Significant Changes

TO THE *NEC*® 2020

electrical training ALLIANCE
IBEW - NECA

IN COLLABORATION WITH

NECA
NATIONAL ELECTRICAL CONTRACTORS ASSOCIATION

This book conveys the information related to each change as of August 1, 2019, but does not reflect potential additional action(s) taken by the NFPA editors or the NFPA Standards Council.

Significant Changes to the *NEC* is intended to be an educational resource for the user and contains procedures commonly practiced in industry and the trade. Specific procedures vary with each task and must be performed by a qualified person. For maximum safety, always refer to specific manufacturer recommendations, insurance regulations, specific job site and plant procedures, applicable federal, state, and local regulations, and any authority having jurisdiction. The *electrical training ALLIANCE* assumes no responsibility or liability in connection with this material or its use by any individual or organization.

© 2019 *electrical training ALLIANCE*

This material is for the exclusive use by the IBEW-*NECA* JATCs and programs approved by the *electrical training ALLIANCE*. Possession and/or use by others is strictly prohibited as this proprietary material is for exclusive use by the *electrical training ALLIANCE* and programs approved by the *electrical training ALLIANCE*.

All rights reserved. No part of this material shall be reproduced, stored in a retrieval system, or transmitted by any means whether electronic, mechanical, photocopying, recording, or otherwise without the express written permission of the *electrical training ALLIANCE*.

1 2 3 4 5 6 7 8 9 – 19 – 9 8 7 6 5 4 3 2 1

Printed in the United States of America

Contents

Chapter 1

Contents

Chapter 2

Contents

Chapter 3

Contents

Chapter 4

Contents

Chapter 5

Articles 500–590...172
Special Occupancies

Contents

Chapter 6

Contents

Contents

Chapter 7

Chapter 8

Introduction

The *National Electrical Code®* (*NEC®*) is the most widely used electrical installation standard in the United States and North America. In fact, the *NEC* is being adopted more globally as electrical codes and standards evolve internationally. It is a living document and is in a continuous state of evolution. As new technologies, equipment, wiring methods, and industry needs evolve, the *NEC* must stay current to effectively address essential installation and safety requirements. An established three-year revision cycle effectively facilitates a dynamic and timely development process. The *NEC* is integral to the electrical business and is used daily by electrical contractors, electricians, maintainers, inspectors, engineers, designers, and others.

The *NEC* development process begins with the submission of public inputs (PIs). The National Fire Protection Association (NFPA) recently implemented a new revision process for all codes and standards that they publish. In previous revision cycles, the public submitted proposals, which are known in the new process as public inputs or PIs. There were 3,730 PIs submitted this cycle, which resulted in 1,400 first revisions (FRs). In January 2018, the technical committees (commonly referred to as Code-Making Panels or CMPs) met to act on all PIs to begin revising existing and developing new requirements. After the CMPs meet and act on all PIs and final balloting is complete, the results are made publicly available on the Internet in a document titled *National Electrical Code First Draft*. NFPA no longer publishes a paper copy of the results in a book form. The public then has an opportunity to modify or reverse the actions initially taken by the technical committees by submitting public comments on any FR or PI. There were 1,930 PCs submitted this cycle resulting in 634 second revisions (SRs). In November 2018, the CMPs met to act on all PCs submitted. There were 73 Correlating First Revisions and four new articles emerged in the 2020 *NEC*.

After the CMP meetings and final balloting is complete on the PCs, the results are made available to the public on the Internet in a document titled *National Electrical Code Second Draft*. Throughout this entire process, the *NEC* Correlating Committee reviews the work in the First Draft and Second Draft stages to ensure that there are no conflicting actions between the work of the CMPs and that all revisions conform to the *NEC Style Manual* and NFPA Regulations Governing Committee Projects. Once the Second Draft is made available, there is a final opportunity for the public to submit a "notice of intent to make a motion" (NITMAM) directed at any revision accepted during this process, as well as any public comment submitted. Actions on these motions are made during the Technical Session at the NFPA annual meeting. The NFPA Standards Council reviews these NITMAMs, and all that are in order become "certified amending motions" (CAMs). At the NFPA annual meeting, the work of the CMPs can be modified by such motions, if accepted by the body present at the Technical Meeting. The NFPA annual meeting for the 2020 *NEC* was held in San Antonio in June 2019. Appeals can be submitted to the NFPA Standards Council by any individual or any organization. The NFPA Standards Council met in Boston in August 2019 to hear appeals. After appeals had been heard and acted upon by the Standards Council, they issued the 2020 *NEC*.

This open consensus revision process provides all users of the *NEC* with an opportunity to mold the next edition through individual and organizational participation. As readers learn about these significant changes for the 2020 *NEC*, they should be sure to note their ideas for an improved *Code* and submit them as PIs for the next edition of the *NEC*.

Many of the changes and new rules in this edition specifically address new technologies such as expanded use of energy storage systems and equipment, micro-grid installations, and large-scale photovoltaic system installations. This edition of the *NEC* also includes incorporation of several additional requirements for reconditioned equipment, a process that began in the 2017 *NEC*.

About This Book

This text is written to inform electrical contractors, electricians, maintenance personnel, inspectors, engineers, and system designers of the most significant revisions and new requirements in the 2020 *National Electrical Code* (*NEC*). The coverage of each change provides readers with an authoritative review by providing insight and detailed information about the reasons for the changes and how these changes impact the industry, daily work, and business operations. The information in this book is a must for active electrical contracting businesses that need to stay current on the installation requirements they manage every day. This textbook is used most effectively in conjunction with the actual 2020 *NEC* textbook.

Features

RELOCATE　**NEW**　**DELETION**
REORGANIZE　**REVISION**

Icons graphically show the Type of Change.

551.72(E) & 551.72(F)　　NEW

Article 551 Recreational Vehicles and Recreational Vehicle Parks
Part VI Recreational Vehicle Parks

Connected Devices, Connection to RV Site Equipment

Code Language

551.72 Distribution System.

(E) Connected Devices. The use of autotransformers shall not be permitted. The use of listed surge protective devices shall be permitted.

(F) Connection to Recreational Vehicle Site Equipment. Each recreational vehicle shall be powered by only one 30-ampere or one 50-ampere external power supply cord.

Informational Note: The requirement in 551.72(F) does not preclude the use of the 15- or 20-ampere receptacle convenience outlet on the recreational vehicle supply equipment.

(See NEC for actual text)

The **Code Language** is "ripped" from the 2020 *National Electrical Code.*

Photos and **Graphics** visually illustrate each change.

Change Summary

- New 551.71(E) prohibits the use of autotransformers and permits surge protective devices.
- New 551.71(F) requires that each recreational vehicle be powered by only one 30-amp or one 50-amp external power cord.

Significance of the Change

New first-level subdivision 551.71(E) provides requirements for connected devices. This revision specifically prohibits the use of autotransformers, such as a buck-boost type transformer. Substantiation provided to support this revision claims that where autotransformers are used severe additional stress is applied to the surrounding electrical infrastructure. RV park operators have reported that low-voltage conditions typically exist when surrounding RV sites use these "add on devices." Additionally, this new subdivision permits the use of listed surge protective devices. While this text may be new in Article 551 *RV Parks and Recreational Vehicles*, they have always been permitted to use listed surge protective devices.

New first-level subdivision 551.71(F) now requires each recreational vehicle to be powered by only one 30-amp or one 50-amp external power supply cord. This will prevent modified recreational vehicles from plugging into more than one source. Substantiation provided to support this revision explained that many large recreational vehicles are modified by their owners to require two 50-amp circuits. Supplying a recreational vehicle from more than one source is a dangerous practice. This new requirement now limits each recreational vehicle to one power source, meaning it can be supplied by only one 30-amp or one 50-amp external power supply cord.

FRs: 8414, 8472
SR: 7681

214　Chapter 5 • Articles 500–590

The **First Revisions** sequence numbers and **Second Revisions** sequence numbers are provided to allow the user the ability to do additional research on a particular change.

Features

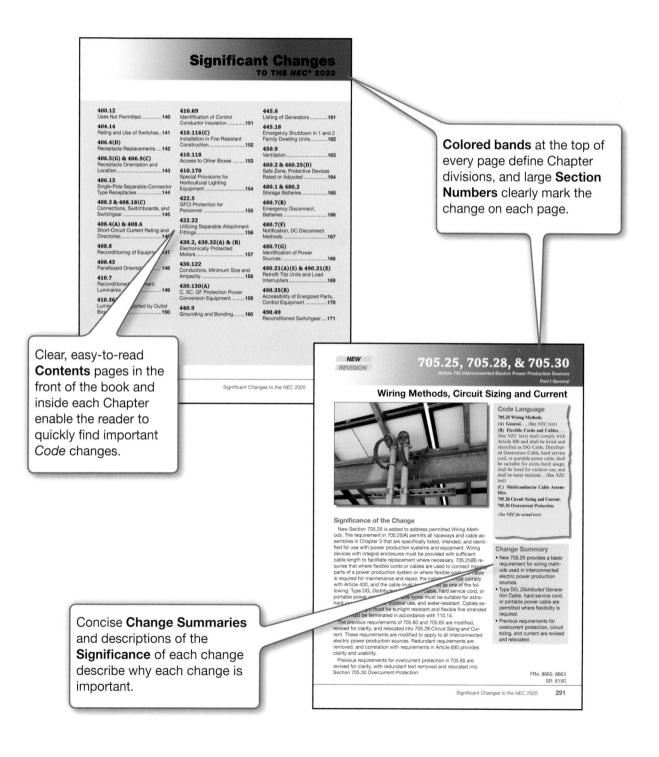

Colored bands at the top of every page define Chapter divisions, and large **Section Numbers** clearly mark the change on each page.

Clear, easy-to-read **Contents** pages in the front of the book and inside each Chapter enable the reader to quickly find important *Code* changes.

Concise **Change Summaries** and descriptions of the **Significance** of each change describe why each change is important.

Acknowledgments

ABB
Donny Cook
Copperweld Bimetallics LLC
Eaton
Electronic Theatre Controls Incorporated
Mark Hilbert
Independence LED Lighting, LLC
Koninklijke Philips Electronics N. V-Lightolier
Legrand

Marina Electrical Equipment
MedPharm Holdings, member of American Trade Assn of Cannabis and Hemp
National Fire Protection Association
National Electrical Contractors Association
Craig Rose
Sky Technologies (formerly Safety Quick Lighting & Fans)
Tesla Energy

NFPA 70®, *National Electrical Code*, and *NEC®* are registered trademarks of the National Fire Protection Association, Quincy, MA.

Contributing Developers

Michael J. Johnston is NECA's executive director of standards and safety. Prior to working with NECA, he worked for the International Association of Electrical Inspectors as the director of education, codes, and standards. He also worked as an electrical inspector and electrical inspection field supervisor for the City of Phoenix, AZ, and achieved all IAEI and ICC electrical inspector certifications. Johnston achieved a bachelor of science in business management from the University of Phoenix. Mike chaired the *NEC* Correlating Committee for the 2014, 2017, and 2020 *NEC* development cycles and is a member of the NFPA Standards Council. He also served on *NEC* Code-Making Panel 5 in the 2002, 2005, 2008 cycles and has chaired the Code-Making Panel 5 representing NECA during the 2011 *NEC* cycle. Among his responsibilities for managing the codes, standards, and safety functions for NECA, Johnston is secretary of the NECA Codes and Standards Committee. He has been a consistent contributor to the *electrical training ALLIANCE* curriculum, authoring titles such as the *Health Care Systems*, *Hazardous Locations*, *Applied Grounding and Bonding*, and *Significant Changes to the NEC*. Johnston is a member of the IBEW and has experience as an electrical journeyman wireman, foreman, and project superintendent. Johnston is an active member of IAEI, ICC, NFPA, ASSE, SES, the NFPA Electrical Section, Education Section, the UL Electrical Council, and National Safety Council.

Jim Dollard is a journeyman wireman in IBEW Local 98 in Philadelphia, PA. Jim is currently retired and is continuing to represent the IBEW in the codes and standards process. Jim worked as an instructor and most recently as the safety coordinator. He is a master OSHA 500 instructor and works with the *electrical training ALLIANCE* training authorized instructors with the goal of safe working conditions on all jobs. As a current member of the following NFPA committees, Dollard plays a significant role in the development of electrical codes and standards: The *National Electrical Code* Correlating Committee, Code-Making Panels 10 and 13, *NFPA 70E: Standard for Electrical Safety in the Workplace*, and *NFPA 90A: Standard for the Installation of Air-Conditioning and Ventilating Systems*.

Dollard is also a member of the Underwriters Laboratories Electrical Council. He is the author of several *electrical training ALLIANCE* titles: the *Codeology* textbook, the 2008 *NEC Significant Changes*, co-author of the 2011 and 2017 *NEC Significant Changes*, and the 2015 and 2018 *ALLIANCE*/NECA *NFPA 70E Significant Changes*. Dollard is an author with a monthly *NEC* column in the Electrical Contractor magazine. His excellent presentation skills, knowledge of the electrical industry, extensive background in the electrical construction field, and involvement in electrical safety and codes/standards allow Dollard to make the most complex requirements easy to understand and apply.

Reconditioned Equipment

This cycle, there are significant revisions throughout the *Code* to address reconditioned equipment. These changes have a global impact on application of the *NEC*. A new definition of *Reconditioned* is added in Article 100 to provide clarity in the application of multiple new requirements. These revisions include modifications in 110.21(A)(2), which requires that reconditioned equipment be identified as reconditioned and the original listing mark be removed. Examples of requirements for reconditioned equipment include a prohibition to recondition molded case circuit breakers and transfer switches. Low voltage power circuit breakers, and more, are permitted to be reconditioned.

GFCI Requirements

A global effort in the *NEC* now provides clarity in Chapters 5, 6, and 7 with respect to the general GFCI requirements in 210.8. Where GFCI requirements existed in Chapters 5, 6, and 7, there was a common misconception that the general rules in 210.8 did not apply. These revisions provide clarity with text to inform the *Code* user that the general rules of 210.8 apply unless specifically modified in a Chapter 5, 6, or 7 article. Sections 210.8 and 422.5 are correlated to clarify the application of GFCI requirements for appliances.

Definitions

Article 100 is significantly revised by adding a new Part III that will contain all of the hazardous (classified) location definitions. A global effort reviewed the use and location of all definitions in the *NEC*. The *general* rule is that where a word or term is defined and is used in more than one article, the definition is located in Article 100, and where used only in a single article, it is located in the XXX.2 section of that article. However, many definitions for cable assemblies, raceways, and systems exist in the XXX.2 section of an article but apply throughout the *Code*. The net result of these changes is to add parent text in each XXX.2 section to explain which definitions apply only within that article, and those that apply globally. These revisions increase clarity and usability.

Fault Current

The use of the terms *short circuit current*, *fault current*, and *available fault current* were reviewed globally and correlated. The result of this effort provides significant clarity. Equipment has a *short circuit current* rating. Installers must ensure that the *available fault current* does not exceed the *short circuit current* rating. Two new definitions are added for clarity, *Fault Current* and *Available Fault Current*.

Disconnects for Emergency Responders

The need for a means to remove power quickly and safely for one- and two-family dwelling units during a fire or other emergency has been discussed in the *NEC* for multiple cycles. There are multiple new requirements to add a means to disconnect power (and signage) on the outside of the dwelling unit. These revisions include new requirements for services, generators, energy storage systems, and alternative energy sources.

2020 NEC® Code-Wide Revisions

Outside Feeders and Service Disconnects

The *NEC* continues to move the needle in the direction of safety by modifying long-standing requirements that some thought could never be changed. This is safety by design; we are revising the *NEC* to provide installer/maintainers with the ability to create electrically safe working conditions and where that state cannot be implemented by reducing the likelihood and level of exposure. The text of 230.71 is significantly revised and will no longer permit a panelboard to contain six disconnecting means. The general rule now is that each service enclosure must contain only one disconnecting means. Switchboards, switchgear, and metering centers with separate compartments and barriers may contain up to six disconnects.

A new 225.30(B) now addresses common supply equipment and will allow six feeders instead of a single large feeder under prescribed conditions. This is a significant safety-driven revision that will allow installers to create electrically safe working conditions on a part of the building supply. This also results in smaller conductors and a reduction in available fault current. This requirement mandates that (not more than six) feeders originate in the same equipment and terminate in the same location.

Chapter 8

An effort to reorganize and clarify the application of Chapter 8 requirements began this cycle and will continue into the 2023 revision cycle. A new Article 800 *General Requirements for Communications Systems* is added and removes redundancies that existed throughout this Chapter. Existing Article 800 for *Communications Circuits* is editorially renumbered as Article 805.

Article 242 Overvoltage Protection

Articles 280 and 285 from the 2017 *NEC* have been combined into a single article titled "Overvoltage Protection." Articles 280 and 285 have been combined to form a new Article 242 titled Overvoltage Protection. The article has three parts, General, Surge Protective Devices (SPDs) 1000 Volts or Less, and Surge Arresters Over 1000 Volts. Technical responsibility for Article 242 and its associated definitions in Article 100 has been shifted from CMP-5 to CMP-10.

Article 311 Medium Voltage Conductors and Cables

Article 328 in the 2017 *NEC* has been deleted, and its content has been relocated to a new Article 311 titled Medium Voltage Conductors and Cables. Requirements for medium voltage cables and conductors rated over 2000 volts and located formerly in Article 310 have also been incorporated into this new article. This new article covers the use, installation, construction specifications, and ampacities for Type MV medium voltage conductors and cable.

Article 337 Type P Cable

A new article titled "Type P Cable" has been added to *NEC* Chapter 3. Article 337 addresses the use and installation of Type P cable (marine shipboard cable). Type P cable has been commonly used in land-based oil and gas rigs for over four decades, but the *NEC* has never addressed its permitted use. Type P cable is limited to industrial installations and hazardous locations.

Article 800 General Requirements for Communications Systems and Article 805 Communications Circuits

Article 800 has been revised to include all the common general requirements from all the Chapter 8 communications articles into a single article. The remaining specific rules in former Article 800 have been included in a new Article 805 titled "Communications Circuits." This revision addresses the usability of *NEC* rules for all communications systems and removes a significant amount of redundancy. The revisions resulted from work of a usability task group specifically assigned by the *NEC* Correlating Committee.

Chapter 1

Articles 90, 100, and 110
Introduction, Definitions, and Requirements for Electrical Installations

Expanded Scope Electric Vehicles and Marinas

Code Language

90.2(A) Covered. This *Code* covers the installation and removal of electrical conductors…(See *NEC* text)

(5) Installations supplying shore power to ships and watercraft in marinas and boatyards, including monitoring of leakage current

(6) Installations used to export electric power from vehicles to premises wiring or for bidirectional current flow

(See NEC for actual text)

Change Summary

- The words "in marinas and boatyards" have been added to 90.2(A)(5).
- A new (6) has been added to 90.2(A) to address installations used to export power from electric vehicles to premises wiring.
- Bidirectional flow of power is typically accomplished using utility interactive inverters.

Significance of the Change

The words "in marinas and boatyards" have been added to 90.2(A)(5). The addition of marinas and boatyards clarifies that the scope of the *Code* covers power installations from shore to small craft and the mooring of floating buildings covered by Article 555. This also aligns with the deletion of Article 553 and the incorporation of its content to a new Part III titled "Floating Buildings" in Article 555 of the 2020 *NEC*.

A new (6) has also been added to 90.2(A) to address installations used to export power from electric vehicles to premises wiring. This new item (6) provides clarification that installations used to export power from electric vehicles to premises wiring systems fall under the scope of the *NEC*. This revision provides an approach consistent with generators that are used to power premises wiring, which are also covered by *NEC* requirements. This new information in (6) also correlates with the scope revisions that CMP-12 incorporated in 625.1 as a result of the addition of power export equipment and bidirectional current flow equipment used with some electric vehicles.

FRs: 8370, 8206, 8211, 8385
SR: 7891

Article 100 Scope (.2)

Article 100 Definitions

Scope. This article contains only those definitions essential to the application of this *Code*. It is not intended to include commonly defined general terms or commonly defined technical terms from related codes and standards. In general, only those terms that are used in two or more articles are defined in Article 100. Definitions are also found in XXX.2 sections of other articles…(See *NEC* Text)…

An example of Definitions provided in XXX.2 of an *NEC* article:

240.2 Definitions. The definitions in this section shall apply only in this article.

Current-Limiting Overcurrent Protective Device. A device that, when interrupting currents in its current-limiting range, reduces the current flowing in the faulted circuit to a magnitude substantially less than that obtainable in the same circuit if the device were replaced with a solid conductor having comparable impedance.

Supervised Industrial Installation. For the purposes of Part VIII, the industrial portions of a facility where all of the following conditions are met:

(1) Conditions of maintenance and engineering supervision ensure that only qualified persons monitor and service the system.
(2) The premises wiring system has 2500 kVA or greater of load used in industrial process(es), manufacturing activities,
or both, as calculated in accordance with Article 220.
(3) The premises has at least one service or feeder that is more than 150 volts to ground and more than 300 volts phase-to-phase.

(…See *NEC* text…)

Code Language

Scope. This article contains only those definitions essential to the application of this *Code*. It is not intended to include commonly defined general terms or commonly defined technical terms from related codes and standards. In general, only those terms that are used in two or more articles are defined in Article 100. Definitions are also found in XXX.2 sections of other articles.

Part I of this article contains definitions intended to apply wherever the terms are used throughout this *Code*. (See *NEC* text)

(See NEC for actual text)

Significance of the Change

The scope of *NEC* Article 100 has been revised with respect to how definitions in both Article 100 and the second section (.2) sections apply. Section 2.2.2.1 of the *NEC Style Manual* requires that in general definitions that appear in two or more articles be located in Article 100. Section 2.2.2.2 requires that where an individual article contains definition(s), they be located in .2 of the article. The style manual does not prohibit a definition in .2 of an article from applying elsewhere in the *NEC*. The style manual clearly states that in general definitions that appear in two or more articles shall be located in Article 100, which is still accurate. A new sentence in the first paragraph simply informs *Code* users that definitions are also found in the second section (.2) of other articles. This revision is supplemented with companion revisions to the .2 section of articles containing definitions. New parent text is proposed for these sections for correlation and to increase clarity and usability. For any .2 containing definitions that apply only within that article, text has been added to indicate that definitions in the .2 section apply only within that article. For any .2 containing definitions that apply within the individual article and throughout the *Code*, text has been added to indicate definitions apply within that article and throughout the *Code*.

Change Summary

- The scope of Article 100 has been revised to indicate that definitions are also provided in the .2 section of some articles.
- The second (.2) section of various articles have been revised to address when the defined terms apply only within that article.
- The second (.2) section in some cases will indicate that the defined term applies within that article and throughout the *NEC*.

FR: Global 8758
SR: None

Article 100 Scope (Parts I, II, and III)

Code Language

Scope. This article contains only those definitions essential to the application of this *Code*. It is not intended to include commonly defined general terms or commonly defined technical terms from related codes and standards. In general, only those terms that are used in two or more articles are defined in Article 100. Definitions are also found in XXX.2 sections of other articles.

Part I of this article contains definitions intended to apply wherever the terms are used throughout this *Code*. Part II contains definitions applicable to installations and equipment operating at over 1000 volts, nominal. Part III contains definitions applicable to Hazardous (Classified) Locations.

(See NEC for actual text)

Change Summary

- The scope of Article 100 has been revised to indicate that definitions are also provided in the .2 section of some articles.

- The second paragraph of the scope now indicates that Part III of Article 100 includes definitions applicable to Hazardous (Classified) Locations.

- Both changes revise the scope to align with the representation contained in Article 100.

Article 100 Definitions

Scope. This article contains only those definitions essential to the application of this *Code*. ...(See *NEC* text)...

Part I of this article contains definitions intended to apply wherever the terms are used throughout this *Code*. Part II contains definitions applicable to installations and equipment operating at over 1000 volts, nominal. Part III contains definitions applicable to Hazardous (Classified) Locations.

Part I. General

Accessible (as applied to equipment) Capable of being reached for operation, renewal, and inspection. (CMP-1)

Accessible (as applied to wiring methods) Capable of being removed or exposed without damaging the building structure or finish or not permanently closed in by the structure or finish of the building. (CMP-1) ...(See *NEC* text)...

Part II. Over 1000 Volts, Nominal

Electronically Actuated Fuse. An overcurrent protective device that generally consists of a control module that provides current sensing, electronically derived time–current characteristics, energy to initiate tripping, and an interrupting module that interrupts current when an overcurrent occurs. Electronically actuated fuses may or may not operate in a current limiting fashion, depending on the type of control selected. (CMP-10)

Fuse. An overcurrent protective device with a circuit-opening fusible part that is heated and severed by the passage of overcurrent through it. (CMP-10) ...(See *NEC* text)...

Part III. Hazardous (Classified) Locations (CMP-14).

Aircraft Painting Hangar. An aircraft hangar constructed for the express purpose of spray/coating/dipping applications and provided with dedicated ventilation supply and exhaust. (CMP-14) ...(See *NEC* text)...

Significance of the Change

The scope of *NEC* Article 100 has been revised with respect to how definitions in both Article 100 and the second (.2) sections apply. Section 2.2.2.1 of the *NEC Style Manual* requires that in general definitions that appear in two or more articles be located in Article 100. New text has been added within all affected .2 sections globally throughout the *NEC*. The scope of Article 100 has also been revised to include a new last sentence that indicates Part III of Article 100 contains definitions applicable to hazardous (classified) locations. Action by CMP-14 on FR 7761 relocates all of the hazardous location definitions in the Chapter 5 Hazardous (Classified) Locations articles to a new Part III of Article 100 titled "Hazardous (Classified) Locations." This revision is a significant enhancement in the usability of the *Code*, while reducing confusion. The relocation also brings the *NEC* more in compliance with the *NEC Style Manual* relative to duplicate definitions in chapter 5 of the *NEC* that previously appeared in more than two of the chapter 5 articles. The words and terms included in this part remain under the technical responsibility of CMP-14.

FR: Global 8758, 7766
SR: None

Definition of Accessible (as applied to equipment)

Code Language

Accessible (as applied to equipment). Capable of being reached for operation, renewal, and inspection. (CMP-1)

(See NEC for actual text)

Significance of the Change

Code-Making Panel 1 acted favorably to Public Input 1009 which proposed a simplified revision to the definition of the term *accessible*, as it applies to equipment. As identified in the substantiation for PI 1009, the 2017 *NEC* definition of accessible (as applied to equipment) contradicts and even conflicts with other sections of the *NEC*. The use of a locked equipment room is common practice under controlled or supervised conditions. By stating that equipment is not accessible, if guarded by locked doors, contradicts 110.26(F) and causes inconsistency in field applications and for the code enforcement community. *Equipment* is a broadly defined term that has far-reaching application in the *Code*. Equipment can still be considered accessible, despite being elevated. Sections 110.26(A)(4), 300.23, and 600.21(F) identify and address equipment that is installed above lay-in suspended ceilings as accessible. The term *other effective means* is vague and not conducive to interpretation. The revised definition is clear and concise and provides for a more uniform and consistent use by users, especially inspectors. The revised definition also is more closely aligned with the recently revised definition of the term *readily accessible*, which is more restrictive as indicated by definition.

Change Summary

- The definition of the term *Accessible (as applied to equipment)* has been revised and simplified.
- The revision provides a clearer differentiation from the definition of the term *readily accessible*.
- Rules containing this term have a more accurate meaning by definition.

FR: 8304
SR: None

Definition of Bonding Jumper, Supply-Side

Code Language

Bonding Jumper, Supply-Side. A conductor installed on the supply side of a service or within a service equipment enclosure(s), or for a separately derived system, that ensures the required electrical conductivity between metal parts required to be electrically connected. (CMP-5)

(See NEC for actual text)

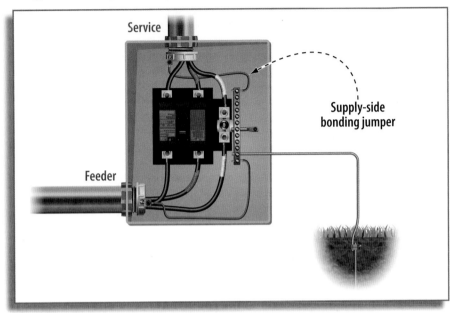

Change Summary

- The definition of the term *Bonding Jumper, Supply-Side* has been deleted from 250.2.
- The definition, without revision, has been located into Part I of Article 100.
- This relocation aligns with the requirements of Section 2.2.2.1 of the *NEC Style Manual*.

Significance of the Change

Action by CMP-5 in SR 9007 deletes the term *bonding jumper, supply side* from Section 250.2 and relocates the term, without revision, to Part I of Article 100. Section 2.2.2.1 of the *NEC Style Manual* requires that Article 100 generally contain definitions of terms that appear in more than one article. While the term is used most often in Article 250, it is also used in other articles such as Articles 230, 310, 408, 450, 694 and so forth. This action effectively does away with Section 250.2 as all grounding and bonding words and terms now appear in Article 100. *Code* Panel 5 retains technical responsibility for the definition. In the larger scheme of things, this is a good indication that the use of defined grounding and bonding terms is becoming consistent throughout the *NEC*. The term *supply-side bonding jumper* relates to a conductor in the grounding and bonding scheme that is typically present both at the service and at the source of separately derived systems. This bonding jumper is installed on the supply side of the service overcurrent device, usually a main, and is typically installed with supply-side ungrounding conductors to the first system overcurrent device enclosure. This bonding jumper, if of a wire type, has strengthened sizing requirements that must comply with Section 250.102(C) which relate directly to the size of the largest ungrounded service conductor or the largest ungrounded derived phase conductor connected at the source of a separately derived system.

FR: 9007
SR: None

Definition of DC-to-DC Converter

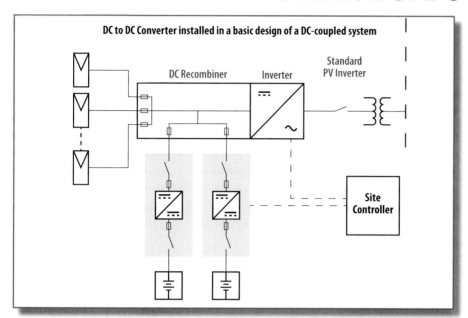

DC to DC Converter installed in a basic design of a DC-coupled system

Code Language

DC-to-DC Converter. A device that can provide an output dc voltage and current at a higher or lower value than the input dc voltage and current. (CMP-4)

(See NEC for actual text)

Significance of the Change

The terms *DC-to-DC Converter*, *DC to DC Converter*, and *DC-DC Converter* are used in Articles 690, 706, and 712 but only defined in 690.2. The definition of a DC-to-DC Converter has been relocated to Article 100 to align with the requirements of Section 2.2.2.1 of the *NEC Style Manual*, which indicates that Article 100 shall contain definitions of terms that appear in two or more other articles of the *NEC*. The words "installed in the PV source circuit or PV output circuit" have been removed as these words are not necessary since new definitions of DC-to-DC converter source circuit and DC-to-DC converter output circuit were added in 690.2 of the 2017 *NEC*. Also, this type of equipment could be installed with systems other than just solar photovoltaic (PV) systems. Examples of articles that address these types of equipment are Article 706 addressing energy storage systems and Article 712 addressing Direct Current Microgrids. As indicated in the definition, this type of equipment converts an output dc voltage and current at a higher or lower value than the input dc voltage and current.

Change Summary

- The varying versions of the term *DC-to-DC Converter* have been removed from Articles 690, 606, and 712.
- One common definition of the term has been incorporated into Article 100.
- CMP-4 retains technical responsibility of the term in the 2020 *NEC*.

FR: 8938
SR: None

Definition of Equipotential Plane

Code Language

Equipotential Plane. Accessible conductive parts bonded together to reduce voltage gradients in a designated area. (CMP-17)

(See NEC for actual text)

Change Summary

- The definition of the term *equipotential plane* has been simplified and relocated in Article 100.
- This definition applies to Articles 680 and 682.
- The definition of "equipotential plane" in Section 547.2 remains in that section and applies only to agricultural facilities.

Significance of the Change

The definition of the term *Equipotential Plane* in Section 682.2 has been modified and relocated to Article 100. The *NEC Style Manual* states at 2.2.2.1 that Article 100 shall contain definitions of terms that appear in two or more articles of the *NEC*. This modified and relocated definition applies to Article 682 and Article 680. Text concerning conductive elements in or under walking surfaces was considered to be a requirement and was moved to 682.33(C).

The original Public Input 8916 sought to combine the definition from 547.2 and 682.2, and as modified, located it in Article 100. While these definitions said nearly the same thing, uniqueness in the equipotential plane definition in 547.2 was identified in the Second Revision stage of the *NEC* development process. As a result, CMP-7 acted to retain it in 547.2. Action by CMP-7 SR 7781 added the words "as applied to agricultural buildings" in parenthesis following the definition title "equipotential plane." In the panel statement to SR 7781, *Code* Panel 7 emphasized that the equipotential plane defined in 547.2 is a very specific definition that applies only to agricultural buildings. The definition in Article 100 does not apply to this particular case and therefore the 547.2 definition remains.

FR: 8916
SRs: 7181, 8029

Definition of Fault Current and Available Fault Current

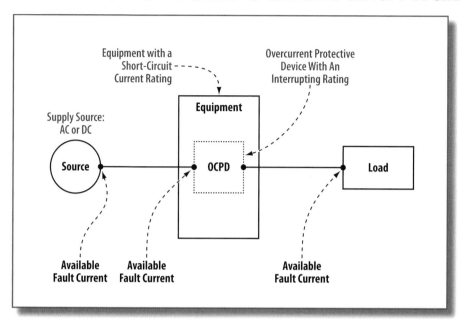

Code Language

Fault Current. The current delivered at a point on the system during a short-circuit condition. (CMP-10)

Fault Current, Available (Available Fault Current). The largest amount of current capable of being delivered at a point on the system during a short-circuit condition. (CMP-10)

Informational Note: A short-circuit can occur during abnormal conditions such as a fault between circuit conductors or a ground fault. See Informational Note Figure 100.1.

(See NEC for actual text)

Significance of the Change

Two new definitions for "Fault Current" and "Available Fault Current" have been added to Article 100. This action is based upon the results of an *NEC* Correlating Committee task group that reviewed the use of the terms *fault current*, *short circuit current*, and the qualifiers "maximum," and "available." These new definitions are part of a global effort to increase clarity in the use of these terms throughout the *NEC* and other standards that use the terms, such as NFPA 70E *Standard for Electrical Safety in the Workplace*. The term *fault current* simply means a level of current at any point on a system where a fault or short circuit occurs. The definition of fault current, available (available fault current) includes the wording "largest amount of current," to clarify that a "short circuit" as used in this definition is of negligible impedance. The term *available fault current* appears throughout the *NEC* and is prominent in Section 110.24 where the available fault current value is addressed in a marking requirement for service equipment in new installations and for modifications to existing installations. The new informational note clarifies that a short circuit can be the ungrounded circuit conductors, or it can be a ground fault.

Change Summary

- New definitions of the terms *fault current* and *fault current, available* have been added to Article 100.

- A new informational note and associated figure have been added to enhance clarity and usability.

- This revision aligns with similar recent revisions in other standards that use the terms, such as *NFPA 70E*.

FRs: 8190, 8191
SR: 7950

Definition of Habitable Room

Code Language

Habitable Room. A room in a building for living, sleeping, eating, or cooking, but excluding bathrooms, toilet rooms, closets, hallways, storage or utility spaces, and similar areas. (CMP-2)

(See NEC for actual text)

Change Summary

- A new definition of the term *habitable room* has been added to Article 100.
- The new definition describes what constitutes a habitable room and differentiates it from one that is not.
- The new definitions align with the same defined term that is included in *NFPA 5000* with similar context to the defined term in the IRC and IBC.

Significance of the Change

The obvious is "habitable room" which is vague text in the *NEC*. The IRC and IBC define habitable space, which clearly fit into the context of habitable rooms. A new definition of the term *habitable room* has been added to Article 100. This term is used multiple times in the *NEC*, but there was never any clear guidance in the *NEC* on what constitutes a habitable room as compared to a room that is considered not habitable. The new definitions provide the needed clarity and a differentiation from rooms within a building that do not qualify as habitable. Rooms such as living rooms, dining rooms, kitchens, and bedrooms are habitable according to this definition, while rooms such as toilet rooms, utility closets, hallways, and closets are not. This is an essential change because it can affect the wiring requirements in those rooms or spaces. This new definition also aligns with the same term that is used in *NFPA 5000*, *Building Construction and Safety Code* and promotes consistency of its use. *Code* Panel 2 has been assigned technical responsibility for this new definition as the most common uses of this term reside within the articles under its jurisdiction.

FR: 7666
SR: None
SCR: 15

Definition of Interactive Inverter

Courtesy of Eaton

Code Language

Interactive Inverter. An inverter intended for use in parallel with power source(s) such as an electric utility to supply common loads and capable of delivering power to the utility. (CMP-13)

(See NEC for actual text)

Significance of the Change

The definition of the term *interactive inverter* has been revised to clarify its operational relationship to a serving utility. This revision is editorial and provides warranted clarification in the definition of interactive inverter. Interactive inverters can be interactive with any appropriate ac power source, not just sources generated by a public utility. Since these inverters are used in many different applications, including in stand-alone systems as an example, this definition should not be exclusive to only a utility source. It is important that non-interactive inverters not be installed in systems that require the safety features inherent to listed interactive inverter-based sources. This change also better aligns this definition with the use of this term in other articles, including in Article 705, and better matches the definition of an interactive system in Article 100. It is commonly understood that interactive inverters may also deliver power to the utility. This revised definition also recognizes the evolution of interactive inverter types that may warrant separate definitions in future editions of the *NEC*. Section 705.6 indicates that interactive inverters are required to be listed and field labeled for the intended interconnection service or application. Interactive inverters are an essential component in microgrid applications.

Change Summary

- The definition of the term *interactive inverter* has been revised and clarified.
- The term *interactive inverter* is no longer limited in use within *NEC* rules addressing interaction with a utility.
- Interactive inverters are capable of delivering power to the utility where identified for that use in accordance with Section 705.6.

FR: 7750
SR: 7545

Definition of Inverter

Code Language

Inverter. Equipment that changes dc to ac. (CMP-4)

(See NEC for actual text)

Change Summary

- The definition of the term *Inverter* has been revised and simplified.
- The definition has been relocated to Article 100 to comply with the *NEC Style Manual*.
- The term *inverter* is applicable to multiple types of systems and not limited in application to just photovoltaic (PV) systems.

Significance of the Change

The definition of "Inverter" has been revised and simplified to minimum terminology and relocated to Article 100. The revision provides significant clarity, and relocation signifies that the term is no longer limited in application to just photovoltaic (PV) systems. The *NEC Style Manual*, Section 2.2.2.1 indicates that Article 100 shall contain definitions of terms that appear in two or more other articles of the *NEC*. While the existing definition worked well for several editions of the *Code*, the definition aged and is no longer completely accurate. The inverter simply changes dc to ac, so that is what the revised definition indicates. Since the term was introduced into Article 690, its use across the *NEC* has expanded beyond that article. The term is used in multiple different articles qualifying it for placement in Article 100. As a result, the simplified definition has consistent application about the performance of an inverter that is the same within whichever article of the *NEC* that it appears. Code-Making Panel 4 retains technical responsibility for this revised and relocated definition.

FR: 8982

SR: None

Definition of Labeled – New Informational Note

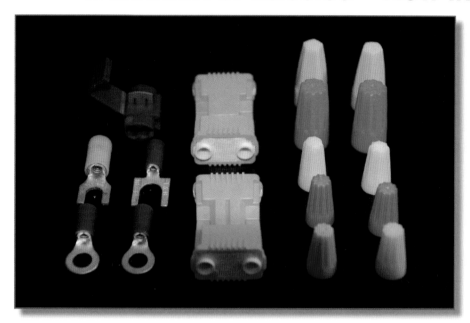

Code Language

Labeled. Equipment or materials to which has been attached a label, symbol, or other identifying mark of an organization that is acceptable to the authority having jurisdiction…(See *NEC* text)

Informational Note: If a listed product is of such a size, shape, material, or surface texture that it is not possible to apply legibly the complete label to the product, the complete label may appear on the smallest unit container in which the product is packaged.

(See NEC for actual text)

Significance of the Change

A new informational note has been added following the definition of the term *Labeled*. The added informational note explains that even though a section of the *NEC* may require a product to be labeled, it is common practice to have the label, symbol, or other identifying mark applied to the packaging, or a tag in some instances. Substantiation clearly indicated that labeling of listed equipment is not possible in all cases or conditions, such as, if products are too small to be labeled or for some severe environmental conditions. Some listed products are marked or require markings on the smallest shipping package. Adding this informational note provides significant clarification for the authority having jurisdiction (AHJ) in that even though a section of the *NEC* may require a product to be labeled, it is acceptable to have the label, symbol, or other identifying mark applied to the packaging or a tag in some instances. Without this informational note, if interpreted verbatim and literally by the AHJ, this definition requires the label, symbol, or other identifying mark to be attached to the equipment or material. Without this informational note, confusion may exist in that AHJs may not accept a label that is not on the product and only affixed to the packaging as permitted by the certification organization.

Change Summary

- A new informational note has been added following the definition of the term *Labeled*.
- Clarification has been provided about what constitutes labeling as defined in the *NEC*.
- The labeling can appear on the smallest package of the product in cases where the equipment is small or installed in a harsh environment.

FR: 8360
SR: 7953

Definition of Laundry Area

Code Language

Laundry Area. An area containing or designed to contain a laundry tray, clothes washer, or clothes dryer. (CMP-2)

(See NEC for actual text)

Change Summary

- A new definition of the term *Laundry Area* has been added to Article 100.
- This is an area containing or designed to contain a laundry tray, clothes washer, or clothes dryer.
- The definition of laundry area in Section 550.2 is no longer necessary and has been deleted.

Significance of the Change

A new definition of the term *Laundry Area* has been added to Article 100. The term is used in multiple *NEC* requirements and has not been defined until the 2020 edition of the *NEC*. The definition indicates that this is an area containing or designed to contain a laundry tray, clothes washer, or clothes dryer. As defined, this definition could be applied within dwelling units and beyond dwelling units, such as laundromat facilities. An important feature of this definition is that it does not apply specifically to a room, but rather an area where laundry activity and equipment is present and used. CMP-2 acted favorably to FR 7682 to include this definition in Article 100. A very similar definition of laundry area existed in Section 550.2 and applied to mobile homes. That definition has been deleted as a result of action by CMP-7 on SR 8141 because it is no longer necessary with the new definition in Article 100 applying to all instances of the term *laundry area* used in *NEC* rules. The *NEC* Correlating Committee assigned technical responsibility for the definition to Code-Making Panel 2 as indicated in Second Correlating Revision 16.

FR: 7682
SR: 8151
SCR: 16

Definition of Messenger or Messenger Wire

Code Language

Messenger or Messenger Wire. A wire that is run along with or integral with a cable or conductor to provide mechanical support for the cable or conductor. (CMP-6)

(See NEC for actual text)

Significance of the Change

The term *Messenger Supported Wiring* is defined in Article 396. Although not defined, the terms *messenger* and *messenger wire* are used as stand-alone terms within Article 396 and in other articles of the *Code* such as Articles 646, 680, 727, 820, and 830. Section 2.2.2.1 of the *NEC Style Manual* indicates that Article 100 shall contain definitions of terms that appear in two or more other articles of the *NEC*. Therefore, a definition has been added to Article 100. These terms used together or alone are defined as a wire that is run along with or integral with a cable or conductor to provide mechanical support for the cable or conductor. A messenger wire or messenger can be a current-carrying conductor, such as the bare conductor within service drop cable that contains a messenger for support and attachment at both ends. Some messengers are not current carrying conductors and are typically dead-ended at both ends. In this case, they are only used as the means of support for the circuit conductors. Festoon lighting is another example of an installation that requires a messenger support wire for support of overhead ungrounded conductors if the circuit conductors are larger than 12 AWG, as indicated in Section 225.6(B).

Change Summary

- A definition of the term(s) *messenger* and *messenger wire* have been added to Article 100.
- This unique definition applies to either term used within the *NEC*.
- A messenger can be current carrying or be dead-ended on both ends and used only for support.

FR: 7864
SR: 7573

Definition of Photovoltaic (PV) System

Code Language

Photovoltaic (PV) System. The total components, circuits, and equipment up to and including the PV system disconnecting means that, in combination, convert solar energy into electric energy. (CMP-4)

(See NEC for actual text)

Change Summary

- The definition of the term *Photovoltaic (PV) System* has been revised.
- As revised, the system includes all components, circuits, and equipment up to and including the PV system disconnecting means.
- The text about connecting to a utilization load has been deleted.

Significance of the Change

The definition of the term *Photovoltaic (PV) System* has been revised to clarify that this is a system including all components, circuits, and equipment up to and including the PV system disconnecting means. Language about utilization loads has been removed since a PV system may have no direct connection to loads. The purpose of all electricity is to eventually operate utilization equipment (loads), so the key should be defining what it is, not what electricity is for. DC power systems with multiple sources are becoming common. These are technically "DC Microgrids" which are covered under Article 712 of the *NEC*. There was a demarcation problem caused by the previous definition of Photovoltaic System in Article 100 and the definitions of PV output circuits and dc-dc output circuits still reside in article 690. This results in the marking requirements of 690.31 (every 10 feet) being applied by some AHJs to entire dc microgrid systems, in addition to introducing other confusion. The revised definition clarifies that PV systems terminate at distribution equipment, or at the last disconnecting means prior to connecting any utilization equipment (loads). Code-Making Panel 4 retains technical responsibility for this defined term.

FR: 8553
SR: None

Definition of Prime Mover

Code Language

Prime Mover. The machine that supplies the mechanical horsepower to a generator. (CMP-13)

(See NEC for actual text)

Significance of the Change

A definition of the term *Prime Mover* has been added to Article 100. The term is used in several articles and therefore included in the general definitions of Article 100 to meet the requirements of Section 2.2.2.1 of the *NEC Style Manual*. Because "prime mover" is a specialized term, requiring specific mechanical knowledge to understand, the definition will assist users while adding needed clarity to the *NEC*. The term *Prime Mover* appears in Articles 445, 700, 701, and 708 with no definition provided in any of these articles. The definition clarifies that the power-producing equipment such as a generator, wind turbine, and so forth, functions to produce electrical power when forcing rotation of a generator rotor using mechanical (force) horsepower. A generator set includes both the prime mover and the electrical generator in an assembly; the generator is driven by a prime mover. The term *generator set* appears in multiple articles such as Article 250 and Article 708. Code-Making Panel 13 has technical responsibility of the newly defined term in Article 100.

Change Summary

- A definition of the term *Prime Mover* has been added to Article 100.
- It is defined as the machine that supplies mechanical horsepower to a generator.
- CMP-13 has been assigned technical responsibility of this term.

FR: 7886
SR: 7549

Definition of Receptacle – New Informational Note

Code Language

Receptacle. A contact device installed at the outlet for the connection of an attachment plug, or for the direct connection of electrical utilization equipment designed to mate with the corresponding contact device. A single receptacle is a single contact device with no other contact device on the same yoke or strap. A multiple receptacle is two or more contact devices on the same yoke or strap. (CMP-18)

Informational Note: A duplex receptacle is an example of a multiple receptacle that has two receptacles on the same yoke or strap.

(See NEC for actual text)

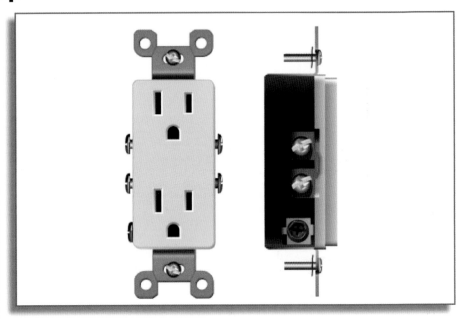

Change Summary

- The words "or strap" have been added following the word "yoke" in two instances within this definition.

- This revision aligns with *NEC* requirements that use the phrase mounting yoke or strap, such as in 314.16(B)(4), 404.10(B), and 406.5.

- The informational note clarifies that a duplex receptacle is two receptacles on a single mounting yoke or strap.

Significance of the Change

It was reported that there was confusion and debate among electricians, inspectors, and others as to whether a typical duplex receptacle is actually two receptacles or just one receptacle on a single mounting yoke or strap. The wording in the 2017 *NEC* seemed to create the illusion of two subcategories of definitions: A "single receptacle" and "multiple receptacle." There are only two other code sections that use the term *multiple receptacle*. The words "or strap" have been added following the word "yoke" in two instances within this definition. This revision aligns with *NEC* requirements that use the phrase mounting yoke or strap, such as in Sections 314.16(B)(4), 404.10(B), and 406.5. An interesting observation is that Section 250.146 does not use the term *mounting strap* but rather "contact yoke" or "device yoke." A new informational note has been added to this definition to clarify that when a multiple receptacle is on the same yoke or mounting strap, such as a duplex receptacle, it is considered two receptacles on a single mounting yoke. The use of the word "receptacles" in the informational note provides the needed clarification to eliminate reported confusion in the field about this issue. The new informational note explains that a duplex receptacle is two receptacles on the same yoke.

FR: 8246
SR: 8223

Definition of Reconditioned

Code Language

Reconditioned. Electromechanical systems, equipment, apparatus, or components that are restored to operating conditions. This process differs from normal servicing of equipment that remains within a facility or replacement of listed equipment on a one-to-one basis. (CMP-10)

Informational Note: The term reconditioned is frequently referred to as rebuilt, refurbished, or remanufactured.

(See NEC for actual text)

Significance of the Change

The term *reconditioned equipment* and related general requirements were introduced in the 2017 *NEC* in Section 110.21(A)(2). During the 2020 *NEC* development process, this term was incorporated into multiple articles that added requirements related to equipment that is either permitted or prohibited from being reconditioned. Accordingly, the *NEC* process yielded a common definition of the term *reconditioned* and included it in Article 100 in compliance with Section 2.2.2.1 of the *NEC Style Manual*. This definition is derived from the NEMA document titled *NEMA Policy on Reconditioned Electrical Equipment*. The wording in this definition retains the essential elements from the NEMA definition without including requirements. The wording also clearly distinguishes both routine maintenance and also one-for-one part or component replacements that are related to reconditioning processes. As described in the informational note, terms such as *rebuilt*, *refurbished*, and *remanufactured* are often used interchangeably with the new *NEC* defined term *reconditioned*. Multiple *NEC* rules have been incorporated that will either permit or prohibit certain equipment from being reconditioned. This new definition and associated rules in the *NEC* will significantly benefit installers, electrical inspectors, owners, and others that periodically have to address the use of reconditioned equipment in existing installations and systems.

Change Summary

- The term *reconditioned* has been added in multiple articles of the *NEC* and is now defined in Article 100.
- The process of reconditioning equipment differs from normal servicing of equipment that remains in place.
- Reconditioned equipment is often referred to as rebuilt, refurbished, or remanufactured.

FR: (None) PI 2935
SRs: 8074, 7992
SCR: 9

Definition of Service Equipment

Code Language

Service Equipment. The necessary equipment, consisting of a circuit breaker(s) or switch(es) and fuse(s) and their accessories, connected to the serving utility and intended to constitute the main control and disconnect of the serving utility. (CMP-10)

(See NEC for actual text)

Change Summary

- The definition of the term *Service Equipment* has been revised.
- The word "usually" has been removed to reduce ambiguity and the word "cutoff" has been replaced by the *NEC* term *disconnecting means.*
- Technical responsibility of this definition has been reassigned from CMP-4 to CMP-10.

Significance of the Change

The definition of the term *Service Equipment* has been revised to improve clarity and ensure proper application of the term. The word "usually" has been deleted because service equipment always consists of a circuit breaker(s) or switch(es) and fuse(s). The word "cutoff" is deleted and replaced with "disconnect" for clarity. This revision clarifies that "service equipment" connects to the utility electric system which may be overhead service conductors or a service lateral. The revision also removes the text related to connection to a building or structure, or other designated area. This was needed because the previous definition was exclusive of other applications that included service equipment. The term *service equipment* as revised clearly applies to premises wiring that is connected to a serving utility. The definition of the term *stand-alone system* includes an informational note that is useful. The note indicates that although stand-alone systems are capable of operating independent of a utility supply they may include a connection to a utility supply for use when not operating in stand-alone mode.

FR: 8199
SR: 8068

Definition of Stand-Alone System

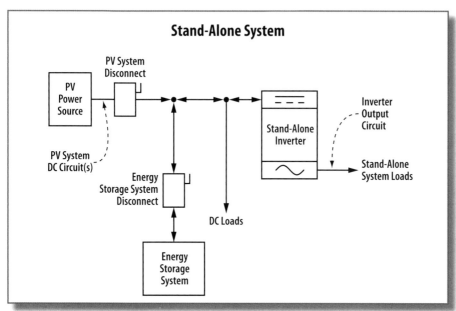

Stand-Alone System

PV System Disconnect

PV Power Source

PV System DC Circuit(s)

Energy Storage System Disconnect

DC Loads

Energy Storage System

Stand-Alone Inverter

Inverter Output Circuit

Stand-Alone System Loads

Code Language

Stand-Alone System. A system that is capable of supplying power independent of an electric power production and distribution network. (CMP-4)

(See NEC for actual text)

Significance of the Change

The definition of the term *Stand-Alone System* has been revised. The revision clarifies that a stand-alone system is capable of supplying power and is independent of an electric power production and distribution network. Article 710 titled *Stand-Alone Systems* was added in the 2017 *NEC*. This new article covers electric power production sources operating in a stand-alone (island) mode. All equipment installed in a stand-alone system is required to be listed for the intended use or purpose. A premises wiring system with a connection to a primary source (often an electric utility) is by definition a microgrid system as defined in 705.2. The term *stand-alone mode* as provided in 710.1 is often used interchangeably with the term *island mode*. Essentially they have similar meaning, which is support by the terminology used in IEEE 1547-2018 - IEEE *Standard for Interconnection and Interoperability of Distributed Energy Resources with Associated Electric Power Systems Interfaces*. Stand-alone systems are typically powered solely by photovoltaic (PV), wind electric systems, fuel cell systems, all of which are often combined with energy storage systems. Premises wiring systems that are stand-alone are often referred to as "off grid" systems.

Change Summary

- The definition of the term *Stand-Alone System* has been revised.
- The revision clarifies that a stand-alone system is capable of supplying power and is independent of an electric power production and distribution network.
- Examples of stand-alone systems are those powered solely by photovoltaic (PV), wind electric systems, fuel cell systems, all of which are often combined with energy storage systems.

FR: 8728
SR: 8218

Definition of Electrical Resistance Trace Heating

Code Language

Electrical Resistance Trace Heating "60079-30-1". Type of Protection for the purpose of producing heat on the principle of electrical resistance and typically composed of one or more metallic conductors and/or an electrically conductive material, suitably electrically insulated and protected.

Informational Note: See ANSI/*UL 60079-30-1:2017, Explosive Atmospheres – Part 30-1: Electrical resistance trace heating – General and testing requirements.*

(See NEC for actual text)

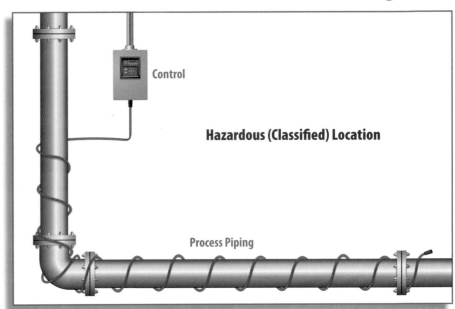

Control

Hazardous (Classified) Location

Process Piping

Change Summary

- A new definition of the term *electrical resistance trace heating* has been incorporated into Part III of Article 100.

- Part III of Article 100 now includes all definitions of words and terms related to hazardous (classified) locations.

- A new informational note refers to the applicable standard (ANSI/*UL 60079-30-1*) for electrical resistance trace heating general and testing requirements.

Significance of the Change

Action by CMP-14 on FR 7761 relocates all of the hazardous location definitions into a new Part III of Article 100 titled Hazardous (Classified) Locations. This relocation addresses two concerns. First, it brings the hazardous locations articles in the *NEC* more into alignment with the *NEC Style Manual* relative to Section 2.2.2.1, which indicates that Article 100 shall contain definitions of terms that appear in two or more other articles of the *NEC*. This revision also improves the usability of the *Code*, eliminates confusion, and enhances safety. The scope of Article 100 has also been revised to recognize that Part III contains definitions applicable to installations and equipment for Hazardous (Classified) Locations. All definitions in this part of Article 100 remain under the technical jurisdiction of CMP-14. A new definition of the term *Electrical Resistance Trace Heating "60079-30-1"* has been added in Part III of Article 100. A new product standard has been introduced for the examination, testing, and marking of electrical resistance trace heating. This equipment is now identified as Type of Protection "60079-30-1" in accordance with ANSI/*UL 60079-30-1:2017*. The new definition applies specifically to electrical resistance heat tracing equipment and systems installed in hazardous (classified) locations.

FR: 7761
SR: None

Definition of Inherently Safe Optical Radiation "op is"

Code Language

Inherently Safe Optical Radiation "op is". Type of protection to minimize the risk of ignition in explosive atmospheres from optical radiation where visible or infrared radiation is incapable of producing sufficient energy under normal or specified fault conditions to ignite a specific explosive atmosphere.

Informational Note: See ANSI/ UL 60079-28-2017, *Explosive Atmospheres — Part 28: Protection of Equipment and Transmission Systems Using Optical Radiation.*

(See NEC for actual text)

Significance of the Change

A new definition of the term *inherently safe optical radiation "op is"* has been added to Article 100. Part III of Article 100 has been designated specifically for the defined terms associated with hazardous (classified) locations. This definition has been added to Part III. This new definition defines inherently safe optical radiation and indicates this type of protection can minimize the risk of ignition in explosive atmospheres from optical radiation where visible or infrared radiation is incapable of producing sufficient energy under normal or specified fault conditions to ignite a specific explosive atmosphere. Although most optical radiation is not a source of ignition, this standard allows determination of those that are a source of ignition and protection techniques that can be used to minimize ignition of explosive atmospheres. The new informational note provides users with a valuable informational reference to ANSI/UL 60079-28 titled *Explosive Atmospheres — Part 28: Protection of Equipment and Transmission Systems Using Optical Radiation.* Additional variations of definitions for optical radiation have been added based on ANSI/*UL 60079 (2017).*

Change Summary

- A new definition of the term *inherently safe optical radiation "op is"* has been added to Article 100.
- Part III of Article 100 has been designated specifically for the defined terms associated with hazardous (classified) locations.
- The new informational note provides an important reference to ANSI/*UL 60079* containing information related to explosive atmosphere ignition concerns.

FR: 7761

SR: None

Definition of Optical Radiation

Code Language

Optical Radiation. Electromagnetic radiation at wavelengths in vacuum between the region of transition to X-rays and the region of transition to radio waves, that is approximately between 1 nm and 1000 μm.

Informational Note: For additional information on types of protection that can be applied to minimize the risk of ignition in explosive atmospheres from optical radiation in the wavelength range from 380 nm to 10 μm, see ANSI/UL 60079-28-2017, *Explosive Atmospheres — Part 28: Protection of Equipment and Transmission Systems Using Optical Radiation.*

(See NEC for actual text)

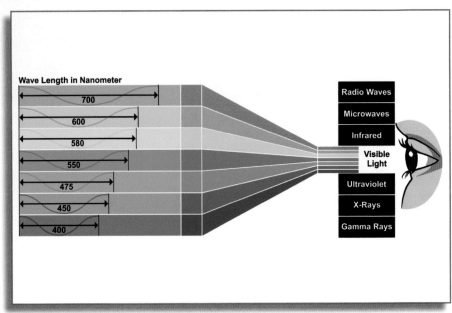

Wave Length in Nanometer

700
600
580
550
475
450
400

Radio Waves
Microwaves
Infrared
Visible Light
Ultraviolet
X-Rays
Gamma Rays

Change Summary

- A new definition of the term *optical radiation* has been added to Part III of Article 100.

- Part III of Article 100 is now designated for defined terms used in *NEC* rules that address hazardous (classified) locations.

- The new informational note provides an important reference to ANSI/*UL 60079* containing information related to explosive atmosphere ignition concerns.

Significance of the Change

A new definition of the term *optical radiation* has been added to Article 100. Part III of Article 100 has been designated specifically for the defined terms associated with hazardous (classified) locations. This definition has been added to Part III. This new definition defines optical radiation and indicates the wavelengths between the region of X-rays and the region of transition to radio wave forms. These wave forms are capable of igniting explosive atmospheres in certain conditions. Optical radiation is identified as a potential "non-electrical" risk of ignition in a hazardous (classified) location largely generated by electrical means. Although most optical radiation is not a source of ignition, this standard allows determination of those that are a source of ignition. The new informational note provides users with a valuable information reference to ANSI/UL 60079-28 titled *Explosive Atmospheres — Part 28: Protection of Equipment and Transmission Systems Using Optical Radiation.* Additional definitions for optical radiation have been added based on ANSI/*UL 60079 (2017)*.

FR: 7761
SR: None

Definition of Protected Optical Fiber Cable

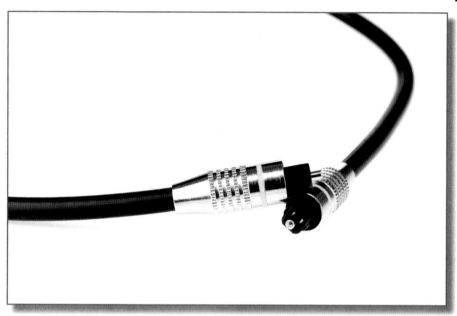

Code Language

Protected Optical Fiber Cable. Optical fiber cable protected from releasing optical radiation into the atmosphere during normal operating conditions and foreseeable malfunctions by additional armoring, conduit, cable tray, or raceway.

Informational Note: See ANSI/UL 60079-28-2017, *Explosive Atmospheres — Part 28: Protection of Equipment and Transmission Systems Using Optical Radiation.*

(See NEC for actual text)

Significance of the Change

A new definition of the term *Protected Optical Fiber Cable* has been added to Article 100. Part III of Article 100 has been designated specifically for the defined terms associated with hazardous (classified) locations. This definition has been added to Part III. This new definition defines protected optical fiber cable and indicates this type of protection as protected from releasing optical radiation into the atmosphere during normal operating conditions and foreseeable malfunctions by additional armoring, conduit, cable tray, or raceway. This means the protection is in the form of protection from damage strengthened means inherent to the cable construction. Although most optical fiber cable is not a source of ignition, this standard allows determination of those that are a source of ignition and protection techniques that can be used to minimize ignition of explosive atmospheres. The new informational note provides users with a valuable information reference to ANSI/UL 60079-28 titled *Explosive Atmospheres — Part 28: Protection of Equipment and Transmission Systems Using Optical Radiation*. Additional variations of definitions for optical radiation have been added based on ANSI/*UL 60079 (2017).*

Change Summary

- A new definition of the term *Protected Optical Fiber Cable* has been added to Article 100.
- Part III of Article 100 has been designated specifically for the defined terms associated with hazardous (classified) locations.
- The new informational note provides an important reference to ANSI/*UL 60079* containing information related to explosive atmosphere ignition concerns and protection techniques that can be used.

FR: 7761
SR: None

Definition of Protected Optical Fiber Radiation

Code Language

Protected Optical Radiation "op pr". Type of protection to minimize the risk of ignition in explosive atmospheres from optical radiation where visible or infrared radiation is confined inside optical fiber or other transmission medium under normal constructions or constructions with additional mechanical protection based on the assumption that there is no escape of radiation from the confinement.

Informational Note: See ANSI/ UL 60079-28-2017, *Explosive Atmospheres — Part 28: Protection of Equipment and Transmission Systems Using Optical Radiation.*

(See NEC for actual text)

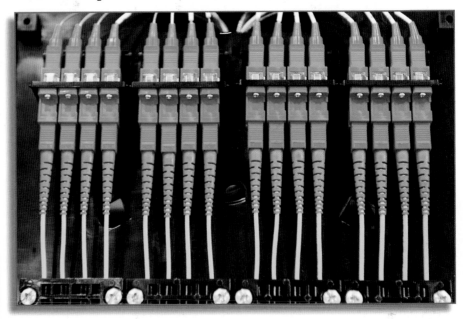

Change Summary

- A new definition of the term *Protected Optical Fiber Radiation* has been added to Article 100.

- Part III of Article 100 has been designated specifically for the defined terms associated with hazardous (classified) locations.

- The new informational note provides an important reference to ANSI/*UL 60079* containing information related to explosive atmosphere ignition concerns and protection techniques.

Significance of the Change

A new definition of the term *Protected Optical Fiber Radiation* has been added to Article 100. Part III of Article 100 has been designated specifically for the defined terms associated with hazardous (classified) locations. This definition has been added to Part III. This new definition defines protected optical fiber radiation and indicates this is a type of protection to minimize the risk of ignition in explosive atmospheres from optical radiation where visible or infrared radiation is confined inside optical fiber or other transmission medium under normal constructions or constructions with additional mechanical protection based on the assumption that there is no escape of radiation from the confinement.

This means the protection is in the form of protection from damage strengthened means inherent to the cable construction. Although most optical fiber cable is not a source of ignition, Standard ANSI/ *UL 60079-28* facilitates determination of those that are a source of ignition and protection techniques that can be used to minimize ignition of explosive atmospheres. The new informational note provides users with a valuable information reference to ANSI/UL 60079-28 titled *Explosive Atmospheres — Part 28: Protection of Equipment and Transmission Systems Using Optical Radiation*.

FR: 7761
SR: None

Installation and Use

Code Language

110.3 Examination, Identification, Installation, Use, and Listing (Product Certification) of Equipment.

(A) Examination. In judging equipment, considerations such as the following shall be evaluated…(See *NEC* text)

(B) Installation and Use. Equipment that is listed, labeled, or both shall be installed and used in accordance with any instructions included in the listing or labeling.

(See NEC for actual text)

Significance of the Change

Section 110.3(B) was revised and reworded to include the words "or both" in the rule. The revision emphasizes that equipment that is listed (certified) either bears the listing mark, bears a label, or both, often in combination. The revision is related to Public Comment No. 531 of the (A2016) Second Draft Report for NFPA 70-2017. This comment was held in the 2017 *NEC* development process in accordance with the Section 4.4.8.3.1 of the NFPA Regulations. The *NEC* Correlating Committee formed a special task group to address the identified confusion with the listing and or labeling issue. This task group work is continuing as evidenced by this slight revision in this section and the new informational note to the definition of the term "labeled" added in the 2020 *NEC*. The new informational note provides meaningful and needed clarification that is beneficial to installers, enforcers, owners, and others. The note indicates that labeling of listed equipment is not possible in all cases or conditions such as if products are too small to be labeled or for some severe environmental conditions. The revision to this section clarifies that equipment could be listed, labeled, or both to provide evidence of product certification.

Change Summary

- Section 110.3(B) was revised and reworded to include the words "or both" in the rule.
- Equipment that is listed (certified), either bears the listing mark, bears a label, or both, often in combination.
- The revision aligns with the fact that most but not all listed (certified) equipment is labeled.

FR: 8392
SR: None

Cables and Conductors – Workmanship

Code Language

(C) Cables and Conductors. Cables and conductors installed exposed on the surfaces of ceilings and sidewalls shall be supported by the building structure in such a manner that the cables and conductors will not be damaged by normal building use. Such cables and conductors... (See *NEC* text)

(See NEC for actual text)

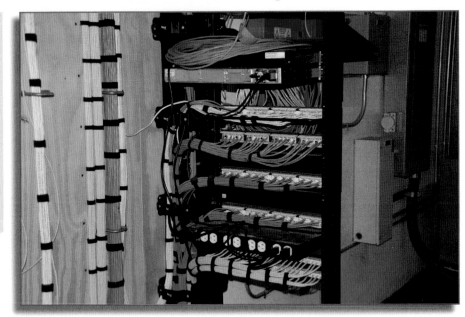

Change Summary

- A new subdivision (C) titled *Cables and Conductors* has been added in Section 110.12 which is titled *Mechanical Execution of Work*.
- It includes relocated requirements from the .24 sections from the communications articles in Chapters 7 and 8.
- Conductor and cable support and concerns about damage are addressed in both 110.12(C) and in 800.24.

Significance of the Change

A new subdivision (C) titled *Cables and Conductors* has been added in Section 110.12 which continues to be titled *Mechanical Execution of Work*. This revision coordinates the actions to relocate the content of sections 760.24, 770.24, 725.24, 800.24, 820.24, 830.24, and 840.24 to Section 110.12(C). This revision aligns with the recommendation of the Correlating Committee Usability task group to improve usability of *NEC* communications articles in chapters 7 and 8. This action consolidates redundant requirements and relocating them into a general rule in Chapter 1. Even though the requirements for support and damage from the communications articles have been relocated to this new subdivision, the requirements still apply within unless specifically addressed otherwise within the communications articles in Chapter 8. Conductor and cable support and concerns about damage are addressed in this rule in 110.12(C) and in 800.24. The two mirror each other in the 2020 *NEC*. Article 800 in the 2020 *NEC* has been restructured to contain only the common general requirements for the chapter 8 communications articles. Articles 810 through 840 contain the more specific rules related to installations of each of these different communications systems and their associated wiring.

FR: 8484
SR: 8047

Terminal Connection Torque

Significance of the Change

The title of subdivision (D) has been changed from "Installation" to "Terminal Connection Torque" to reflect the content of this subdivision. The first sentence of this rule has been completely revised and a new second sentence has been added requiring an approved means to be used to achieve required torque values as indicated by the manufacturer. The word calibrated has been deleted from this section as use of a calibrated tool for performing torqueing functions is inherently implied and a responsibility of the installer. Helpful informational notes have been added to provide needed guidance and insight into providing correct torque for threaded connections and terminations. A new requirement for an approved means was introduced to allow viable and practical approaches by authorities having jurisdiction (AHJ) that the installation conforms to the appropriate torqueing requirements. Informational Note No. 1 provides guidance to help ensure that a proper torque has been achieved, including an option for visual indicators. The revisions to this section provide installers with all necessary information related to the torqueing process and removes the language related to "calibrated tools" which results in ease of enforceability by the AHJ.

Code Language

(D) Terminal Connection Torque. Tightening torque values for terminal connections shall be as indicated on equipment or in installation instructions provided by the manufacturer. An approved means shall be used to achieve the indicated torque value.

Informational Note No. 1: Examples of approved means of achieving the indicated torque values include torque tools or visual indicators that demonstrate that the proper torque has been applied.

Informational Note No. 2: Informative Annex I of UL *Standard 486A-486B, Standard for Safety-Wire Connectors,* provides torque values in the absence of manufacturer's recommendations.

Informational Note No. 3: Additional information for torqueing threaded connections and terminations can be found in Section 8.11 of NFPA 70B-2016, *Recommended Practice for Electrical Equipment Maintenance.*

(See NEC for actual text)

Change Summary

- The title of subdivision (D) has been changed from "Installation" to "Terminal Connection Torque."
- The term *calibrated* has been deleted from this section.
- Three new informational notes provide practical guidance for installers and inspectors.

FR: 8510
SR: 8069

Reconditioned Equipment Exception

Code Language

Exception: In industrial occupancies, where conditions of maintenance and supervision ensure that only qualified persons service the equipment, the markings indicated in 110.21(A)(2) shall not be required for equipment that is reconditioned by the owner or operator as part of a regular equipment maintenance program.

Informational Note No. 1: Industry standards are available for application of reconditioned and refurbished equipment.

Informational Note No. 2: The term "reconditioned" may be interchangeable with the terms "rebuilt," "refurbished," or "remanufactured."

(See NEC for actual text)

Change Summary

- The exception has been revised to provide clarification as to when this exception can be applied.
- New Informational Note No. 2 explains that terms such as *refurbished*, *rebuilt*, or *remanufactured* are often used interchangeably with the term *reconditioned*.
- New Informational Note No. 3 explains that the original listing mark could include the mark of the certifying body, and not an entire label.

Significance of the Change

Section 110.21(A)(2) requires that reconditioned equipment be marked with the name, trademark, or other descriptive marking by which the organization responsible for reconditioning the electrical equipment can be identified, along with the date of the reconditioning. Reconditioned equipment is required to be identified as "reconditioned" and the original listing mark should be removed. Approval of the reconditioned equipment shall not be based solely on the original listing of the equipment. The exception has been revised by adding the words "for equipment that is reconditioned by the owner or operator as part of a regular equipment maintenance program." This revision provides clarity as to when the exception applies. Informational Note No. 2 provides terms such as *refurbished*, *rebuilt*, or *remanufactured* that are often used interchangeably with *reconditioned*. Normal servicing of equipment that remains within a facility should not be considered reconditioning or refurbishing. The intent of the Exception to 110.21(A)(2) is to provide practical relief from the marking requirement when industrial facilities maintain and refurbish equipment as a part of their regularly maintenance cycle for safety and reliability under controlled conditions that adhere to applicable standards.

FR: 8550
SR: 8079
SCR: 71

Disconnect Marking

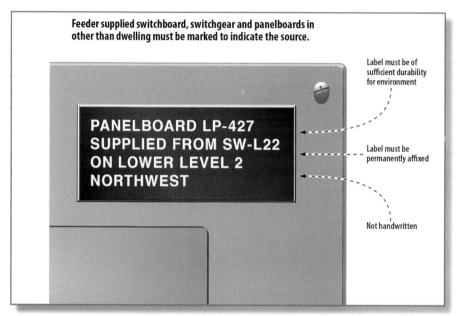

Feeder supplied switchboard, switchgear and panelboards in other than dwelling must be marked to indicate the source.

Label must be of sufficient durability for environment

PANELBOARD LP-427 SUPPLIED FROM SW-L22 ON LOWER LEVEL 2 NORTHWEST

Label must be permanently affixed

Not handwritten

Code Language

(A) General. Each disconnecting means shall be legibly marked to indicate its purpose unless located and arranged so the purpose is evident. In other than one- or two-family dwellings, the marking shall include the identification of the circuit source that supplies the disconnecting means. The marking shall be of sufficient durability to withstand the environment involved.

(See NEC for actual text)

Significance of the Change

A new second sentence has been added to Section 110.22(A) that reads "In other than one- or two-family dwellings, the marking shall include the identification of the circuit source that supplies the disconnecting means." This source circuit identification requirement provides direct correlation with the same requirement in Section 408.4. Identifying the source of a circuit or feeder at the disconnecting enclosure enhances electrical safety for workers at times subsequent to the original installation. The maintenance electrician, contract electrician, or owner will be able to identify and shut off the disconnect in case of a problem with a minimal amount of time. The first sentence of this rule relaxes the source circuit identification requirement when by location and arrangement, the purpose is evident. This is usually accomplished through compliance with a "within sight from" requirement. This revision also helps facilitate the process of establishing an electrically safe work condition required by *NFPA 70E: Standard for Electrical Safety in the Workplace*. The information about the marking being durable for the environment has not been changed by this revision.

Change Summary

- A new second sentence has been added to Section 110.22(A).
- Identification of the source circuit supplying the disconnecting means is now required for other than one- and two-family dwelling installations.
- The revision enhances the ability to establish an electrically safe work condition as addressed in *NFPA 70E*.

FR: 8600

SR: NA

110.24(A)

Article 110 Requirements for Electrical Installations

Part II 1000 Volts, Nominal, or Less

Published Values of Available Fault Current

Code Language

(A) Field Marking. Service equipment at other than dwelling units shall be legibly marked in the field with the available fault current. (See *NEC* text)

Informational Note No. 1: The available fault-current marking(s) addressed in 110.24 is related to required short-circuit current ratings of equipment…(See *NEC* text)

Informational Note No. 2: Values of available fault current for use in determining appropriate minimum short-circuit current ratings of service equipment are available from electric utilities in published or other forms.

(See NEC for actual text)

SES#	1 PH 120/240 POLE/PAD XFMR		3 PH 120/240 Closed Delta POLE TOP XFMR		3 PH 120/240 Open Delta POLE TOP XFMR		3 PH 120/240 Open Delta PAD XFMR (based upon a 167/75kva transformer)		3 PH 120/208 POLE TOP XFMR		3 PH 120/208 PAD XFMR		3 PH 277/480 POLE TOP XFMR		3 PH 277/480 PAD XFMR	
AMPS	kVA	Isc	kVA	Isc	kVA	ISC	kVA	Isc	kVA	Isc	kVA	Isc	kVA	Isc	kVA	Isc
100	50	8,890	3-25	9,948	75-75	19,953	167-75	23,971	3-25	8,895	112.5	12,684	75	5,192	112.5	8,688
125	50	8,890	3-25	9,948	75-75	19,953	167-75	23,971	3-25	8,895	112.5	12,684	150	9,613	112.5	8,688
150	50	8,890	3-25	9,948	75-75	19,953	167-75	23,971	3-25	8,895	112.5	12,684	150	9,613	112.5	8,688
200	75	14,318	3-25	10,478	75-75	25,625	167-75	33,705	3-25	10,483	112.5	16,178	150	10,347	150	12,076
*400	100	20,955	3-50	20,034	75-75	28,369	167-75	39,681	3-50	21,553	150	27,478	300	20,938	300	25,573
600	167	32,755	3-75	28,369	100-75	35,297	167-75	44,187	3-75	33,789	225	39,066	500	31,615	500	25,773
800	167	36,451	3-100	33,208	167-75	44,186	167-75	44,187	**3-100	43,106	300	49,505			750	25,773
1,000									**3-100	45,740	300	53,011			750	25,773
1,200											500	53,011			1,000	25,773
1,600											500	56,194			1,500	32,990
2,000											750	56,194			1,500	33,207
2,500											750	56,194			2,000	44,250
3,000											1,000	56,194			2,000	44,346

Sample Published Available Fault Current Levels for Utility Service

Change Summary

- Section 110.24(A) has been revised for accuracy and clarification.
- The word "maximum" has been deleted in front of "available fault current" because it is not necessary.
- New Informational Note No. 2 explains that available fault current values are typically provided and published by utilities.

Significance of the Change

Section 110.24(A) has been revised for accuracy and clarification. The word "maximum" has been deleted in front of "available fault current" because it is not necessary. The reference to *NFPA 70E* in Informational Note No. 1 has been updated to the latest edition (2018). A new Informational Note No. 2 was added to advise that values of available fault current for use in determining appropriate minimum short circuit current ratings of service equipment are available from electric utilities in published or other forms. The words "and interrupting ratings" have been added in both informational notes to clarify that the equipment ratings implied here include both the short-circuit current and interrupting ratings of the equipment to better align with Section 110.9. It was reported in some areas that utilities were reluctant to provide the available fault current of their system that supplies an electric service. This information is required. The new informational note will assist users and emphasize that the available fault current from the serving utility must be provided and known to allow for compliant designs and installations relative to using equipment within their applicable ratings. A general requirement of the *NEC* in 110.10.

FR: 8617
SR: 8089

Planning for an Electrically Safe Work Condition

Code Language

110.26(A) Working Space. Working space for equipment operating at 1000 volts, nominal, or less to ground and likely to require examination, adjustment, servicing, or maintenance while energized shall comply with…(See *NEC* text)

Informational Note: NFPA 70E-2018, *Standard for Electrical Safety in the Workplace*, provides guidance, such as determining severity of potential exposure, planning safe work practices including establishing an electrically safe work condition, arc flash labeling, and selecting personal protective equipment.

(See NEC for actual text)

Significance of the Change

Section 110.26(A) provides general requirements for and minimum dimensions (distances) of required working space about electrical equipment. These are installation requirements that ensure minimum working space is provided to allow for safe examination, adjustment, servicing, or maintenance while in an energized state. The existing informational note to Section 110.26(A) has been revised and expanded. The date of *NFPA 70E* has been changed from 2015 to 2018 to reference the current edition of the standard. The phrase "including establishing an electrically safe work condition" has been incorporated. Including this language is important because it provides increased emphasis on the main purpose of *NFPA 70E* which is to remove electrical hazards and risks as the first requirement rather than resorting directly to the use of PPE as the first choice. The general requirements of *NFPA 70E* are to eliminate the hazard through the implementation of an electrically safe work condition. The *NEC* is an installation standard, not a work practice standard, and does not convey any position on work practices related to energized electrical work, whether justified or not.

Change Summary

- The informational note to Section 110.26(A) has been revised and expanded.
- The date of *NFPA 70E* has been changed from 2015 to 2018 to reference the current edition.
- The phrase "including establishing an electrically safe work condition" has been incorporated.

FR: 8621
SR: 8097

Sum of Service Disconnect Ratings Added

Code Language

110.26(C)(2) Large Equipment. For large equipment that contains overcurrent devices, switching devices, or control devices, there shall be one entrance to and egress...(See *NEC* text)

(1) For equipment rated 1200 amperes or more and over 1.8 m (6 ft) wide

(2) For service disconnecting means installed in accordance with 230.71 where the combined ampere rating is 1200 amperes or more and over 1.8 m (6 ft) wide

Open equipment doors shall not impede the entry to or egress from the working space.

(See NEC for actual text)

Change Summary

- Section 110.26(C)(2) has been revised and restructured into a list format.
- Two entrances and egress paths from the work space are required if the sum of the two-to-six service disconnects is 1200 amperes or more.
- Open equipment doors on large equipment shall not impede the entry to or egress from the required working space.

Significance of the Change

Section 110.26(C)(2) continues to address large equipment and is restructured into second level subdivisions to comply with the *NEC Style Manual* and to improve clarity. The text "For equipment rated 1200 amperes or more and over 1.8 m (6 ft) wide" has been relocated to second level subdivision (1). Subdivision (2) triggers the two entrances and egress path from equipment for service disconnecting means installed in accordance with 230.71 where the combined ampere rating is 1200 amperes or more and over 1.8 m (6 ft) wide. This means that when using the two-to-six service disconnect rule, the sum of the six service disconnect ratings must be used to determine the requirement for two entrances and egress paths from the working space. This revision is safety driven and is intended to recognize the common practice of separating large services into multiple separate disconnecting means. Requirements have also been added to 110.26(C)(2) to prohibit open equipment doors from impeding the entry to or egress from the working space of large equipment in order to minimize the chance of entrapment between open equipment doors and an obstruction, such as a wall facing the equipment.

FR: 8672
SR: 8104

Listed Fire Exit Hardware

Code Language

(3) Personnel Doors. Where equipment rated 800 amperes or more that contains overcurrent devices, switching devices, or control devices is installed and there is a personnel door(s) intended for…(See *NEC* text)… working space, the door(s) shall open in the direction of egress and be equipped with listed panic hardware or listed fire exit hardware.

Informational Note: For information on panic hardware, see UL 305, *Standard For Safety For Panic Hardware*. For fire exit hardware, see UL 305, *Standard For Panic Hardware*, and UL 10C, *Standard for Safety for Positive Pressure Fire Tests of Door Assemblies.*

(See NEC for actual text)

Significance of the Change

The words "or listed fire exit hardware" have been added to 110.26(C)(3). A new informational note references two UL standards applicable to the door hardware referred to in this rule. Adding listed fire exit hardware as an alternative to listed panic hardware will correlate with the terminology used in the building and fire codes. Panic hardware is used for egress doors installed in a non-fire-resistance rated wall, whereas, fire exit hardware is used for egress doors installed in a fire-resistance rated wall. As previously written in the 2017 *NEC*, an AHJ may not accept hardware listed as "Fire Exit Hardware" as it is not identified as "Panic Hardware." Doors in fire rated assemblies are required to be listed fire-rated doors and the installation of panic hardware on fire doors is prohibited by the Life Safety *Code* and other model building codes. For examples of areas that require fire rated separation, see section 450.21(B) of the *NEC* and Section 7.2 of *NFPA 110*. *NFPA 101*, Section 7.2.1.7.2 prohibits the installation of panic hardware on fire rated doors along which is consistent with other model building codes. Both panic hardware and fire exit hardware are listed to UL 305. However, fire exit hardware is additionally tested to UL 10C.

Change Summary

- The words "or listed fire exit hardware" have been added to 110.26(C)(3).
- An informational note has been added that references two UL standards that apply to the door hardware referred to in this rule.
- The revision differentiates listed panic hardware from listed fire exit hardware.

FR: 8658
SR: None

Dusttight Enclosure Use and Application

Code Language

Informational Note No. 3: Dusttight enclosures are suitable for use in hazardous locations in accordance with 502.10(B)(4), 503.10(A)(2), and 506.15(C)(9).

Informational Note No. 4: Dusttight enclosures are suitable for use in unclassified locations and in Class II, Division 2; Class III; and Zone 22 hazardous (classified) locations.

(See NEC for actual text)

Courtesy of Eaton

Significance of the Change

Two new informational notes have been added to Section 110.28. The new informational notes add clarity relative to installing enclosure types in the specified environments. Type 4, 4X, 6, and 6P are considered dusttight and are added to Informational Note No. 1 for clarity. Prior to the 2020 *NEC*, it was reported that there was confusion in the field that Types 3, 3X, 3SX, 3X, 5, 12, 12K, and 13 enclosures that were marked as "dusttight" were not suitable for any hazardous locations. These rated enclosures are suitable for use in hazardous locations that contain dust in accordance with the sections identified in the new Informational Note. Basically, Informational Note No. 3 references the specific "uses permitted" sections with Article 502, 503, and 506 while new Informational Note No. 4 indicates that these types of enclosures are permitted in any unclassified location and limited in hazardous (classified) locations to only Class II, Division 2 locations and Class III locations and Zone 22 locations. The new informational note should remove the confusion about which locations dusttight equipment is permitted to be installed in.

Change Summary

- Two new informational notes have been added to Section 110.28.
- Informational Note No. 3 references the specific "uses permitted" sections with Articles 502, 503, and 506.
- Informational Note No. 4 indicates that these types of enclosures are permitted in any unclassified location and limited to Class II, Division 2; Class III, and Zone 22 hazardous (classified) locations.

FR: 8672
SR: 8109

Listed Panic and Fire Exit Hardware

Code Language

(4) Locks. Doors shall be equipped with locks, and doors shall be kept locked, with access allowed only to qualified persons. Personnel doors shall open in the direction of egress and be equipped with listed panic hardware or listed fire exit hardware.

(See NEC for actual text)

Significance of the Change

Section 110.31(A)(4) has been revised to address the door opening direction and to include both listed panic hardware and listed fire-rated hardware. This revision will align with similar requirements in Section 110.26(C)(3) while clarifying the direction of opening of personnel doors. They must open in the direction of egress. The phrase "panic bars, pressure plates, or other devices…" has been removed because it is adequately covered and included in listed panic hardware or fire exit hardware. Listed panic hardware is not permitted to be installed on fire rated doors unless so rated. Some electrical equipment rooms are required to be enclosed with fire-rated construction and doors in fire rated walls are required to be fire rated. The term listed is added to "fire exit hardware" because both "listed panic hardware" and "listed fire exit hardware" are evaluated to the *Standard for Panic Hardware, UL 305*, with "listed fire exit hardware" evaluated to both *UL 305* and the *Standard for Positive Pressure Fire Tests for Door Assemblies, UL 10C*. The new informational note to Section 110.26(C)(3) provides references to these two door hardware UL standards.

Change Summary

- Section 110.31(A)(4) has been revised to clarify the personnel door opening must be in the direction of egress.
- The terms *listed panic hardware* and *listed fire exit hardware* have been incorporated in this section.
- The informational note to Section 110.26(C)(3) provides references to two UL standards that address listed panic hardware and listed fire exit hardware.

FR: 8682
SR: 8110

Work Space About Equipment

Code Language

110.32 Work Space About Equipment. Sufficient space shall be provided... (See *NEC* text)...shall be not less than 2.0 m (6 $\frac{1}{2}$ ft) high (measured vertically from the floor or platform) and the width of the equipment or 914 mm (3 ft) wide (measured parallel to the equipment), whichever is greater. The depth shall be... (See *NEC* text) Within the height requirements of this section, other equipment that is associated with the electrical installation and is located above or below the electrical equipment shall be permitted to extend not more than 150 mm (6 in) beyond the front of the electrical equipment. Working space required by this section shall not be used for storage. When normally enclosed live parts are exposed for inspection or servicing, the working space, if in a passageway or general open space, shall be suitably guarded.

(See NEC for actual text)

Change Summary

- This section has been revised and expanded to align with similar requirements in 110.26(A) and (B).
- The work space shall not be used for storage.
- Live parts that are exposed for inspection or servicing must be suitably guarded.

Significance of the Change

This section has been revised and expanded to align with similar requirements in 110.26(A) and (B). The word "or" is changed to "and" to require both conditions because it is a combination of height and width that creates the work space. The "width of the equipment" and the words "whichever is greater" requirement have been added for clarity in the second sentence. Three new sentences have been added to be consistent with requirements for equipment installations that are less than 1000 volts. The first new sentence indicates that other equipment that is associated with the electrical installation and is located above or below the electrical equipment shall be permitted to extend not more than six inches beyond the front of the electrical equipment. The second new sentence is consistent with the prohibiting of working space being used for storage. The third sentence mirrors Section 110.26(B) and requires that when normally enclosed live parts are exposed for inspection or servicing, the working space, if in a passageway or general open space, must be suitably guarded.

FR: 8686
SR: None

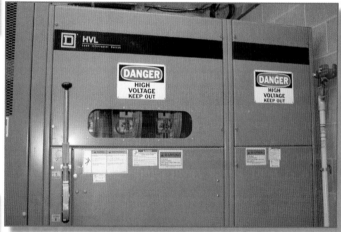

Chapter 2

Articles 210–250
Wiring and Protection

REVISION

Connection to Grounded System

Code Language

200.3 Connection to Grounded System. Premises wiring shall not be electrically connected to a supply system unless the latter contains, for any grounded conductor of the premises wiring system, a corresponding conductor that is grounded. For the purpose of this section, *electrically connected* shall mean connected so as to be capable of carrying current, as distinguished from connection through electromagnetic induction.

Exception: Listed interactive inverters identified for use in distributed resource generation systems such as photovoltaic... (See NEC text)

(See NEC for actual text)

Change Summary

- Section 200.3 has been revised for improved clarity and usability.
- The word *utility* has been deleted from this section as it was redundant and implied by definition of premises wiring.
- The term *direct electrical connection* provides a clear distinction from a connection through electromagnetic induction.

Significance of the Change

The first sentence was revised to make it clear that this text refers to all premises wiring, not just interior wiring. The sentence was also reworded for clarity. The word *utility* was deleted because it is redundant based on the definition of interactive inverter as provided in Article 100. The second sentence in 200.3 was revised to provide additional clarity and a clear differentiation between a solid direct electrical connection and a connection that is made through magnetic coupling. The connection sought by this requirement of the *Code* is a solid grounding connection that is supported by the definition of the term *grounded solidly*. Section 200.3 is directly related to the requirements contained in Section 250.24 that includes mandatory language about grounded conductors supplied from utility sources for a service. This section requires that where an ac system operating at 1000 volts or less is grounded at any point, the grounded conductor(s) shall be routed with the ungrounded conductors to each service disconnecting means and shall be connected to each disconnecting means grounded conductor(s) terminal or bus. This connection must be a solid connection.

FR: 7614

SR: None

Identification of Grounded Conductor Terminals

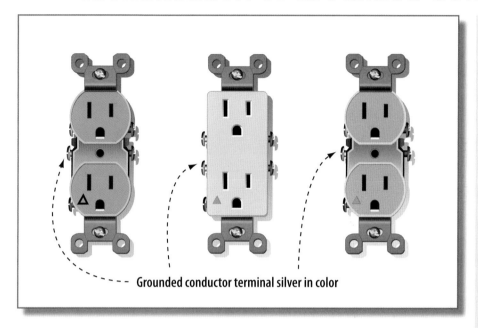

Grounded conductor terminal silver in color

Code Language

200.10 Identification of Terminals
(B) Receptacles, Plugs, and Connectors. Receptacles, polarized attachment plugs, and cord connectors for plugs and polarized plugs shall have the terminal intended for connection to the grounded conductor identified as follows:

(1) Identification shall be by a metal or metal coating that is substantially white or silver in color or by the word *white* or the letter *W* located adjacent to the identified terminal.

(2) If the terminal... (See *NEC* text)

(See NEC for actual text)

Significance of the Change

Section 200.10 is titled "Identification of Terminals" and should include all methods of identification of terminals for grounded conductors. Terminals of devices and equipment specifically referenced in this section must be identified by one of the means indicated in this section. In the prior editions of the *Code*, these identification means included the color "White" or the letter "W" for identification of the conductor terminal connections. Although manufacturers can utilize the color white and the letter W, the most common means used is to use a screw that is silver or chrome in color. This provides the contrast between terminals for connecting ungrounded conductors to the devices, which are typically brass or gold in color. The revision to this section reflects accuracy in what is most commonly utilized in the field for terminal identification on receptacles, plugs, and connectors. The options of the word "White" and the letter "W" still exist. What is interesting is the absence of the word "Gray" from this section, which must reflect the common practices of manufacturers of these types of equipment and devices.

Change Summary

- The words "or silver" have been added to second level subdivision (1).
- Receptacles, polarized attachment plugs, and cord connectors for plugs and polarized plugs typically include a terminal that is silver or chrome in color, as compared to brass or gold color.
- The revision reflects the common identification means employed by product manufacturers.

FR: 7631
SR: None

Identification of Ungrounded Conductors

Code Language

210.5(C)(1) Branch Circuits Supplied from More Than One Nominal Voltage System. ...(See *NEC* Text) each ungrounded conductor of a branch circuit shall be identified by phase or line and by system voltage class at all termination, connection, and splice points in compliance with 210.5(C)(1)(a) and (b). Different systems within the same premises that have the same system voltage class shall be permitted to use the same identification.

(See NEC for actual text)

NECA Electric, Bethesda MD 20814	
Ungrounded Conductor Identification	
Voltage Class	
Less than 150 volts to ground and not over 300 volts to phase to phase	Over 150 volts to ground and not over 300 volts to phase to phase
A-Phase Black	A-Phase Brown
B-Phase Red	B-Phase Orange
C-Phase Blue	C-Phase Yellow
Neutral White	Neutral Gray

Change Summary

- 210.5(C)(1) now requires ungrounded conductors be identified by phase or line and *by system voltage class*.
- Clarification is provided to permit different voltage systems within the same premises with the same *system voltage class* to use the same means of identification.

FR: PI 454

SR: 7525

Significance of the Change

Section 210.5 contains requirements for the identification of branch circuits. First level subdivision 210.5(C) contains requirements for the identification of ungrounded conductors. 210.5(C)(1) requires that where a premise wiring system has branch circuits supplied from more than one nominal voltage system, each ungrounded conductor of a branch circuit must be identified. In the 2017 *NEC*, these ungrounded branch circuit conductors are required to be identified by "phase or line and system." This marking requirement is revised for the 2020 *NEC* and the identification is now required to be by "phase or line and *by system voltage class*." This is a very significant revision as the *NEC* now recognizes that a single facility may have several voltage systems but only two system voltage classes. This revision recognizes that if each individual system were required to be individually identified, it would be next to impossible. A new last sentence in the parent text of 210.5(C)(1) provides significant clarity as follows: "Different systems within the same premises that have the same system voltage class shall be permitted to use the same identification." For example, consider a facility that contains several systems including: 240/120 single phase, 208/120 three phase (wye), 240/120 three phase (delta), and 480/277 three phase (wye). As written in 2017 we would need four different means of identification. This revision now recognizes that in the example provided above there are only two voltage classes. The first is less than 150 volts to ground and not over 300 volts phase-to-phase. The second is over 150 volts to ground and less than 1000-volts phase-to-phase.

GFCI Protection for Personnel

Code Language

210.8 Ground-Fault Circuit-Interrupter Protection for Personnel... (See *NEC* Text)

Informational Note No. 3. See 555.9... (See *NEC* Text)

Informational Note No. 4. See Chapters 4, 5 and 6... (See *NEC* Text)

For the purposes of this section, when determining the distance from receptacles... (See *NEC* text) the shortest path the supply cord of an appliance connected to the receptacle would follow ... (See *NEC* text) without passing through a ... (See *NEC* text)

210.8(A)(11) Indoor Damp and wet locations

(See NEC for actual text)

Significance of the Change

Section 210.8 *GFCI Protection for Personnel* is significantly modified. The parent text now references first level subdivisions 210.8(A) through (F). Two subdivisions are relocated in the *NEC* and three new subdivisions are added. Existing first level subdivision (C) is deleted and relocated into new section 555.9. A new informational note is added to the parent text to send the code user to 555.9 for GFCI requirements for boat hoists. An additional informational note is added to inform the code user that additional GFCI requirements for specific circuits and equipment are located in chapters 4, 5, and 6. This is extremely important as the general requirement in 210.8 for GFCI protection for personnel applies to all buildings, structures, and other locations. The last paragraph of the parent text provides prescriptive information on how to determine the distance from receptacles when a distance is provided within this section. The distance is determined by measuring the shortest path the supply cord of an appliance connected to a receptacle would follow without piercing a floor, wall, ceiling or fixed barrier or the shortest path without passing through a window. It is extremely significant to note that the terms *door* and *doorway* are deleted. This text was new in the 2017 *NEC* and exempted GFCI protection of receptacles in cabinets with doors in kitchens, next to bathtubs, and shower stalls, as well as under or next to sinks. For example, a receptacle installed in the cabinet directly under a sink must now be GFCI protected.

Change Summary

- Measuring distance from receptacles is modified. Doors or doorways do not eliminate GFCI requirements.
- 210.8(C) for boat hoists is relocated into 555.9. An informational note is added.
- In 210.8 two first level subdivisions are deleted and three are added.

FR: 7863
SR: 7685

210.8(A)

Article 210 Branch Circuits

Part I General Provisions

GFCI, Dwelling Units

Code Language

210.8(A) Dwelling Units. All 125-volt through 250-volt receptacles installed in the locations specified in 210.8(A)(1) through (A)(11) and supplied by single-phase branch circuits rated 150 volts or less to ground shall have ground-fault circuit-interrupter protection for personnel.

(5) Basements

(11) Indoor damp and wet locations

(See NEC for actual text)

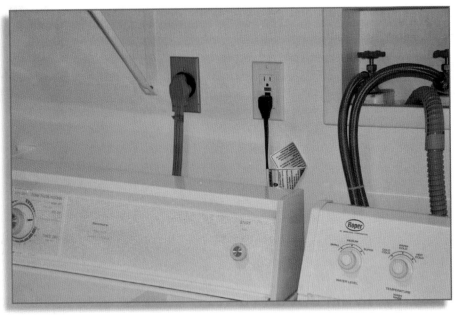

Change Summary

- The parent text in 210.8(A) is expanded to include all 125-volt through 250-volt receptacles rated 150 volts or less to ground.

- List item 210.8(A)(5) is no longer limited to unfinished areas and applies to all receptacles in basements.

- New list item 11 requires GFCI protection for indoor damp and wet locations.

Significance of the Change

The parent text of section 210.8(A) is significantly modified. This revision mandates that all 125-volt through 250-volt receptacles rated 150 volts or less to ground have ground-fault circuit-interrupter protection (GFCI) for personnel. This revision now requires that all receptacles installed in the locations specified in 210.8(A)(1) through (A)(11) be GFCI protected. It is important to note that there is no limitation to the amp rating of the receptacle. This will require, for example, GFCI protection of 250-volt, 30 amp receptacles for electric clothes dryers. See new first level subdivision 210.8(F), which addresses outdoor outlets for dwelling units.

List item (5) for basements is no longer limited to unfinished areas or areas that are considered to be non-habitable rooms. This list item now requires GFCI protection for all receptacles in dwelling unit basements. Substantiation for this revision included the fact that conductive floor surfaces on concrete are common in dwelling unit basements. Additionally, all dwelling unit basements are prone to moisture, including the possibility of flooding.

A new list item (11) *Indoor damp and wet locations* is added to require GFCI protection in areas that would include a dog washing space or a mud room.

FRs: 8119, 8120, 8121, 8122, 7705

SR: 7697

210.8(B)

Article 210 Branch Circuits

Part I General Provisions

GFCI, Other Than Dwelling Units

Code Language

210.8(B) Other Than Dwelling Units.

(2) Kitchens or areas with a sink and permanent provisions for either food preparation or cooking

(11) Laundry areas

(12) Bathtubs and shower stalls — where receptacles are installed within 1.8 m (6 ft) of the outside edge of the bathtub or shower stall

(See NEC for actual text)

Significance of the Change

Section 210.8(B) provides *GFCI Protection for Personnel* requirements for other than dwelling units. The parent text is revised for clarity. The previous text referenced receptacles rated at 150 volts to ground or less. Receptacles do not have an identified voltage to ground rating that can be determined by the installer. Therefore, the parent text is modified to reference "... all receptacles supplied by single/three-phase branch circuits rated at 150 volts to ground or less." The amp ratings are not revised. List item 210.8(B)(2) *Kitchens*, is expanded to include "or areas with a sink and permanent provisions for either food preparation or cooking." This revision is safety driven, recognizing that permanent provisions for cooking or food preparation together with a sink have the same potential for shock hazards as a kitchen. List item 210.8(B)(8) is revised to add "accessory buildings," which would include, but not be limited to, sheds, storage buildings, utility buildings, pool houses, and others that contain the same potential for shock as a garage or service bay. List item 210.8(B)(10) is revised for clarity. Two new list items are added in 210.8(B) to correlate with similar list items for dwelling units in 210.8(A). A new list item (11) *Laundry areas*, is added because the same potential for shock exists in all areas used for laundry. A new list item (12) is added to include *Bathtubs and shower stalls*, where receptacles are installed within 6 feet of the outside edge of the bathtub or shower stall. These revisions recognize that the same potential for shock exists in all of these locations.

Change Summary

- Parent text in 210.8(B) is revised for clarity. Accessory buildings are added in 210.8(B)(8).
- 210.8(B)(2) Kitchens include areas with a sink and permanent provisions for either food preparation or cooking.
- Two new list items are added to include laundry areas, bathtubs and shower stalls.

FRs: 7705, 7791
SRs: 7697, 7724

GFCI Protection for Personnel

Code Language

210.8 GFCI Protection for Personnel

(D) Specific Appliances. (references 422.5 to coordinate GFCI protection for appliances)

(E) Equipment Requiring Servicing. (references 210.63)

(F) Outdoor Outlets. (general requirement for outdoor outlets other than lighting outlets excluding 210.8(C))

(See NEC for actual text)

Change Summary

- Existing 210.8(D) is deleted and GFCI requirements for dishwashers are expanded and relocated to 422.5.

- New 210.8(D) references 422.5 to coordinate GFCI protection.

- New 210.8(E) references 210.63 requiring GFCI protection and new (F) includes general GFCI requirements for outdoor outlets other than those in 210.8(A)(3) Exception.

Significance of the Change

Existing section 210.8(D) requiring GFCI protection of the kitchen dishwasher branch circuit in dwelling units is deleted and relocated to 422.5. In order to correlate GFCI requirements in 210.8 and 422.5, a new 210.8(D) *Specific Appliances* is added. This rule simply restates the requirements in Article 422. See the revisions in Article 422. Appliances requiring GFCI protection are identified in 422.5(A) and a new list item (7) is titled *Dishwashers*. It is important to note that as revised, this GFCI requirement is no longer limited to dwelling units. A new GFCI requirement is added in 210.8(E) for *Equipment Requiring Servicing* with a reference to all receptacles required by 210.63. This includes all HVAC equipment and in other than dwelling units all indoor service entrance equipment and all indoor equipment that requires dedicated equipment space in accordance with 110.26(E). A new requirement is added in 210.8(F) to require GFCI protection for all outdoor outlets for dwelling units. This will apply to all outlets other than those covered in 210.8(A)(3) Exception that are supplied by single-phase branch circuits rated 150 volts to ground or less and 50 amps or less. An exception is added for all lighting outlets other than those covered in 210.8(C) for crawl spaces. This revision will now require GFCI protection for HVAC systems, outdoor condensing units and any other outdoor hard-wired electrical equipment. Substantiation provided to support this revision included a fatality that occurred when an individual came in contact with the energized housing of a condensing unit and a nearby metal fence.

FRs: 7852, 7889
SRs: 7737, 7587, 7676

210.11(C)(3) & (C)(4)

Bathroom and Garage Branch Circuits

120-Volt 20-Amp branch circuit required for bathroom receptacle outlets required by 210.52(D) and any countertop and similar work surface receptacle outlets

Code Language

210.11(C)(3) Bathroom Branch Circuits... one or more 120-volt, 20-ampere branch circuit shall be provided to supply bathroom(s) receptacle outlet(s) required by 210.52(D) and any countertop and similar work surface receptacle outlets...(See *NEC* text)

(C)(4) Garage Branch Circuits... at least one 120-volt, 20-ampere branch circuit shall be installed to supply receptacle outlets required by 210.52(G)(1) for attached garages and in detached garages...(See *NEC* text)

(See NEC for actual text)

Significance of the Change

Section 210.11 requires that a minimum number of branch circuits be provided for lighting, appliances, etc. in accordance with 220.10 and for dwelling unit loads as specified in 210.11(C).

The existing text in 210.11(C)(3) required at least one 120-volt, 20-amp branch circuit for bathroom receptacle outlets. This inferred that all receptacle outlets in the bathroom must be supplied by 120-volt, 20-amp branch circuits. 210.11(C)(3) is revised to provide clarity. New text is added to clarify that one or more 120-volt, 20-amp branch circuits must be provided to supply bathroom receptacle outlets as required by 210.52(D) (receptacle outlet required within 3 feet of the outside edge of each basin) and for any countertop and similar work surface receptacle outlets. This revision clarifies that a receptacle outlet at an additional countertop space such as a "make up counter" must be supplied by a 120-volt, 20-amp branch circuit. This also clarifies that a general purpose receptacle outlet in a large bathroom area may be supplied by a 120-volt, 15-amp branch circuit.

A new second-level subdivision 210.11(C)(4) was added in the 2017 *NEC* revision cycle for garage branch circuits. Section 210.52 provides requirements for receptacle outlets. Existing 210.52(G)(1) requires at least one receptacle outlet be installed in each vehicle bay of attached and detached garages with electric power. New text is added in 210.11(C)(4) to clarify that the required 120-volt, 20-amp branch circuit supplies the receptacle outlets required by 210.52(G)(1). This revision provides necessary correlation.

Change Summary

- Requirements for branch circuits in 210.11 are modified for clarity.
- The required receptacle outlet(s) in 210.52(D) and any other countertop or similar work surface receptacle outlets in bathrooms must be supplied by one or more 120-volt, 20-amp branch circuits.
- The required 120-volt, 20-amp branch circuit in 210.11(C)(4) is intended to supply the required receptacle outlet(s) in 210.52(G)(1).

FRs: 7547, 7549

SR: None

AFCI Protection, Dwelling Units

Code Language

210.12(A) Dwelling Units

210.12(A)(6) Exception: AFCI protection shall not be required for an individual branch circuit supplying a fire alarm system installed in accordance with 760.41(B) or 760.121(B). The branch circuit shall be installed in a metal raceway, metal auxiliary gutter, steel-armored cable, Type MC or Type AC, meeting the applicable requirements of 250.118, with metal boxes, conduit bodies, and enclosures.

(See NEC for actual text)

Courtesy of Eaton

Change Summary

- The exception for an individual branch circuit supplying a fire alarm system is modified to permit any metal raceway, metal auxiliary gutter, steel armored cable, Type MC or Type AC cable.
- The IN reference to UL Subject 1699C, *Outline of Investigation for System Combination Arc-Fault Circuit Interrupters* is retained.

Significance of the Change

Section 210.12(A) list item (6) permits the installation of a listed outlet branch circuit type AFCI at the first outlet where metal or nonmetallic conduit or tubing or Type MC cable is encased in not less than 2 inches of concrete from the branch circuit overcurrent device to the first outlet. The existing exception permitted an individual branch circuit supplying a fire alarm system to not be AFCI protected under specific conditions. The exception identified specific types of metal raceway. This revision deletes the list of raceway types and now requires that the branch circuit be installed in a metal raceway, metal auxiliary gutter, steel-armored cable, Type MC or Type AC, meeting the applicable requirements of 250.118, with metal boxes, conduit bodies, and enclosures. This will now permit the use of LFMC and FMC. A similar revision occurred in 210.12(A)(5).

The general requirement in 210.12(A)(4)(d) permits a combination of a branch-circuit overcurrent device and an outlet branch-circuit AFCI that is listed and identified as meeting the requirements for a system combination-type AFCI to be used. Informational Note No. 1 references UL 1699C *Outline of Investigation for System Combination Arc-Fault Circuit Interrupters* for information on system combination AFCIs. This standard was never finalized or adopted and was deleted in the first draft stage. It was replaced when the second revision failed the ballot.

FRs: 8130, 8131
CC: 7740

...Sleeping Rooms, Nursing, Limited-Care Facilities

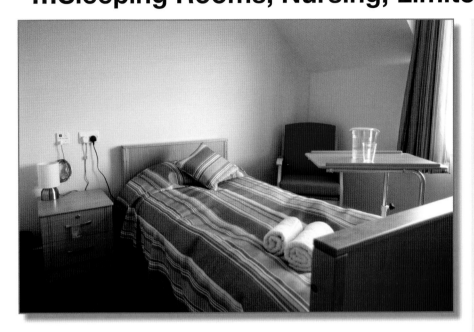

Code Language

210.12(C) Guest Rooms, Guest Suites, and Patient Sleeping Rooms in Nursing Homes and Limited-Care Facilities. All 120-volt, single-phase, 15- and 20-ampere branch circuits supplying outlets and devices... (See *NEC* Text) and patient sleeping rooms in nursing homes and limited-care facilities shall be protected by any of the means described in 210.12(A)(1) through (6).

(See NEC for actual text)

Significance of the Change

The requirements in 210.12(C) for guest rooms and guest suites are expanded to include patient sleeping rooms in nursing homes and limited care facilities. This is a logical expansion of AFCI protection. Patient sleeping rooms in nursing homes and limited care facilities are very often furnished by the occupant. This results in sleeping spaces very similar to those found in dwelling units. These spaces are wired in a similar manner to dwelling units and quite often with the same wiring methods. While Article 210 does not contain definitions for these spaces, we can look to 517.2 for more information.

The definition of nursing home is extracted from *NFPA 101: Life Safety Code* as follows:

A building or portion of a building used on a 24-hour basis for the housing and nursing care of four or more persons who, because of mental or physical incapacity, might be unable to provide for their own needs and safety without the assistance of another person. [101: 3.3.148.2]

The definition of limited care facility is defined as follows:

A building or portion thereof used on a 24-hour basis for the housing of four or more persons who are incapable of self-preservation because of age; physical limitation due to accident or illness; or limitations such as mental retardation/developmental disability, mental illness, or chemical dependency.

Change Summary

- The AFCI requirements of 210.12 are expanded to include patient sleeping rooms in nursing homes and limited care facilities.
- These sleeping rooms are very similar in nature to those found in dwelling units, guest rooms, guest suites, and dormitory units.

FR: 7977
SR: None

BC Extensions/Modifications, Guest Rooms/Suites

Code Language

210.12(D) Branch Circuit Extensions or Modifications — Dwelling Units, Dormitory Units, and Guest Rooms and Guest Suites. (See *NEC* text) ... shall be protected by one of the following:

(1) By any of the means described in 210.12(A)(1) through (A)(6)

(2) *No change.*

Exception: (See NEC text) ..., other than splicing devices. This measurement shall not include the conductors inside an enclosure, cabinet, or junction box.

(See NEC for actual text)

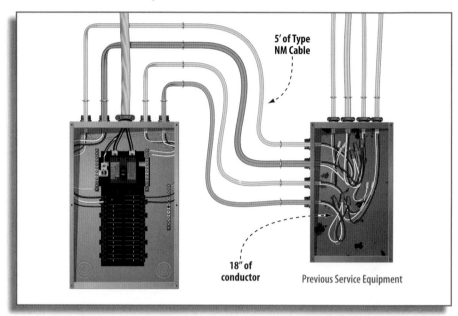

5' of Type NM Cable

18" of conductor

Previous Service Equipment

Change Summary

- 210.12(D) is expanded to include guest rooms and guest suites.
- New text is added to clarify the exception for branch circuit conductor extensions not more than 6 feet.
- Splicing devices are permitted. The 6-foot measurement does not include conductors inside an enclosure, cabinet, or junction box.

Significance of the Change

Section 210.12(D) provides requirements for AFCI protection where existing branch circuit conductors are extended or modified. The title is expanded to include guest rooms and guest suites. Where branch circuit wiring in any of the areas specified in 210.12(A), (B), or (C) are modified, replaced or extended, the branch circuit is required to be AFCI protected by one of two methods. The first method is revised to permit any of the means described in 210.12(A) through (6). The second method continues to permit a listed outlet branch circuit type AFCI located at the first receptacle outlet of the existing branch circuit. The existing exception is modified to provide clarity. The exception is clarified and AFCI protection is not required where the extension of the existing branch circuit conductors is not more than six feet and does not include any additional outlets or devices other than splicing devices. Wire nuts are considered devices. This revision clarifies that the use of wire nuts or other devices to splice conductors does not trigger an AFCI requirement. Additional text is added to the exception to clarify that the six-foot measurement does not include conductor length inside an enclosure, cabinet, or junction box. This is a significant clarification of this exception. For example, a service upgrade in an older home may require that existing branch circuits be extended 5 $\frac{1}{2}$ feet just to reach the new panelboard. An additional foot or two may be needed inside necessary junction boxes and in the cabinet containing the panelboard. This revision clarifies that in this case AFCI protection would not be required.

FR: 7963

SR: None

Conductors, Minimum Ampacity and Size

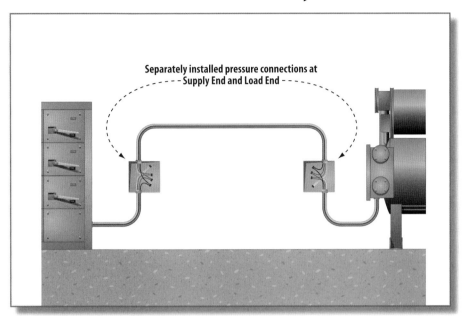

Separately installed pressure connections at
- - - Supply End and Load End - - -

Code Language

210.19(A)(1) General… (See *NEC* text)

Exception No. 2 to (1)(a) and (1) (b): Where a portion of a branch circuit is connected at both its supply and load ends to separately installed pressure connections as covered in 110.14(C)(2), it shall be permitted to have an allowable ampacity, in accordance with 310.15, not less than the sum of the continuous load plus the noncontinuous load. No portion of a branch circuit installed under this exception shall extend into an enclosure containing either the branch-circuit supply or the branch-circuit load terminations.

(See NEC for actual text)

Significance of the Change

Section 210.19(A)(1) provides requirements for minimum size and ampacity of branch circuit conductors supplied at not more than 600 volts. The parent text is modified with a reference to 110.14(C) for equipment terminations. The existing exception for overcurrent protective devices listed for operation at 100% of their rating is modified to apply only to 210.19(A)(1)(a). A new exception is added to correlate with 215.2(A)(1)(a). This new exception applies to both 210.19(A)(1) (a) and (A)(1)(b) and permits portions of the branch circuit (not the full length) to have an allowable ampacity of not less than the sum of the continuous load, plus the noncontinuous load, relieving the requirement for 125% of the continuous load. In order to apply this exception, these portions of the branch circuit must be connected at both the supply and load ends to separately installed pressure connectors as covered in 110.14(C)(2). These portions of the branch circuit are not permitted to extend into an enclosure containing either the branch circuit supply or the branch circuit load terminations as covered in 110.14(C)(1). The full-size conductor in accordance with 210.19(A)(1)(a) or (A)(1)(b) is required at the termination points because the larger conductor acts as a heatsink for connected devices to accommodate continuous loading. This exception allows installers to consider cost-effective options.

Change Summary

- The minimum ampacity and size of branch circuit conductors must also comply with 110.14(C) for equipment terminations.
- The existing exception is clarified to apply to only 210.19(A) (1)(a).
- A new Exception No. 2 is added to permit portions of the branch circuit (not the full length) to have an allowable ampacity of not less than the sum of the continuous load plus the noncontinuous load.

FR: 7981
SR: 7752

Common Area Branch Circuits

Code Language

210.25 Branch Circuits in Buildings with More Than One Occupancy

(B) Common Area Branch Circuits...

Informational Note: Examples of public or common areas include, but are not limited to, lobbies, corridors, stairways, laundry rooms, roofs, elevators, washrooms, store rooms, driveways (parking), and mechanical rooms.

(See NEC for actual text)

Change Summary

- A new informational note is added in 210.25(B) to provide examples of common areas or public spaces.
- These areas include, but are not limited to, lobbies, corridors, stairways, laundry rooms, roofs, elevators, washrooms, storerooms, driveways (parking), and mechanical rooms.

Significance of the Change

Section 210.25 provides requirements for branch circuits in buildings with more than one occupancy. 210.25(B), titled *Common Area Branch Circuits*, prohibits equipment (panelboards, load centers etc.) that supply branch circuits for an individual dwelling unit or tenant space from supplying branch circuits for lighting, central alarm, signal, communications, or other purposes, for public or common areas of a two-family dwelling, a multifamily dwelling, or a multi-occupancy building. Practical application of this requirement is open to interpretation as to what is a "common area." A new informational note is added following 210.25(B) to provide the *Code* user with examples of public or common areas. This revision is based on the public input that sought to add a definition for *Common Areas (Public Areas)*. The *Code* Making Panel chose not to add a definition, because doing so would limit common areas to spaces identified in the definition. The informational note provides examples that include, but are not limited to, lobbies, corridors, stairways, laundry rooms, roofs, elevators, washrooms, store rooms, driveways (parking) and mechanical rooms.

FR: 7517

SR: None

Receptacle Outlets, Countertops and Work Surfaces

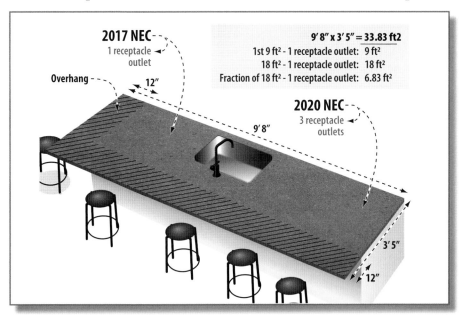

2017 NEC — 1 receptacle outlet

Overhang — 12"

9' 8" x 3' 5" = 33.83 ft2

1st 9 ft2 - 1 receptacle outlet: 9 ft2
18 ft2 - 1 receptacle outlet: 18 ft2
Fraction of 18 ft2 - 1 receptacle outlet: 6.83 ft2

2020 NEC — 3 receptacle outlets

9' 8"

3' 5"

12"

Significance of the Change

Requirements for receptacle outlets for countertops and work surfaces in 210.52(C) are significantly revised. Requirements for a receptacle outlet at each wall countertop/workspace 12 inches or wider is retained in the parent text along with the exception for spaces behind a range counter-mounted cooking unit or sink; and 210.52(C)(1) is retitled *Wall Spaces*. New text is added to address the use of multioutlet assemblies. Where they are used, each section 12 inches or wider containing two or more receptacles in individual or continuous lengths, is considered to be one receptacle outlet. Existing requirements for all island and peninsular counter/worktop spaces are deleted and replaced with new 210.52(C)(2). All island and peninsular countertop/work spaces require receptacle outlet(s). Previous requirements that included measurements to determine the need for a receptacle outlet are deleted. At least one receptacle outlet must be provided for the first 9 ft.^{2} or fraction thereof. An additional receptacle outlet must be provided for every 18 ft.^{2} or fraction thereof. Peninsular counter/worktop spaces must have at least one receptacle outlet within 2 feet of the outer end of the peninsular counter/worktop space. Requirements for receptacle outlet location are relocated from 210.52(C)(5) to (C)(3). The previous exception is deleted, and permission for receptacle outlets not more than 12 inches below the space where the surface does not extend more than 6 inches beyond its base are included in 210.52(C)(3). This revision will significantly revise receptacle outlet requirements for large island and peninsular counter/worktop spaces.

Code Language

(2) Island and Peninsular Countertops and Work Surfaces.

Receptacle...outlets with 210.52(C)(2)(a) and (C)(2)(b).

(a) ...one receptacle outlet ...for the first (9 ft²), or fraction thereof... receptacle outlet shall be provided for every additional (18 ft²), or fraction thereof, of the countertop or work surface.

(b) At least one receptacle outlet shall be located within (2 ft) of the outer end of a peninsular countertop or work surface... Additional... as determined by the installer, designer, or building owner.

A peninsular countertop shall be measured from the connected perpendicular wall.

(See NEC for actual text)

Change Summary

- Requirements for island and peninsular countertops are combined.
- 9 ft.^{2} of space or any fraction will require a receptacle and one more for every 18 ft.^{2} or any fraction thereof.
- A peninsular countertop work surface must have a receptacle outlet within 2 feet of the end of the countertop on work surface.

FRs: 7521, 7537
SRs: 7644, 8246

210.52(E) & (G)

Article 210 Branch Circuits
Part III Required Outlets

Outdoor Outlets and Basements, Garages, ...

Code Language

210.52(E)(3) Balconies, Decks, and Porches. Balconies, decks, and porches that are attached within (4 in.) horizontally... (See *NEC* text) dwelling unit and are accessible from inside the dwelling unit shall have at least one receptacle

(G) Basements, Garages, and Accessory Buildings. For one- and two- family dwellings, and multi-family dwellings...(See *NEC* text)

Exception: Garage spaces not attached to an individual dwelling unit of a multifamily dwelling shall not require a receptacle outlet in each vehicle bay.

(See NEC for actual text)

Change Summary

- New text modifies receptacle outlet requirements for decks and porches; accessibility from inside and attachment is no longer required.
- Multifamily dwellings must now comply with 210.52(G).
- Garage spaces not attached in multifamily dwellings are not required to have a receptacle outlet in each vehicle bay.

Significance of the Change

Section 210.52(E) provides requirements for outdoor receptacle outlets in one-family, two-family and multifamily dwellings. Previous requirements mandated a receptacle outlet be installed on all balconies, decks, and porches that were: (1) attached to the dwelling unit, and (2) accessible from inside the dwelling unit. This revision requires a receptacle outlet on balconies, decks, and porches that are within 4 inches horizontally of the dwelling unit. If it is attached, it is within 4 inches. The previous requirement for the balcony, deck, or porch to be accessible from inside the dwelling unit is deleted. For example, a stand-alone deck on the outside of a dwelling unit that does not have a door or other means to access the deck from the inside of the dwelling unit will require a receptacle outlet. Previous text requiring receptacle outlets in basements, garages, and accessory buildings in 210.52(G) applied only to one- and two-family dwellings. This revision expands these requirements to include multifamily dwellings. This includes at least one receptacle outlet in each vehicle bay for garage spaces attached to an individual dwelling of a multifamily dwelling unit. An exception is added for garage spaces that are not attached to an individual dwelling unit of a multifamily dwelling unit. In this case, a receptacle outlet will be required, but a receptacle outlet in each vehicle bay is not required.

FRs: 7598, 7604
SR: None

Equipment Requiring Servicing

Code Language

210.63 Equipment Requiring Servicing.

(A) Heating, Air-Conditioning, and Refrigeration Equipment…

(B) Other Electrical Equipment…

(1) Indoor Service Equipment…

(2) Indoor Equipment Requiring Dedicated Equipment Spaces. Where equipment, other than service equipment, requires dedicated equipment space as specified in 110.26(E), the required receptacle outlet shall be located within the same room or area as the electrical equipment and shall not be connected to the load side of the equipment's branch-circuit disconnecting means.

(See NEC for actual text)

Significance of the Change

Sections 210.63 and 64 are revised and combined into a single section titled, 210.63 *Equipment Requiring Servicing*. The parent text of this section requires a 125 volt, single phase, 15 or 20-amp receptacle outlet within 25 feet of the equipment identified in two new first level subdivisions 210.63(A) and (B). The requirements for HVAC and refrigeration equipment are relocated into 210.63(A) with only editorial revisions. New 210.63(B) is titled *Other Electrical Equipment*. 210.63(B)(1) *Indoor Service Equipment*, mandates that the receptacle outlet required in the parent text be in the same room or area as the service equipment. The previous edition of the *Code* included two exceptions to this rule that are deleted. These exceptions excluded one and two-family dwellings and services where the voltage to ground is greater than 120 volts for services dedicated to equipment covered in Articles 675 and 682.

A new requirement in 210.63(B)(2) is added to address all indoor equipment requiring dedicated equipment space. This is a significant revision that now requires all indoor electrical equipment requiring dedicated equipment space as specified in 110.26(E), to locate the required receptacle outlet within the same room as the electrical equipment. The receptacle outlet required in 210.63(B)(2) cannot be connected to the load side of the dedicated equipment branch-circuit disconnecting means.

Change Summary

- 210.63 and 210.64 are revised and combined into a single section.
- The exceptions to 210.64 are deleted.
- A new requirement now mandates a receptacle outlet for all indoor equipment requiring dedicated equipment space.

FR: 7588
SR: 7566

Meeting Rooms

Code Language

210.65 Meeting Rooms

(A) General. ...(See *NEC* text)

(B) Receptacle Outlets Required.

(1) Receptacle Outlets in Fixed Walls. ...(See *NEC* text) required number of receptacle outlets...(See *NEC* text) determined in accordance with 210.52...(See *NEC* text) located as determined by the installer, designer, or building owner

(2) Floor Outlets. ...(See *NEC* text) any floor dimension 12 ft or greater in any direction and that has a floor area of at least 215 ft² shall have at least one floor receptacle outlet, or at least one floor outlet to serve receptacle(s), located at a distance not less than 1.8 m (6 ft) from any fixed wall for each 215 ft² or major portion of floor space.

(See NEC for actual text)

Change Summary

- Meeting room receptacle requirements are relocated from 210.71 to 210.65.
- Clarity is provided for the number of, and location of, receptacle outlets in fixed walls.
- Revisions also address non-rectangular meeting rooms and floor outlets to supply receptacles that could be in hardwired furniture.

Significance of the Change

Requirements for receptacle outlets in meeting rooms were added in the 2017 *NEC* into section 210.71. These requirements are modified and relocated into new section 210.65 to group this requirement with other rules for required receptacle outlets. The permissive requirement for receptacle outlets in fixed walls to be located by the installer, designer, or building owner are relocated into 210.65(B)(1) for clarity. The 2017 *NEC* 210.71(B)(1) required that receptacle outlets in fixed walls be installed in accordance with 210.52(A)(1) through (A)(4). The intent of this requirement has always been that the number of receptacle outlets is to be determined in accordance with 210.52(A)(1) through (A)(4) and the location of these outlets will be determined by the installer, designer, or building owner.

210.65(B)(2) *Floor Outlets* is modified to add clarity where an odd shaped room, such as a round meeting room is encountered. The text now requires a meeting room with any floor dimension 12 feet or greater *in any direction* that has a floor area of 215 ft.² to have one floor receptacle outlet, or at least one floor outlet to serve receptacles located a distance not less than 6 feet from any fixed wall. A floor receptacle outlet or floor outlet is required for every 215 ft.² or major portion of floor space.

This revision adds clarity and also recognizes that a floor outlet can meet this requirement where it is used to supply receptacles in hardwired furniture or other equipment.

FR: 7593

SR: None

Lighting Outlets Required

Code Language

230.70 Lighting Outlets Required.
(A) Dwelling Units. ... (See *NEC* text)
(1) Habitable Rooms. At least one lighting outlet controlled by a listed wall-mounted control device shall be installed in every habitable room, kitchen, and bathroom. The wall-mounted control device shall be located near an entrance to the room on a wall.

(See NEC for actual text)

Significance of the Change

Section 210.70 provides requirements for required lighting outlets in (A) *Dwelling Units*, (B) *Guest Rooms or Guest Suites*, and (C) *All Occupancies*. Each of these requirements is modified to require lighting outlets "controlled by a listed wall-mounted control device." The previous text required "wall switch-controlled" lighting outlets. This revision now recognizes technologies that are readily available to communicate wirelessly to control a lighting outlet for a receptacle for lighting and other purposes. As written, a typical wall switch controlled (typical snap switch) lighting outlet is permitted provided it is listed. This revised text is seen throughout 210.70, as well as in list item (2) in the parent text of 210.52.

The previous requirement in 210.70(A)(3), which applied only to dwelling units, is deleted and the requirement is relocated into first level subdivision (C) *All Occupancies,* which was very similar. This requirement is significantly revised to mandate that a point of control must be at each entry that permits access to attics, underfloor spaces, utility rooms, or basements. The previous text permitted a single point of control where there was more than one way to access a space. Where the required lighting outlet is installed for equipment that requires service, the lighting outlet must be installed at or near the equipment. This applies to all occupancies including dwelling units.

Change Summary

- 210.70 is modified to require lighting outlets "controlled by a listed wall-mounted control device."
- Listed snap switches are permitted.
- This revision recognizes technology that utilizes remote devices that wirelessly communicate to control a lighting outlet or receptacle.

FRs: 7589, 7590, 7592, 7612

SR: None

Ground Fault Protection of Equipment

Code Language

215.10 Ground-Fault Protection of Equipment. ...(See *NEC* text)

Exception No. 3: If temporary feeder conductors are used to connect a generator to a facility for repair, maintenance, or emergencies, ground-fault protection of equipment shall not be required. Temporary feeders without ground-fault protection shall be permitted for the time period necessary but shall not exceed 90 days.

(See NEC for actual text)

Change Summary

- New Exception No. 3 now permits temporary feeders to be installed without ground-fault protection for the time necessary to repair and maintain equipment.

- This permission is limited to the time period necessary, but not more than 90 days.

- Editorial revisions were made in the remainder of this section.

Significance of the Change

A new Exception No. 3 is added to the ground-fault protection requirements of 215.10. This new exception recognizes that the connection of feeder conductors from a generator used on a temporary basis for the repair, maintenance, or failure of an existing generator creates significant issues with existing ground fault protection. All standby generators require regular maintenance. An oil change on a larger generator may require a significant amount of time to complete. Where additional work is required, a standby generator could be offline for days or weeks. When repair, maintenance, or emergencies impact a standby generator, it is typical to use portable generators and temporary feeders. This exception now permits the installation of temporary feeders without ground fault protection for the time period necessary for maintenance or repair, but not more than 90 days. Providing ground-fault sensing at a portable generator would require the removal of, and/or relocation of bonding jumpers and ground fault sensing equipment in other equipment. This could be extensive and may not be feasible. Shutdowns would be required and bonding jumper terminations would be subject to wear and damage. Another concern is that the original system connections may not be properly restored after the temporary generator and feeders are removed. This exception recognizes that it is feasible to incur the loss of ground-fault protection for the short period of time needed to perform required repair or maintenance on existing generators.

FR: 8361
SR: 7858

NEW
REVISION

220.11, 220.12(A) & (B)
Article 220 Branch-Circuit, Feeder, and Service Load Calculations
Part II Branch Circuit Load Calculations

Floor Area, Lighting Load Non-Dwelling Occupancies

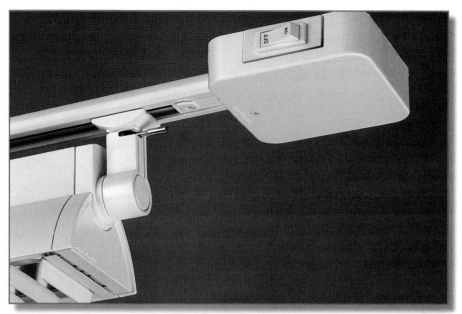

Courtesy of Koninklijke Philips Electronics N. V-Lightolier

Code Language

220.12 Lighting Load for Non-Dwelling Occupancies.

(A) General. A unit load of not less than that specified in Table 220.12 for non-dwelling occupancies and the floor area determined in 220.11 shall be used to calculate the minimum lighting load... (See *NEC* text)

(B) Energy Code. ... (See *NEC* text)

(4) The continuous load multiplier of 125% shall be applied.

(See NEC for actual text)

Significance of the Change

Section 220.12 Is significantly modified and is now titled *Lighting Load for Non-Dwelling Occupancies.* The parent text is modified to clarify that this section no longer applies to dwelling occupancies. Previous text that provided the *Code* user with the method to determine the floor area for each floor is relocated into a new section 220.11 *Floor Area.* A new last sentence clarifies that motors rated less than $\frac{1}{8}$ HP connected to a lighting circuit are considered as part of the general lighting load. Existing exception number one is deleted and relocated into a new 220.12(B) *Energy Code.* Placing requirements that address installations built to an energy code in positive text increases clarity and usability. Requirements for a power monitoring system are modified to permit automatic means to take action reducing the connected load if it exceeds the values set by the *Energy Code.* Where 220.12(B) is applied, new list item (4) requires that the continuous load multiplier of 125% be applied. Existing exception number two is deleted because the lighting load values in Table 220.12 are revised.

Change Summary

- The parent text of 220.12 is modified editorially and relocates requirements to determine floor area to a new section 220.11.
- Energy Code requirements are added in 220.12(B) and exception number one is deleted.
- Exception No. 2 is deleted as the values in Table 220.12 are revised.

FRs: 8104, 8075

SR: None

Table 220.12

Article 220 Branch-Circuit, Feeder, and Service Load Calculations

Part II Branch Circuit Load Calculations

General Lighting Loads by Non-Dwelling Occupancy

Code Language

Type of Occupancy	VA ft^2
Automotive facility	1.5
Convention center	1.4
Courthouse	1.4
Dormitory	1.5
Exercise center	1.4
Fire station	1.3
Gymnasium[a]	1.7
Health care clinic	1.6
Hospital	1.6

(See NEC for actual text)

Change Summary

- Table 220.12 is now limited to non-dwelling occupancies.
- Significant revisions are included for types of occupancies to correlate with ASHRAE 90.1.
- The unit load for most occupancies has been significantly reduced.

Significance of the Change

Table 220.12 Is significantly revised, and is now titled *General Lighting Loads by Non-Dwelling Occupancy*. The types of occupancies are significantly revised and are correlated with those found in the ASHRAE 90.1 standard. This results in the majority of the previous occupancies being deleted from the body of the table. There are numerous table notes to explain how previously listed occupancies are now addressed in the new table. The unit load for all but four occupancies are reduced and correlated with the data provided by and the values provided in the ASHRAE 90.1 standard. This reduction in value is the reason that previous Exception No. 2 in 220.12 is deleted. An example of the reduction in unit load is seen in the previous occupancy types for banks and offices. The previous unit load was 3 $\frac{1}{2}$ volt-amps per square foot for each of these occupancies. The new unit load for banks and offices is reduced by 37% to 1.3 volt-amps, which is a significant reduction in load calculation. The table revision includes many types of occupancies, which previously did not exist, including, but not limited to, automotive facilities, convention centers, dormitories, exercise centers, fire stations, gymnasiums, health care clinics, penitentiaries, sports arenas, and many more. A new table note clarifies that the 125% multiplier specified in 210.20(A) for continuous loads is included in the unit loads of the revised table. There are eight additional table notes to explain where previous types of occupancies now fall in this table. For example, banks are office types of occupancies, and clubs are considered restaurant occupancies.

FR: 8075

SR: None

Dwelling Units, Office Buildings, Hotels, and Motels

Code Language

220.14 Other Loads-All Occupancies

(J) Dwelling Units... Motors rated less than $\frac{1}{8}$ HP and connected to a lighting circuit shall be considered part of the minimum lighting load.

(1) ...(See *NEC* text) and 210.11(C)(4)

(K) Office Buildings. ...

(1) The calculated load from 220.14(I) after all demand factors have been applied

(M) Hotel and Motel Occupancies. ...

(2) The receptacle outlets specified in 210.52(E)(3)

(See NEC for actual text)

Significance of the Change

First level subdivisions 220.14(J) & (K) are revised to correlate with the revisions in Table 220.12, which is revised to contain general lighting loads for only non-dwelling occupancies. 220.14(J) is retitled *Dwelling Units* and the minimum unit load from table 220.12 is relocated into this requirement. A new sentence is added in 220.14(J) to correlate with 220.12(A) to clarify that motors rated less than $\frac{1}{8}$ HP and connected to a lighting circuit are considered as part of the general lighting load. The required branch-circuit for dwelling unit garage is added into list item (1) to clarify that it is included in the minimum unit load. 220.14(K) is retitled *Office Buildings* to correlate with the change in types of occupancies in Table 220.12. Clarity is provided in list item (1) for the calculated load of receptacle outlets in 220.14(K) to explain that this value has all demand factors applied. A new first level subdivision 220.14(M) *Hotel and Motel Occupancies* is added to provide clarity for calculations of these venues. Two substantial changes here:

(1) is to clarify that in guest rooms or guest suites of hotels and motels, the lighting and receptacle outlets specified in 220.14(M)(1), (M)(2), and (M)(3) are included in the minimum unit load in Table 220.12, and

(2) adds a reference to 210.52(E) for receptacle outlets on balconies, decks, and porches in list item (3).

Change Summary

- General lighting load requirements for dwelling units are relocated to 220.14(J).
- 220.14(K) now clarifies that the value in (K) has demand factors applied.
- New 220.14(M) clarifies that the minimum unit load in table 220.12 includes the lighting at receptacle outlets specified.

FRs: 8076, 8077, 8071
SRs: 7754, 7758

General Lighting

Code Language

220.42 General Lighting. Hotels and motels, including apartment houses without provision for cooking by tenants

First 20k or less	60%
Above 20k to 100k	50%
Remainder over 100k	35%

(See NEC for actual text)

Change Summary

- Demand factors for derating feeder and service conductors in hospitals are deleted.
- Demand factors for feeder and service conductors in hotels, motels, and apartment houses without provision for cooking, are increased to correlate with revisions in Table 220.12.

Significance of the Change

The demand factors for the general lighting load in hospitals are deleted in section 220.42. The general lighting load for hospitals in Table 220.12 is reduced from 2 to 1.6 volt-amps. The revisions in Table 220.12 are based upon data in ASHRAE 90.1. These reductions in unit load are due to significant advancements in energy reduction in lighting due to the use of LED and other lighting technology. The *NEC* Correlating Committee established an energy task group to review the long-standing values that existed in Article 220. That task group submitted public inputs to revise multiple sections in Article 220. The reduction in the unit load of volt-amps per square foot in hospitals from 2 to 1.6, mandated the deletion of the demand factors in Table 220.42.

The demand factors for the general lighting load of feeder and service conductors in hotels, motels, and apartment houses without provisions for cooking, are increased to correlate with the reduction in volt-amps per square foot seen in Table 220.12. The unit load in Table 220.12 for hotels, motels, including apartment houses without provisions for cooking by tenants, has been reduced from 2 volt-amps to 1.7 volt-amps per square foot.

FR: 8080
SR: 7759

Determining Existing Loads

Code Language

220.87 Determining Existing Loads. The calculation of a feeder or service load for existing installations shall be permitted to use actual maximum demand to determine the existing load under all of the following conditions... (See *NEC* text)

Exception: If the feeder or service has any renewable energy system (i.e., solar photovoltaic systems or wind electric systems) or employs any form of peak load shaving, this calculation method shall not be permitted

(See NEC for actual text)

Significance of the Change

Section 220.87 provides requirements for determining existing loads. The calculation of a feeder or service load for these existing installations is permitted to use actual maximum demand to determine the existing load under the three conditions listed. (1) The maximum demand data has to be for a one-year period, (2) The maximum demand at 125% plus the new load cannot exceed the ampacity of the feeder or service conductors and, (3) The feeder must have overcurrent protection in accordance with 240.4 and service conductors must have overload protection in accordance with 230.90.

Where feeder or service conductors are supplied by any form of renewable energy or a peak load shaving system exists, the actual peak demand load seen by the meter will not reflect the actual peak demand for the feeder or service conductors. Since there is no effective way to determine the contribution from these renewable systems to determine the peak demand, an exception is added to prohibit the use of this calculation method if the feeder or service has any renewable energy system, or if there is any form of peak load shaving.

Change Summary

- 220.87 permits actual maximum demand values to determine existing loads.
- Where feeder or service conductors have a renewable energy system, or any form of peak load shaving, actual maximum demand is not obtainable and Section 220.87 cannot be applied.

FR: 8081
SR: 7756

Wiring on Buildings (or Other Structures)

Code Language

225.10 Wiring on Buildings (or Other Structures).

(17) Type SE cable

(18) Type TC-ER cable

230.43 Wiring Methods for 1000 Volts, Nominal, or Less.

(20) Type TC-ER cable

230.44 Cable Trays.

(6) Type TC-ER cable

(See NEC for actual text)

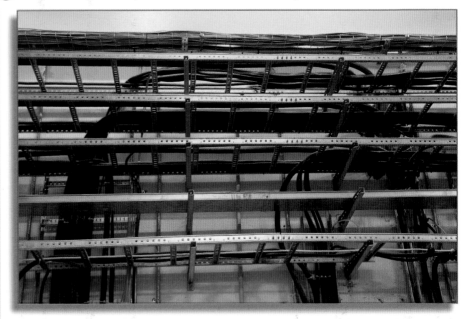

Change Summary

- Type TC-ER cable is now a permitted wiring method for outside feeders and branch circuits and services.
- Type TC-ER cable complies with the crush and impact requirements of Type MC cable.
- Type SE cable is now specifically identified as permitted in 225.10, 230.43, and 230.44.

Significance of the Change

Section 225.10 provides the *Code* user with a prescriptive list of permitted wiring methods for outside feeders and branch circuits. This section is similar to 230.43, which provides permitted wiring methods in services, and 230.44 for wiring methods permitted as service conductors in cable tray. Throughout the *NEC* there are numerous requirements that simply reference Chapter 3 wiring methods as being suitable for a given purpose. These revisions now recognize Type TC-ER cable as suitable for use as outside branch circuits and feeders, and as service conductors. Type TC-ER cable (power and control tray cable) is addressed in Article 336. See uses permitted 336.10(7), which permits Type TC-ER between cable tray and utilization equipment. 336.10(7)(d) explains that Type TC-ER complies with the crush and impact requirements of Type MC cable. New in 225.10 is list item (17) for Type SE cable. This was necessary due to the deletion of previous list item (10) for multiconductor cable. This list item was deleted because it permitted all types of multiconductor cable, including Type SE cable, which was not intended. New list item (20) in 230.43 and list item (6) in 230.44 now permits Type TC-ER cable.

FR: 8274
SR: 7863

Supports Over Buildings

Code Language

225.15 Supports over Buildings.
Outside branch-circuit and feeder
conductors passing over a building
shall be securely supported.

(See NEC for actual text)

Significance of the Change

Section 225.15 is revised to remove the reference to 230.29, which addresses service conductors that pass over a roof. The requirement in 230.29 requires: (1) service conductors that pass over a roof be securely supported by substantial structures, and (2) that where the service conductors are a grounded system, and the support structure is metal, the grounded conductor must be bonded to the metal support structure. This requirement is specifically directed at the use of messenger supported wiring where an exposed, bare grounded service conductor is used. The requirement in 230.29 does not apply to service drop conductors, as they are under the exclusive control of the serving utility. Previous text in 225.15 required that supports over a building comply with 230.29. This meant that any outside feeder or branch-circuit that is supported by metal supports over a building, had to have the grounded conductor bonded to that metal support structure. This is a clear violation of 250.142(B). Additionally, outside branch-circuits and feeders are typically installed in raceways or cable assemblies.

Change Summary

- Section 225.15 is revised by removing the reference to 230.29.
- The requirement for outside branch-circuits and feeders supported over a building is that they be "securely supported."
- Applying the requirements of 230.29 in Article 225, and bonding the grounded conductor to metal support structures violates 250.142(B).

FR: 8275
SR: None

Overhead Spans Open/Multiconductor Cable

Code Language

225.19 Clearances from Buildings for Conductors of Not over 1000 Volts, Nominal. Overhead spans of open conductors and open multiconductor cables shall comply with 225.19(A), (B), (C), and (D).

(See NEC for actual text)

Change Summary

- Parent text is added to clarify that this section applies only to overhead spans of open conductors and open multiconductor cables.
- Cable assemblies, such as Type SE or UF are not "open multiconductor cables."
- The requirements of 225.19 do not apply to raceways or cable assemblies.

Significance of the Change

Parent text is added in 225.19 to clarify that all of the requirements in this section apply only to overhead spans of open conductors and open multiconductor cables. The requirements in this section have always been intended to address the installation of outside branch circuits, and feeders installed as open conductors and open multiconductor cables:

(1) above roofs in 225.19(A)

(2) from nonbuilding or non-bridge structures in 225.19(B)

(3) horizontal clearances in 225.19(C)

(4) for final spans of outside feeders or branch circuits in 225.19(D)

(5) zones for fire ladders covered in 225.19(E).

This revision clarifies that 225.19 does not apply to outside feeders or branch circuits installed in raceways or cable assemblies with an outer jacket, such as Type SE or UF cable.

FR: 8277
SR: None

NEW

225.30(A)
Article 225 Outside Branch Circuits and Feeders
Part II Buildings or Other Structures Supplied by a Feeder(s) or Branch Circuit(s)

Special Conditions (Number of Supplies)

Code Language

225.30(A) Special Conditions. Additional feeders or branch circuits shall be permitted to supply the following: (8) Docking facilities and piers

(See NEC for actual text)

Significance of the Change

Section 225.30 requires that a building or other structure that is served by a branch circuit or feeder on the load side of a service disconnecting means be supplied by only one feeder or branch circuit unless permitted in first level subdivisions 225.30(A) through (E). This requirement mirrors 230.2, which limits the number of permitted services to a building or structure. Section 225.30(A) permits additional feeders or branch circuits to supply fire pumps, emergency systems, legally required standby systems, optional standby systems, parallel power production systems, systems design for connection to multiple sources of supply for the purpose of enhanced reliability, and electric vehicle charging systems. A new list item (8) is added in 225.30(A) to permit additional feeders or branch circuits for docking facilities and piers. This revision recognizes the need for increased levels of ground fault protection on branch circuits and feeders supplying docking facilities and piers. Without this revision, a single feeder supplying a large docking facility may need to have the required ground fault protection level increased to prevent nuisance tripping. Installing multiple smaller feeders and branch circuits will permit lower levels of ground fault protection resulting in a safer installation. Section 555.35 requires shore power receptacles to have ground fault protection not exceeding 30 mA. Feeders and branch circuits must have ground fault protection set to open at not more than 100 mA.

Change Summary

- 225.30(A) is modified to permit additional feeders or branch circuits for docking facilities and piers.
- This revision recognizes the need for increased levels of ground fault protection in marinas and similar installations.
- Section 555.35 requires shore power receptacles to have GFPE not exceeding 30 mA. Feeders and branch circuits must have GFPE set to open at not more than 100 mA.

FR: 8281
SR: None

Common Supply Equipment

Code Language

225.30(B) Common Supply Equipment. Where feeder conductors originate in the same panelboard, switchboard, or other distribution equipment, and each feeder terminates in a single disconnecting means, not more than six feeders shall be permitted. Where more than one feeder is installed in accordance with this section, all feeder disconnects supplying the building or structure shall be grouped in the same location, and the requirements of 225.33 shall not apply. Each disconnect shall be marked to indicate the load served.

(See NEC for actual text)

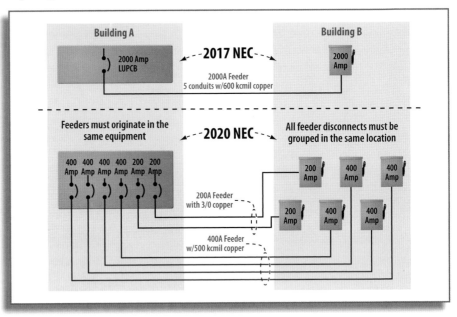

Change Summary

- 225.30(B) now permits up to six feeders to supply a separate building or structure.
- All of the feeder conductors must originate in the same panelboard, switchboard, or other distribution equipment.
- Each feeder must terminate in a single disconnecting means, and all of the feeder disconnects in the building or structure supplied, must be grouped in the same location.

Significance of the Change

The general rule in the parent text of 225.30 permits only one feeder or branch circuit to supply a building or other structure unless permitted in 225.30(A) through (F). This includes a new first level subdivision (B) titled *Common Supply Equipment*. This revision will now permit up to six feeders to supply a separate building or structure under prescriptive conditions. All of the feeder conductors must originate in the same panelboard, switchboard, or other distribution equipment. Each feeder must terminate in a single disconnecting means and all of the feeder disconnects in the building or structure supplied must be grouped in the same location. This revision is safety driven and recognizes that a single large feeder typically results in high levels of incident energy at the building or structure supplied. The incident energy is based upon the arcing current, (which is a factor of available fault current) and the clearing time of the upstream overcurrent protective device. The use of multiple feeders results in reduced conductor sizes, lowering the amount of available fault current, and lower amp ratings on upstream overcurrent protective devices to reduce incident energy levels. The use of multiple feeders instead of a single large feeder, also allows for the creation of an electrically safe work condition on a portion of the electrical distribution in the building or structure supplied. Where a single feeder is installed, there is a greater likelihood of unjustified energized work.

FR: 8280
SR: 7866

Spliced and Tapped Conductors

Code Language

230.46 Spliced and Tapped Conductors... Power distribution blocks, pressure connectors, and devices for splices and taps shall be listed. Power distribution blocks installed on service conductors shall be marked "suitable for use on the line side of the service equipment" or equivalent.

Effective January 1, 2023, pressure connectors and devices for splices and taps installed on service conductors shall be marked "suitable for use on the line side of the service equipment" or equivalent.

(See NEC for actual text)

Significance of the Change

Section 230.46 permits service entrance conductors to be spliced or tapped in accordance with 110.14, 300.5(E), 300.13, and 300.15. This revision relocates the requirement for power distribution blocks installed on service conductors to be listed and marked as "suitable for use on the line side of service equipment," or equivalent. This requirement is moved into 230.46 from 314.28(E)(1). This revision expands the listing requirements to include power distribution blocks, pressure connectors, and all devices used for splices and taps of service conductors. Additionally, a new requirement, effective January 1, 2023, will require all pressure connectors and devices for splices and taps installed on service conductors to be marked "suitable for use on the line side of service equipment" or equivalent. The *Code*-Making Panel was provided with test documentation that showed failures of some devices (split bolts) used for the termination of service conductors at higher amounts of available fault current.

Change Summary

- The requirement for marking power distribution blocks used on service conductors is moved from 314.28(E)(1) to 230.46.
- All power distribution blocks, pressure connectors, and devices for splices and taps of service conductors must be listed.
- Effective January 1, 2023, pressure connectors and devices for splices and taps on service conductors must be marked as suitable.

FR: 8454
SR: 7871

NEW

Barriers

Code Language

230.62(C) Barriers. Barriers shall be placed in service equipment such that no uninsulated, ungrounded service busbar or service terminal is exposed to inadvertent contact by persons or maintenance equipment while servicing load terminations.

(See NEC for actual text)

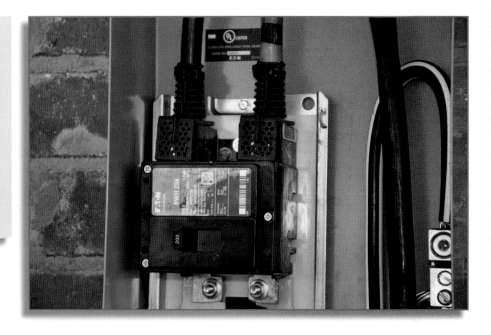

Change Summary

- The requirements of 408.3(A)(2) are relocated and expanded into new 230.62(C).

- All service equipment is now required to be provided with barriers to prevent line side inadvertent contact.

- This includes, but is not limited to panelboards, switchboards, switchgear, motor control centers, individual circuit breaker enclosures, SUSE rated transfer switches, and fused disconnects.

Significance of the Change

Section 230.62 contains requirements to enclose and/or guard energized parts of service supplied equipment, to prevent them from being exposed to inadvertent/accidental contact. A new first level subdivision 230.62(C) is added to require additional protection against inadvertent contact in the form of a barrier. Section 230.62(C) titled *Barriers*, now requires that barriers be placed in all service equipment, so that no uninsulated, ungrounded service busbar, or service terminal is exposed to inadvertent contact by persons while servicing load terminations. This requirement previously existed in 408.3(A)(2) in the 2017 *NEC*. The previous requirement required protection from inadvertent contact only for service supplied panelboards, switchboards, and switchgear. As written, this new requirement now applies to all service equipment. This includes, but is not limited to panelboards, switchboards, switchgear, motor control centers, individual circuit breaker enclosures, SUSE rated transfer switches and fused disconnects. This revision is safety driven, and mirrors the requirement in the *Canadian Electrical Code*, which requires service terminations to be completely enclosed. This is an example of how the *NEC* incorporates safety driven design requirements, to allow the installer/maintainer to safely maintain, expand, and to troubleshoot in service equipment.

FR: 8459
SR: 7896

Surge Protection, Dwelling Units

Significance of the Change

A new section 230.67 now requires services supplying dwelling units, to be provided with a surge protective device. There is significant data that proves electrical surges can, and do, cause significant damage within dwelling units and other structures. Within the *NEC*, for example, we have requirements for AFCIs, GFCIs, IDCIs, and other sensitive electronic equipment that is easily damaged by an electrical surge. These devices are required by the *NEC*, because they save lives. It is practical, feasible, and prudent to require surge protection to be provided for all dwelling unit service equipment. One significant example of documentation supporting this revision is the changes to the product standard for GFCIs that occurred around 2002. The standard was modified to require GFCIs have a self-test feature to determine if they were damaged by an electrical surge. New 230.67 mandates that an SPD be an integral part of the service equipment or immediately adjacent to the service equipment. An exception, allows the SPD to not be located in service equipment, provided that an SPD is located at each next level distribution equipment downstream towards the load. The SPD is required to be a Type 1 or Type 2 SPD. First level subdivision 230.67(D) requires that where service equipment is replaced, all of the requirements of this section apply.

Code Language

230.67 Surge Protection.

(A) Surge Protective Device. All services supplying dwelling units shall be provided with a surge protective device (SPD).

(B) Location...(See *NEC* text) an integral part of the service equipment or shall be located immediately adjacent thereto.

Exception: ... (See NEC text) if located at each next level distribution equipment downstream toward the load.

(C) Type. The SPD shall be a Type 1 or Type 2 SPD.

(D) Replacement. Where service equipment is replaced, all of the requirements of this section shall apply.

(See NEC for actual text)

Change Summary

- New 230.67 requires services supplying dwelling units to be provided with an SPD.
- The SPD must be located in or next to the service equipment. An exception permits an alternate location, provided an SPD is located at each next level distribution equipment downstream toward the load.
- All of the requirements in this new section apply where service equipment is replaced.

FR: 8546
SR: 7898

Maximum Number of Disconnects, Two to Six

Code Language

(B) Two to Six Service Disconnecting Means…Two to six service disconnects shall be permitted … (See *NEC* text) to consist of a combination of any of the following:

1 Separate enclosures with a main service disconnecting means in each enclosure

2 Panelboards with a main service disconnecting means in each panelboard enclosure

3 Switchboard(s) where there is only one service disconnect in each separate vertical section where there are barriers separating each vertical section

4 Service disconnects in switchgear or metering centers where each disconnect is located in a separate compartment

(See NEC for actual text)

Change Summary

- The requirements in 230.71(B) permitting up to six service disconnects are significantly revised.
- Panelboards, for example, must be provided with a single main in each enclosure.
- 230.71(B)(1) through (4) outline the permitted methods for two to six service disconnects.

FR: 8463
SR: 7901

Significance of the Change

The general rule in 230.71(A) permits only one service disconnecting means, unless the requirements of 230.71(B) are met. First level subdivision 230.71(B), is significantly revised and is retitled *Two to Six Service Disconnecting Means*. Two to six service disconnects are still permitted for each service permitted by 230.2, or for each set of service-entrance conductors permitted by 230.40 Exceptions 1, 3, 4, and 5. The previous permission for six disconnects permitted them all to be in a single enclosure, such as a panelboard. This revision provides four list items that outline the permitted two to six *disconnects* as follows: List item (1) permits separate enclosures with the main service disconnecting means in each enclosure. This provision is wide-ranging and includes all types of enclosures that are rated as service equipment. List item (2) permits panelboards, with a main service disconnecting means in each panelboard enclosure. List item (3) permits switchboards where there is only one service disconnect in each separate vertical section, where there are barriers separating each vertical section. List item (4) permits service disconnects in switchgear or metering centers, where each disconnect is located in a separate compartment. This is an extremely significant change in the 2020 *NEC*. This revision recognizes that *NFPA 70E*, prohibits justified energized work in service equipment with more than one service disconnecting means in the same enclosure. Together, with the requirements of 230.62(C) for barriers, this revision is an excellent example of requirements that drive safety through design.

Disconnection of Grounded Conductor

Courtesy of Eaton

Code Language

230.75 Disconnection of Grounded Conductor.

Informational Note: In switchgear or multisection switchboards, the disconnecting means provided for the grounded conductor is typically identified as a neutral disconnect link and is typically located in the bus to which the service grounded conductor is connected.

(See NEC for actual text)

Significance of the Change

Section 230.75 requires that where the service disconnecting means does not open the grounded conductor, some other means must be provided for this purpose in the service equipment. A new informational note is added to explain that in switchgear or multisection switchboards, the disconnecting means provided by the manufacturer for the grounded conductor is typically identified as a "neutral disconnect link" and is typically located in the bus to which the service grounded conductor is connected. The neutral disconnect link is typically a short piece of bus on the grounded bus that can be removed before performance testing of GFPE, which is required by 230.95(C).

Section 230.75 exists because the *NEC* must mandate a means to temporarily isolate for GFPE testing. The removal of a neutral disconnect link is the first step in performance testing GFPE. Without the removal of the neutral disconnect link, performance testing cannot verify that the neutral/grounded conductor is isolated from all grounding connections on the load side of the service disconnecting means.

Change Summary

- A new informational note is added in 230.75, to explain how this requirement is typically met.
- In order to performance test GFPE, there must be a means to disconnect the grounded conductor from premises wiring.
- A short section of bus is typically installed so that it can be easily removed, and it is typically identified as a *neutral disconnect link*.

FR: 8622
SR: None

Equipment...Supply Side of Service Disconnect

Code Language

230.82 Equipment Connected to the Supply Side of Service Disconnect.

(1) Cable limiters

(3) ... (See *NEC* text) available fault current... (See *NEC* text)

(5) Conductors used... (See *NEC* text)

(6) ... (See *NEC* text) if provided with a disconnecting means listed as suitable for use as service equipment, and overcurrent protection as specified in Part VII of Article 230.

(See NEC for actual text)

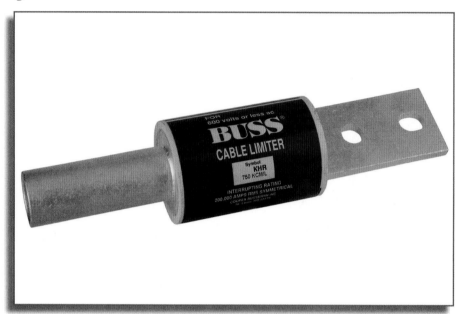

Courtesy of Eaton

Change Summary

- Other current-limiting devices are not permitted to act as a "cable limiter."

- Where service conductors are spliced, the rules of 240.21 do not apply.

- 230.82(6) now requires PV systems, fuel cells, and wind energy, etc. connected on the supply side of the service disconnect to be provided with service rated disconnecting means and overcurrent protection.

FRs: 8627, 8626, 8624, 8625
SR: None

Significance of the Change

Section 230.82 contains a list (11 items) of equipment that is permitted to be connected to the supply side of the service disconnecting means. Multiple revisions are discussed in this change. List item (1) is modified to clarify that other current-limiting devices are not permitted to be used in the same manner as a *current limiter*. The previous text, as written, inferred that a current limiting fuse could be used in the same manner as a current limiter. List item (3) is modified as part of a global revision to reference "available fault current" instead of "available short circuit current" where appropriate. List item (5) now addresses "Conductors used to supply...," instead of "Taps used to supply..." equipment. This revision attempts to eliminate possible confusion with the requirements of 240.21(B) for feeder taps. Where a smaller conductor is tapped to a larger service conductor, it is not a tap conductor as defined in 240.2, it is a service conductor, and the rules in 240.21 do not apply. List item (6) permits PV systems, fuel cells systems, wind electric systems, energy storage systems, and interconnected electric power production sources to be connected to the supply-side of the service disconnecting means. Additional text is added to require that each of these systems must be provided with a disconnecting means that is listed as suitable for use as service equipment and overcurrent protection, as specified in Article 230. This is a significant revision. The alternative energy industry would like to call those conductors *output conductors* and not service conductors.

Equipment...Supply Side of Service Disconnect

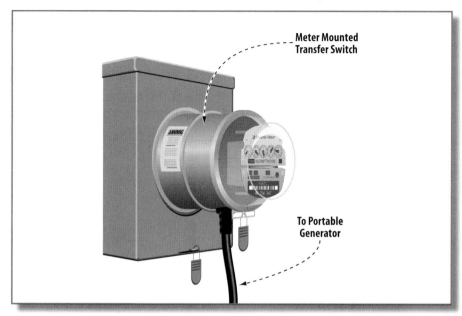

Meter Mounted
Transfer Switch

To Portable
Generator

Significance of the Change

Two new list items are added in section 230.82 for equipment permitted to be connected to the supply side of the service disconnect. List item (10) now permits "emergency disconnects" in accordance with new 230.85, provided all metal housings and service enclosures are grounded in accordance with Part VII, and bonded in accordance with Part V of Article 250. New section 230.85 now requires an emergency disconnect for all one- and two-family dwellings to allow first responders to remove power from the home in an emergency or fire event. Section 230.85 outlines the type of disconnects permitted.

New list item (11) now permits meter mounted transfer switches not over 1000 volts that have a short-circuit current rating equal to, or greater than, the available fault current. These meter mounted transfer switches must be listed and must be capable of transferring load served. This list item requires that meter mounted transfer switches be marked on the exterior: "Meter Mounted Transfer Switch" and "Not Service Equipment." Sections 700.5(C) and 701.5(C) prohibit meter mounted transfer switches from being used as part of an emergency system or a legally required standby system. Meter mounted transfer switches are permitted to be used in optional standby systems as required in 702.5(B).

Code Language

230.82 Equipment Connected to the Supply Side of Service Disconnect.

(10) Emergency disconnects in accordance with 230.85, if all metal housings and service enclosures are grounded in accordance with Part VII and bonded in accordance with Part V of Article 250.

(11) Meter-mounted transfer switches nominally rated not in excess of 1000 volts that have a short-circuit current rating equal to or greater than the available fault current. A meter-mounted transfer switch shall be listed and be capable of transferring the load served. A meter-mounted transfer switch shall be marked on its exterior with both of the following:

(a) Meter-mounted transfer switch

(b) Not service equipment

(See NEC for actual text)

Change Summary

- Emergency disconnects required by 230.85 are permitted to be connected on the supply side of the service disconnect.

- Meter mounted transfer switches are added in list item (11) and are permitted for optional standby use.

FRs: 8623, 8628
SR: 7912

Emergency Disconnects

Code Language

230.85 Emergency Disconnects. For one and two family dwelling units, all service conductor shall terminate in disconnecting means... In a readily accessible outdoor location. More than one disconnect is provided, they shall be grouped... (See *NEC* text)

(1) Service disconnects... (See *NEC* for text)

(2) Meter disconnects installed per 230.82... (See *NEC* text)

(3) Other listed disconnect switches or circuit breakers on the supply side of each service disconnect that are suitable for use as service equipment... (See *NEC* text)

(See NEC for actual text)

Change Summary

- All services for one and two family dwellings are now required to have emergency disconnects installed in a readily accessible outdoor location.

- These disconnects are necessary for first responders in a fire or other emergency.

- Similar requirements are added in this *NEC* cycle for energy storage systems and permanently mounted generators.

FR: 8462
SR: 7924

Courtesy of Craig Rose

Significance of the Change

New section 230.85 now requires that all services supplying one- and -two-family dwelling units terminate into a disconnecting means having a short circuit current rating equal to or greater than the available fault current that is installed in a readily accessible outdoor location. This new requirement recognizes the need of first responders to remove power from the dwelling unit in the event of fire or other emergency. This requirement made it to the floor of the NFPA annual meeting in the last cycle and was overturned. If more than one service disconnect is provided, the service supplied emergency disconnects must be grouped. There are three options provided as follows:

(1) Service disconnects marked as both: EMERGENCY DISCONNECT and SERVICE DISCONNECT. This permits the required service disconnecting means to be installed at a readily accessible outdoor location complying with both 230.70 and 230.85.

(2) Meter disconnects installed per 230.82(3) marked as: EMERGENCY DISCONNECT, METER DISCONNECT, NOT SERVICE DISCONNECT.

(3) Other listed disconnect switches or circuit breakers on the supply side of each service disconnect that are suitable for use as service equipment and marked: EMERGENCY DISCONNECT, NOT SERVICE DISCONNECT.

For example, this permits a listed circuit breaker enclosure to be installed outdoors in an accessible location ahead of the main in a panelboard used as service equipment. In this case, the circuit breaker enclosure is the emergency disconnect and would not be considered the service disconnecting means.

Restricted Access Adjustable-Trip Circuit Breakers

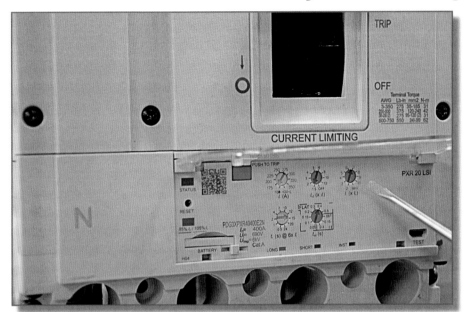

Courtesy of Eaton

Code Language

240.6(C) Restricted Access Adjustable-Trip Circuit Breakers. ...(See *NEC* text)

(1) Located behind removable and sealable covers over the adjusting means

(2) Located behind bolted equipment enclosure doors

(3) Located behind locked doors accessible only to qualified personnel

(4) Password protected, with password accessible only to qualified personnel

(See NEC for actual text)

Significance of the Change

Section 240.6 provides requirements for standard ampere ratings of overcurrent protective devices. These requirements address: (A) *Fuses and Fixed Trip Circuit Breakers*, the rating of which is the fixed overload rating on the device and (B) *Adjustable Trip Circuit Breakers*, requires that the rating of these devices be the maximum setting possible. This revision addresses first level subdivision (C) *Restricted Access Adjustable-Trip Circuit Breakers*. 240.6(C) modifies the requirements for adjustable trip circuit breakers in (B). This requirement allows an adjustable trip circuit breaker to be rated at the *adjusted current rating*, which is the long-time pickup setting, provided that device has restricted access. This revision modifies what the *Code* considers to be "restricted access." There are now four methods to achieve restricted access. The first three methods are existing and are editorially modified as follows: (1) located behind removable and sealable covers over the adjusting means, (2) located behind bolted equipment enclosure doors, and (3) located behind locked doors accessible only to qualified personnel. A new list item (4) is added to recognize password protected devices with the password accessible only to qualified personnel. This new means to achieve restricted access recognizes the capability of modern electronic trip units, to keep unauthorized users from changing the settings.

Change Summary

- Adjustable trip circuit breakers may be rated at the adjusted current setting, provided there is restricted access to the device.
- 240.6(C) list items (1) through (3) are editorially modified for clarity.
- New list item (4) permits an adjustable trip circuit breaker that is password-protected with the password accessible only to qualified personnel to be considered as having restricted access.

FR: 8636
SR: 7955

Feeder Taps

Code Language

(B) Feeder Taps. Conductors shall be permitted to be tapped, without overcurrent protection at the tap, to a feeder as specified in 240.21(B)(1) through (B)(5). The tap shall be permitted at any point on the load side of the feeder overcurrent protective device. Section 240.4(B) shall not be permitted for tap conductors.

(See NEC for actual text)

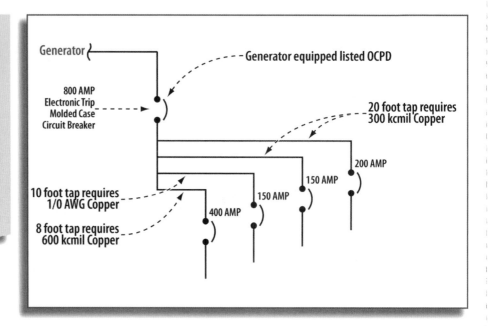

Change Summary

- The parent text 240.21(B) is modified for clarity.
- Feeders are permitted to be tapped at any point on the load side of the feeder overcurrent protective device.
- Generator supplied feeder tap conductors are often installed in this manner. See 445.13(B).

Significance of the Change

Feeder tap requirements in 240.21(B) are modified to clarify where along the length of the feeder a tap is permitted. The parent text of this first level subdivision is modified with a new sentence that states "The tap shall be permitted at any point on the load side of the feeder overcurrent protective device." The load side of the overcurrent protective device begins at the load terminals of the circuit breaker or fused disconnect. For example, consider a 400 amp molded case circuit breaker that is provided with two lugs (termination points) on the load side of the device for each phase. In this case, the 400-amp circuit breaker is permitted to supply two loads through two sets of tap conductors provided the requirements of 240.21(B) are met. For example, two 1/0 copper tap conductors could supply two 150-amp circuit breaker enclosures in accordance with 240.21(B). This type of installation is typical for standby generators and is specifically permitted in 445.13(B).

FR: 1811
SR: 7956

NEW

240.62, 240.88, & 240.102

Article 240 Overcurrent Protection

Part VI Cartridge Fuses... Part VII Circuit Breakers and Part IX Overcurrent Protection...

Reconditioned Equipment

Courtesy of Eaton

Code Language

240.62/88/102 Reconditioned Equipment.

240.62... (See *NEC* text) low-voltage fuseholders and low-voltage non-renewable fuses... (See *NEC* text)

240.88... (See *NEC* text) molded case, low and medium voltage power, and high-voltage circuit breakers... (See *NEC* text) electronic trip units, electromechanical protective relays encourage transformers... (See *NEC* text)

240.102... medium voltage fuseholders and medium voltage nonrenewable fuses... (See *NEC* text)

(See NEC for actual text)

Significance of the Change

Three new sections are added in Article 240 to address reconditioned equipment. The term *reconditioned* means that electromechanical systems, equipment, apparatus or components are restored to operating conditions. It is imperative to note that some equipment lends itself very well to the reconditioning process and other equipment cannot be reconditioned. This process (reconditioning) is significantly different from normal servicing of equipment that remains within a facility. Additionally, it is important to note that replacement of listed equipment on a one-to-one basis does not constitute "reconditioned equipment." Additional terms to describe this process include: *rebuilt*, *refurbished*, or *remanufactured*.

Sections 240.62 and 240.102 prohibit low/medium-voltage fuse holders and low/medium voltage nonrenewable fuses from being reconditioned. Section 240.88 provides requirements for reconditioning circuit breakers (CBs) and associated components. Molded case CBs are not permitted to be reconditioned. Low voltage power CBs, medium voltage power CBs, and high-voltage CBs are permitted to be reconditioned. Section 240.88(B) addresses reconditioned trip units, protective relays, and current transformers. Low voltage power CB trip units are not permitted to be reconditioned. Electromechanical protective relays and current transformers are permitted to be reconditioned. See the "NEMA Policy on Reconditioned Electrical Equipment" for more information.

Change Summary

- Low and medium voltage fuse holders/non-renewable fuses are not permitted to be reconditioned.
- Molded case circuit breakers and low voltage power circuit breaker electronic trip units are not permitted to be reconditioned.
- Low, medium voltage power CBs, high voltage CBs, electromechanical protective relays, and current transformers are permitted to be reconditioned.

FR: None
SRs: 7974, 8011, 8048

Arc Energy Reduction

Code Language

240.67(A) Documentation. ... (See *NEC* text) Documentation shall also be provided to demonstrate that the method chosen to reduce clearing time is set to operate at a value below the available arcing current.

(B) Method to Reduce Clearing Time.

(4) Current limiting electronically actuated fuses

(See NEC for actual text)

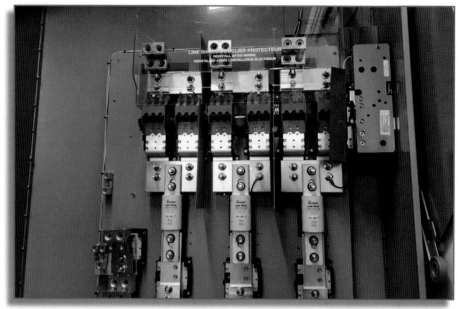

Courtesy of Eaton

Change Summary

- Documentation is now required to demonstrate that the method chosen to reduce clearing time will operate at a value below the arcing current.

- 240.67(B) requires that the method chosen to reduce clearing time operates at a value below the arcing current.

- Current limiting electronically actuated fuses are now a permitted arc energy reduction method in 240.67.

Significance of the Change

Section 240.67 requires that where fuses rated 1200 amps or higher are installed, a means of arc energy reduction must be applied. 240.67(A) requires documentation available to those authorized to design, install, operate, or inspect the installation. This requirement is revised to require documentation to prove that the arc energy reduction method chosen to reduce clearing time is set to operate at a value below the available arcing current. 240.67(B) now requires that the method to reduce clearing time be set to operate at a value less than the available arcing current. 240.67(B) *Method to Reduce Clearing Time* requires a fuse to have a clearing time of 0.07 seconds or less at the available arcing current or one of the listed means to reduce clearing time must be applied. Existing methods include, differential relaying, an energy-reducing maintenance switch with a local status indicator, an energy reducing active arc flash mitigation system, or an approved equivalent means. A new method to reduce clearing time is added as list item (4) *Current limiting, electronically actuated fuses*. While these fuses were already permitted as an approved equivalent method, the specific reference increases clarity and usability for the *Code* user. Current limiting, electronically actuated fuses typically include a very small pyrotechnic charge that can be triggered electronically. For this method, the arc energy reduction system must recognize that an arcing fault is occurring and a signal is sent to the small pyrotechnic charge to open the fuse link.

FR: 8641

SR: 7991

240.67(C) & 240.87(C)

Article 240 Overcurrent Protection

Part VI Cartridge Fuses and Fuseholders and VIII Circuit Breakers

Performance Testing

Courtesy of Eaton

Code Language

240.67(C) Performance Testing. The arc energy reduction protection system shall be performance tested by primary current injection testing or another approved method when first installed on site. This testing shall be conducted by a qualified person(s) in accordance with the manufacturer's instructions.

A written record…

Informational Note: Some energy reduction protection systems cannot be tested using a test process of primary current injection due to either the protection method being damaged such as with the use of fuse technology or because current is not the primary method of arc detection.

(See NEC for actual text)

Significance of the Change

A new first level subdivision (C) *Performance Testing* is added to 240.67 and 240.87, which requires arc energy reduction methods for fuses rated 1200 amps or higher, and for circuit breakers where the actual overcurrent device installed is rated at, or can be adjusted to, 1200 amps or more. This new text requires methods to reduce clearing time be performance tested when first installed on site. An example of existing performance testing requirements is found in 230.95 for ground fault protection of equipment. The required performance testing must be done by a qualified person in accordance with the manufacturers' instructions. The performance test must be by primary current injection testing or another approved method following the manufacturers' recommended test procedures. Requirements for arc energy reduction are safety driven and exist to address exposure to arc flash. The energy released in an arc flash incident is primarily the product of the arcing current squared (arcing current is a function of the available fault current) multiplied by the clearing time of the upstream overcurrent protective device. The clearing time is directly proportional to the energy released in an arc flash incident. If we can reduce clearing time to 25%, the energy released is reduced to 25%. The intent is to allow persons that will maintain or troubleshoot the system, to reduce exposure to arc flash while performing justified energized work. These changes were modified by Tentative Interim Amendments 1451 and 1452.

Change Summary

- Arc energy reduction methods must be performance tested when first installed onsite.
- Testing must be performed by qualified persons in accordance with the manufacturers' instructions.
- A written record of this testing must be made available to the AHJ.

FR: None
SRs: 8020, 8030

Arc Energy Reduction

Code Language

240.87(A) Documentation....(See *NEC* text) Documentation shall also be provided to demonstrate that the method chosen to reduce clearing time is set to operate at a value below the available arcing current.

(B) Method to Reduce Clearing Time. ... (See *NEC* text) shall be set to operate at less than the available arcing current:

(5) An instantaneous trip setting. Temporary adjustment of the instantaneous trip setting to achieve arc energy reduction shall not be permitted.

(6) An instantaneous override

(See NEC for actual text)

Change Summary

- Temporary adjustment of the instantaneous trip setting to achieve arc energy reduction is prohibited.
- All arc energy reduction methods chosen, must operate at less than the available arcing current. This must be documented.

FR: 8671
SR: 7999

Courtesy of Eaton

Significance of the Change

Section 240.87 *Arc Energy Reduction* is modified in (B) to require that the arc energy reduction method chosen, must be set to operate at less than the available arcing current. Documentation must be provided to demonstrate that the clearing time method chosen, will operate at a value below the available arcing current. Adding this requirement in the parent text of both 240.87(A) and (B) required that list items (5) and (6) be editorially revised to permit an instantaneous trip setting, or an instantaneous override. It is important to note that the parent text now clarifies that the instantaneous trip setting, or the instantaneous override must be set to operate at less than the available arcing current. List item (5) is further modified to clarify that temporary adjustment of the instantaneous trip setting to achieve arc energy reduction is prohibited. Unfortunately, there has been a significant effort to confuse the electrical industry with respect to arc energy reduction and the requirements of 240.87. The use of a circuit breaker that includes an instantaneous trip setting does not mean that the installation is in compliance with 240.87. An instantaneous trip setting cannot be modified to achieve arc energy reduction. This is a very dangerous concept. The average wireman is not qualified to make any adjustments on an electronic trip unit in a circuit breaker. Where this is done there is no guarantee that the individual modified the right setting. There is also no guarantee that the setting will be returned to the original value when the work is complete.

Overvoltage Protection

Code Language

242.1 Scope. This article provides the general requirements, installation requirements, and connection requirements for overvoltage protection and overvoltage protective devices. Part II covers surge-protective devices (SPDs) permanently installed on premises wiring systems of not more than 1000 volts, nominal, while Part III covers surge arresters permanently installed on premises wiring systems over 1000 volts, nominal.

Informational Note: Article 242 combines and replaces Articles 280 and 285 in NFPA 70-2017. (See *NEC* text)

(See NEC for actual text)

Significance of the Change

The content of Articles 280 and 285 have been combined and incorporated into a new Article 242 titled "Overvoltage Protection." These requirements are more appropriately located immediately following Article 240, which covers overcurrent protection. The requirements for surge protective devices and surge arresters are reformatted into a single article with three parts for clarity and usability. Part I includes the General Requirements, Part II includes Surge Protective Devices (SPDs) 1000 Volts or Less, and Part III covers Surge Arresters Over 1000 Volts. The development of this new article required careful coordination by both *Code* Panels 5 and 10, since this revision involved a shift in technical responsibility of the new article. Logically, CMP-10 has responsibility for the article and its associated definitions, because the requirements contained therein address protection from overvoltage events. Definitions of the terms *Surge Protective Device (SPD)* and *Surge Arrester* are appropriately located in Article 100, since these terms appear elsewhere in the *NEC* in more than two articles. There were very few grounding and bonding requirements within former Articles 280 and 285, another justification for this shift in responsibility. Requirements for surge protective devices have expanded in each recent edition of the *NEC*. In the 2020 *NEC*, a new requirement for surge protection in dwelling unit services was added in section 230.67.

Change Summary

- Articles 280 and 285 have been combined to form a new Article 242 titled Overvoltage Protection.
- The article has three parts, General, Surge Protective Devices (SPDs) 1000 Volts or Less, and Surge Arresters Over 1000 Volts.
- Technical responsibility for Article 242 and its associated definitions in Article 100 has been shifted from CMP-5 to CMP-10.

FR: 8221

Global SR: 8083

SR: 8066

Definition of Bonding Jumper, Supply-Side

Code Language

Bonding Jumper, Supply-Side. A conductor installed on the supply side of a service or within a service equipment enclosure(s), or for a separately derived system, that ensures the required electrical conductivity between metal parts required to be electrically connected. (CMP-5)

(See NEC for actual text)

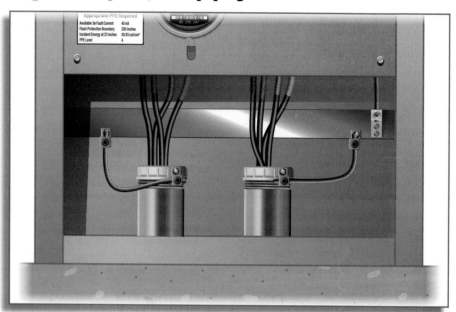

Change Summary

- The definition of the term *Bonding Jumper, Supply-Side* has been deleted from 250.2.
- The definition, without revision has been located into Part I of Article 100.
- This relocation aligns with the requirements of Section 2.2.2.1 of the *NEC Style Manual*.

Significance of the Change

Action by CMP-5 in SR 9007 deletes the term *bonding jumper, supply-side* from Section 250.2, and relocates the term, without revision, to Part I of Article 100. Section 2.2.2.1 of the *NEC Style Manual* requires that Article 100 generally contain definitions of terms that appear in more than one article. While the term is used most often in Article 250, it is also used in other articles such as Articles 230, 250, 310, 408, 450, 694 and so forth. This action effectively does away with Section 250.2 as all grounding and bonding words and terms now appear in Article 100. In the larger scheme of things, this is a good indication that the use of defined grounding and bonding terms is becoming consistent throughout the *NEC*. The term *supply-side bonding jumper* relates to a conductor in the grounding and bonding scheme that is present both at the service, and at the source of separately derived systems. This bonding jumper is installed on the supply side of the service overcurrent device, usually a main, and is typically installed with supply-side ungrounding conductors to the first system overcurrent device enclosure. This bonding jumper, if of a wire type, has strengthened sizing requirements that must comply with Section 250.102(C), which relate directly to the size of the largest ungrounded service conductor, or the largest ungrounded derived phase conductor connected at the source of a separately derived system.

FR: 9007

SR: None

Informational Note References *NFPA 70E*

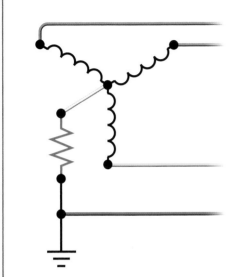

Grounding location is between the grounding electrode conductor and the neutral grounding point.

Neutral conductor has to be fully insulated.

Neutral conductor must have an ampacity no less than the maximum current rating of the grounding impedance.

Grounding connection can only be made through the grounding impedance device.

Code Language

250.20(B) Alternating-Current Systems of 50 Volts to 1000 Volts. (See *NEC* text)

Informational Note: According to Annex O of NFPA 70E-2018, Standard for Electrical Safety in the Workplace, high impedance grounding is an effective tool to reduce arc flash hazards.

250.36 High Impedance Grounded Neutral Systems. (See *NEC* text)

Informational Note: According to Annex O of NFPA 70E-2018, Standard for Electrical Safety in the Workplace, high impedance grounding is an effective tool to reduce arc flash hazards.

(See NEC for actual text)

Significance of the Change

According to *NFPA 70E, Standard for Electrical Safety in the Workplace*, high impedance grounding is an effective tool to reduce arc flash hazard levels. Placing an informational note in 250.20(B) will highlight the safety benefits of high-impedance grounded system prior to making selection for system grounding. A high-impedance grounded neutral system is a system in which an impedance device, usually a resistor, limits the current in a phase-to-ground fault condition to a low level. This allows the system to remain operational during the ground-fault condition. These types of systems are typically installed in industrial applications. High-impedance grounded neutral systems are permitted for use in AC systems with voltages ranging from 480 to 1000 volts, but restrictions must be met as indicated in 250.20(B)(1), (2), and (3). High-impedance grounded neutral systems have special requirements, all of which need to be followed. This type of installation requires special equipment, and various manufacturers produce the equipment designed specifically for these types of installations. Because these systems divert a phase-to-ground fault condition through an impedance or resister, the amount of arc energy at the point of a ground fault is significantly reduced, aligning with objectives expressed in *NFPA 70E*.

Change Summary

- A new informational note has been added following Section 250.20(B) and 250.36.
- The informational note references *NFPA 70E Standard for Electrical Safety in the Workplace, Annex O.*
- High-impedance grounded systems limit arc energy in a first phase-to-ground fault event that occurs in a high impedance grounded system.

FRs: 7643, 7781
SR: None

NEW

Grounding on Supply Side of Disconnect

Code Language

250.25 Grounding Systems Permitted to Be Connected on the Supply Side of the Disconnect. The grounding of systems connected on the supply side of the service disconnect... (See *NEC* text) ...shall comply with 250.25(A) or (B).

(A) Grounded System. If the utility system is grounded... (See *NEC* text) ... shall comply with the requirements of 250.24(A) through (D)

(B) Ungrounded Systems. If the utility system is ungrounded... (See *NEC* text) ...shall comply with the requirements of 250.24(E)

(See NEC for actual text)

Change Summary

- A new section 250.25 titled "Grounding Systems Permitted to Be Connected on the Supply Side of the Disconnect" has been added in Part II of Article 250.

- The new section provides rules for grounding of systems connected to the supply side of the service disconnect as permitted in 230.82.

- The new section addresses systems supplied by grounded and ungrounded utility sources.

Significance of the Change

A new section 250.25 titled "Grounding Systems Permitted to Be Connected on the Supply Side of the Disconnect" has been added in Part II of Article 250, providing grounding rules for grounded and ungrounded systems connected to the supply side of the service disconnect as permitted in 230.82. The new section address systems supplied by grounded and ungrounded utility sources. Not all equipment connected to the utility is considered a service, such as parallel power production equipment, but should be grounded and bonded with the same requirements. In some instances, such as solar installations, the parallel power production equipment is connected in parallel with a service, and in some cases, connected directly to the utility solely for power production to the utility with no service equipment in parallel. The addition of 250.25 referencing the appropriate parts of Section 250.24 ensures that supply-side equipment is connected to a grounding electrode system, has an effective fault path whether it be a grounded service conductor or supply-side bonding jumper, and is bonded using more robust requirements of 250.92 and 250.102(C). The existing structure of Article 250 is maintained, and redundancy is minimized because all necessary grounding and bonding requirements are contained within Article 250.

FR: 8198
SR: 7778

Main Bonding Jumper and System Bonding Jumper

Code Language

250.28 Main Bonding Jumper and System Bonding Jumper.

(A) Material. Main bonding jumpers and system bonding jumpers shall be of copper, aluminum, copper-clad aluminum, or other corrosion-resistant material. A main bonding jumper and a system bonding jumper shall be a wire, bus, screw, or similar suitable conductor.

(B) Construction. ... (See *NEC* text)

(C) Attachment. ... (See *NEC* text)

(D) Size. ... (See *NEC* text)

(See NEC for actual text)

Significance of the Change

The words "aluminum, copper-clad aluminum" have been added to Section 250.28(A). This clarifies the conductive materials permitted to be used as main and system bonding jumpers. This revision also aligns with the permitted materials listed in 250.102(C)(1), and with materials that manufacturers sometimes use for main and system bonding jumpers within listed equipment. Information in Public Input 2862 correctly indicated that the materials in 2017 *NEC* Section 250.28(A) did not contain aluminum and copper-clad aluminum, and consequently did not correspond with 250.102(C)(1) conductor requirements. Action by *Code*-Panel 5 includes these materials within this section to correspond with the materials in Table 250.102(C)(1), for consistency. It should also be noted that manufacturers often construct equipment and use these conductor materials for the main bonding jumpers and system bonding jumpers contained within such equipment. This equipment is typically identified as "suitable for use as service equipment" or "suitable for use only as service equipment" and thus typically includes main and system bonding jumper provisions.

Change Summary

- The words "aluminum, copper-clad aluminum" have been added to Section 250.28(A).
- This clarifies the conductive materials permitted to be used as main and system bonding jumpers.
- This revision also aligns with the permitted materials listed in 250.102(C)(1), and with materials that manufacturers sometimes use for main and system bonding jumpers within listed equipment.

FR: 7685
SR: None

Grounding Separately Derived AC Systems

Code Language

250.30 Grounding Separately Derived Alternating-Current Systems. In addition to complying with 250.30(A) for grounded systems, or as provided in 250.30(B) for ungrounded systems, separately derived systems shall comply with 250.20, 250.21, 250.22, or 250.26, as applicable. Multiple power sources of the same type that are connected in parallel to form one system that supplies premises wiring shall be considered as a single separately derived system and shall be installed in accordance with 250.30.

(See NEC for actual text)

Change Summary

- Multiple separately derived systems connected in parallel are considered a single separately derived system, only where the systems are of the same type.
- Section 250.30(A)(2) was revised to clarify that the system bonding jumper is connected to the enclosure, not the disconnecting means.
- Exceptions were relocated to follow the rule to which they apply to comply with the *NEC Style Manual*.

Significance of the Change

The revised text in the first paragraph of 250.30 clarifies that multiple separately derived systems of the same type connected in parallel are considered to be a single separately derived system. As an example, multiple generators connected in parallel could be considered a single separately derived system. New exception number 4 was added to cover multiple sources of the same type, that are installed as a single separately derived system. The words "enclosure for the" were added to 250.30(A)(2) because the supply side bonding jumper is connected to the enclosure, not the disconnecting means itself. Language was added to 250.30(A)(3) to clarify that a derived system grounded conductor is not required to be larger than the derived system ungrounded conductors. The word "each" was added to the first paragraph of 250.30(A)(6) to emphasize that each separately derived system needs to be connected to the common grounding electrode conductor. The exception to 250.30(A)(6) was relocated under the opening paragraph as Exception No. 3, as that is what it applies to. An exception to 250.30(A)(6)(a)(1) and (b) was added to 250.30(A)(6) to permit reduced sizing of grounding electrode conductors, under the conditions stated, and be consistent with 250.66(A) through (C).

FR: 8097
SR: 7785

Trailer-Mounted Generators

Code Language

250.34 Portable, Vehicle-Mounted, and Trailer-Mounted Generators.

(A) Portable Generators. The frame of a portable generator shall not be required to be connected to a grounding electrode as defined in 250.52 for a system supplied by the generator under both of the following conditions: (See *NEC* text)

(B) Vehicle-Mounted and Trailer-Mounted Generators. (See *NEC* text)

(C) Grounded Conductor Bonding. A system grounded conductor that is required to be grounded by 250.26... (See *NEC* text)

(See NEC for actual text)

Significance of the Change

Action by *Code* Panel 5 on FR 7818, results in the expansion of this section to include trailer-mounted generators. The addition of trailer-mounted generators to 250.34(B) brings clarity that the requirements for vehicle-mounted generators also apply to trailer-mounted generators. The frame of a vehicle or trailer shall not be required to be connected to a grounding electrode as defined in 250.52 for a system supplied by a generator located on this vehicle or trailer under the specific conditions in (1) through (3). The word *vehicle* is typically defined as something that is used to transport people or goods. It typically includes a means of propelling the vehicle, such as an electric or combustion engine. *Portable* is typically defined as able to be easily carried or moved, especially because of being a lighter and smaller version than usual. These definitions do not define a trailer-mounted generator, which can be up to 2 megawatts in size. Second Revision 7793 would have resulted in additional language in 250.34(C), to provide clarity that when any bonded neutral generator is utilized as a temporary source of power, as permitted elsewhere in the *Code*, the connection cannot create objectionable current paths within the premise wiring system. SR 7793 did not pass ballot, which restores 250.34(C) to the text in the 2017 *NEC*.

Change Summary

- The term *trailer-mounted* has been incorporated into Section 250.34(B).
- The requirements apply to portable, vehicle, and trailer-mounted generators.
- Subdivision (C) remains as in the 2017 *NEC* due to Second Revision 7793 failing ballot.

FR: 7818
SR: 7793

250.64(A)

Article 250 Grounding and Bonding

Part III Grounding Electrode System and Grounding Electrode Conductor

Aluminum and Copper-Clad Aluminum Conductors

Code Language

(A) Aluminum or Copper-Clad Aluminum Conductors. Grounding electrode conductors of bare, covered, or insulated aluminum or copper-clad aluminum shall comply with the following:

(1) Bare or covered conductors without an extruded polymeric covering shall not be installed where subject to corrosive conditions or be installed in direct contact with concrete.

(2) Terminations made within outdoor enclosures that are listed and identified for the environment shall be permitted within 450 mm (18 in.) of the bottom of the enclosure.

(3) Aluminum… (See *NEC* text)

(See NEC for actual text)

Change Summary

- This section was restructured into a list format to meet the *NEC Style Manual* requirements.
- The revision in (1) prohibits direct contact with concrete.
- (2) has been revised to permit terminations of aluminum and copper-clad aluminum conductors connections within 18 inches of the earth where within enclosures listed for the environment.

FR: 7973
SR: 7775, 7777

Significance of the Change

The section was formatted into a list format for improved clarity and usability to show three requirements that must be met. Revised language in this section clarifies that terminations located in the interior of the listed equipment are separated from the earth. Substantiation indicated that inspectors in some jurisdictions have rejected installations of aluminum conductors, or copper-clad aluminum conductors, where terminated on equipment grounding busbars, because the termination was less than 18 inches above the concrete slab or pad at the bottom of the equipment. The additional text in (2) clarifies that a concrete bottom on open bottom equipment is not to be considered as earth for application of these requirements. The interior of outdoor rated equipment is considered a dry location in accordance with the applicable UL and IEEE standards, therefore, aluminum terminations within these rated enclosures are not subject to exposure to the earth and related corrosive conditions. In addition, the allowance is provided for aluminum connections to be made outdoors or outside rated enclosures as long as they are listed and identified for the environment. There are standards for this listing and while none exist at this time, this provision will permit manufacturers to develop and list connectors as the market demands. This is a permissive allowance and not a requirement so the lack of having a product on the market at this time is not substantiation to not permit this allowance. Concrete was added to the list of prohibited locations to clarify that concrete is a type of masonry. The bottom of open-bottom enclosures is the material, other than earth, where the enclosure is mounted.

REVISION

250.64(B)(2) & (B)(3)
Article 250 Grounding and Bonding
Part III Grounding Electrode System and Grounding Electrode Conductor

Securing and Protection Against Physical Damage

Significance of the Change

The term *Schedule 80* has been added to second-level subdivisions (2) and (3). The revision clarifies the type of PVC conduit that is suitable and identified to provide protection against physical damage. Schedule 80 PVC conduit provides impact and crush resistant characteristics, while schedule 40 does not. Section 350.10(F) indicates that PVC conduit shall be permitted to be used to provide protection against physical damage where it is identified for that use. The informational note specifically mentions Schedule 80. It should also be noted that Part III of Article 352 provides the construction characteristics of PVC conduit. Section 352.100 indicates that "PVC conduit and fittings shall be composed of suitable nonmetallic material that is resistant to moisture and chemical atmospheres. For use above-ground, it shall also be flame retardant, resistant to impact and crushing, resistant to distortion from heat under conditions likely to be encountered in service, and resistant to low temperature and sunlight effects." Schedule 80 PVC provides the impact and crush resistant characteristics needed for use where protecting a grounding electrode conductor from physical damage is necessary. As a reminder, Table 1, Chapter 9 provides the maximum percentage of fill for a single conductor installed in a circular raceway is 53%.

Code Language

250.64(B) Securing and Protection Against Physical Damage.

(2) Exposed to Physical Damage. A 6 AWG or larger copper or aluminum grounding electrode conductor exposed to physical damage shall be protected in rigid metal conduit (RMC), intermediate metal conduit (IMC), Schedule 80 rigid polyvinyl chloride conduit (PVC), reinforced thermosetting resin conduit Type XW (RTRC-XW), electrical metallic tubing (EMT), or cable armor.

(3) Smaller Than 6 AWG. Grounding electrode conductors smaller than 6 AWG shall be protected in RMC, IMC, Schedule 80 PVC, RTRC-XW, EMT, or cable armor.

(See NEC for actual text)

Change Summary

- The term *Schedule 80* has been added to second-level subdivisions (2) and (3).
- The revision clarifies the type of PVC conduit that is suitable to provide protection against physical damage.
- Schedule 80 PVC conduit provides impact and crush resistant characteristics, while schedule 40 does not.

FR: 7898
SR: None

Raceways and Enclosures for GECs

Code Language

(1) General. Ferrous metal raceways, enclosures, and cable armor for grounding electrode conductors shall be electrically continuous from the point of attachment to cabinets or equipment to the grounding electrode and shall be securely fastened to the ground clamp or fitting. Ferrous metal raceways, enclosures, and cable armor

(3) Size. The bonding jumper for a grounding electrode conductor(s), raceway(s), enclosure(s), or cable armor shall be the same size as, or larger than, the largest enclosed grounding electrode conductor.

(See NEC for actual text)

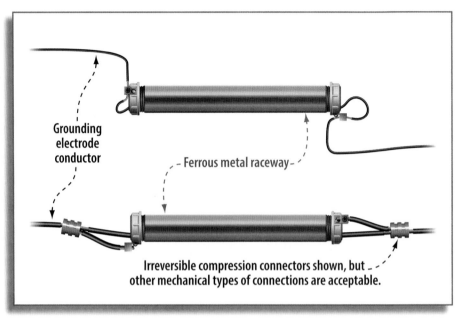

Grounding electrode conductor

- Ferrous metal raceway -

Irreversible compression connectors shown, but other mechanical types of connections are acceptable.

Change Summary

- The term *cable armor* has been added to second-level subdivision (1).
- (3) has been revised to clarify minimum sizing requirements for bonding jumpers that are connected to ferrous metal raceways, or cable armor that encloses a GEC.
- The minimum size must not be smaller than the largest contained GEC in the same enclosure.

Significance of the Change

Section 250.64(E) addresses requirements for ferrous metal enclosures containing grounding electrode conductors. This section does not apply to nonferrous metal enclosures. The word "enclosures" was added for consistency throughout this section. The term *cable armor* has been added to second-level subdivision (1) and second-level subdivision (3) has been revised to clarify minimum sizing requirements for bonding jumpers that are connected to ferrous metal raceways, or cable armor that encloses a single or multiple grounding electrode conductor(s). Ferrous metal armor assemblies that include a grounding electrode conductor are available for installing grounding electrode conductors in a location that warrants protection. Bonding the ferrous metal armor to the contained grounding electrode conductor is a requirement of this section, and there are listed clamps and fittings available specifically for this purpose. The revisions to (3) clarify that when multiple GECs are installed in a single raceway, cable armor, or other enclosure and bonding the enclosure is required, the minimum size for the bonding jumper(s) must not be smaller than the largest contained grounding electrode conductor(s). Bonding ferrous metal enclosures for grounding electrode conductors is necessary to minimize impedance and the choke effect that is imposed on the contained grounding electrode conductor(s).

FRs: 7980, 7902
SR: None

Grounding Electrode Conductor Connections

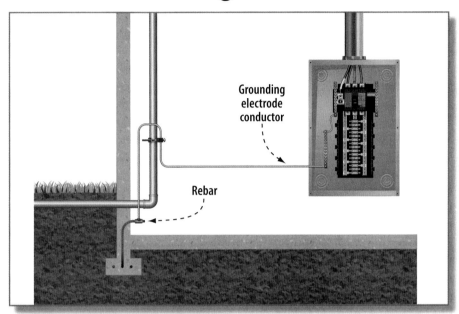

Grounding electrode conductor

Rebar

Significance of the Change

This section has been revised and structured into a list format in accordance with the *NEC Style Manual* for improved clarity and usability. The words "foundation or footing" have been added to clarify where the rebar extension must be connected. The rebar extension must be continuous with the grounding electrode rebar, or shall be connected to the grounding electrode rebar and connected together by the usual steel tie wires, exothermic welding, welding, or other effective means. The idea here is that the rebar is extended outside the concrete footing or foundation so that a connection can be made to it with a grounding electrode conductor. This can be accomplished either continuous (bent from the horizontal base to vertically expose above the foundation or footing) or if a separate piece is installed, as is most commonly done, have the proper overlap as set by the building code and be attached with the usual steel tie wires, exothermic welding, welding, or other approved means. List item (b) clarifies that the rebar extension must not be exposed to contact with the earth without corrosion protection. In list item (c), language has been added that will restrict rebar from being used as a conductor (bonding jumper) to interconnect electrodes of the grounding electrode system.

Code Language

(3) A rebar-type concrete-encased electrode...(See *NEC* text)...from its location within the concrete foundation or footing to an accessible location...(See *NEC* text)...in accordance with the following:

(a) The additional rebar section shall be continuous with the grounding electrode rebar or shall be connected to the grounding electrode rebar and connected together by the usual steel tie wires, exothermic welding, welding, or other effective means.

(b) The rebar extension shall not be exposed to contact with the earth without corrosion protection.

(c) Rebar shall not be used as a conductor to interconnect the electrodes of grounding electrode systems.

(See NEC for actual text)

Change Summary

- The rebar extension must be connected to the rebar in the foundation or footing.
- The rebar extension shall not be exposed to earth contact without corrosion protection.
- The rebar extension shall not be used to interconnect electrodes of the grounding electrode system.

FR: 7985
SR: None

Method of Bonding at the Service

Code Language

(B) Method of Bonding at the Service. Bonding jumpers meeting the requirements of this article shall be used around impaired connections, such as reducing washers or oversized, concentric, or eccentric knockouts. (See *NEC* text) …one of the following methods:

(1) (See *NEC* text)

(2) Connections using threaded couplings or listed threaded hubs on enclosures if made up wrenchtight.

(3) (See *NEC* text)

(4) (See *NEC* text)

(See NEC for actual text)

Change Summary

- The words "listed threaded hubs" have been incorporated into list item (2) of this section.

- Standard hubs that have not been evaluated and listed for use in service bonding applications are not permitted.

- Listed products are identified for the uses for which they are permitted.

Significance of the Change

Section 250.92(B) provides bonding methods for enclosures, raceways, and other normally non–current-carrying metal parts at the service, and on the supply side of the service disconnecting means, and overcurrent protective device. These conductive enclosures contain conductors supplied directly from a utility source that are usually not protected at their ampacity. During ground-fault conditions, these metal enclosures and raceways can carry high levels of fault current for the duration of time it takes for the overcurrent protective device on the primary side of the utility transformer to open. For this reason, bonding requirements for metallic parts on the supply side of the service disconnect are more restrictive, and result in more robust or strengthened bonding installations.

Sections 342.6 and 344.6 address intermediate metal conduit (IMC), and rigid metal conduit (RMC) and associated fittings, and require them to be listed. Hubs are typically intended and designed to receive the threads of RMC and IMC, and if so listed, are suitable for use in wiring methods installed on the supply side of the service. Action by *Code* Panel 5 on SR 7920, affirms that hubs used for a service installation must be listed for that purpose. These hubs should include means of identifying the product as suitable for use in service bonding applications. This information could be obtained from the manufacturer.

FR: 7920

SR: None

Bonding Loosely Joined Metal Raceways

Courtesy of ABB

Code Language

250.98 Bonding Loosely Jointed Metal Raceways. Expansion, expansion-deflection, or deflection fittings and telescoping sections of metal raceways shall be made electrically continuous by equipment bonding jumpers or other means.

(See NEC for actual text)

Significance of the Change

The requirements of Section 300.7(B) were expanded in the 2017 *NEC*, which recognized the use of an expansion-deflection or deflection fittings. Listed products are manufactured for this use. Expansion deflection and deflection fittings were added to the list of fittings required to be made electrically continuous. These products are similar to the more common telescoping expansion fittings, except that they account for increased movement that involves deflection. Section 250.98 previously only addressed bonding requirements for telescoping straight expansion and contraction fittings. Substantiation indicated that the bonding requirements of a straight expansion or telescoping fittings in Section 250.98 should also apply to expansion deflection, and deflection fittings, to maintain the bonding of electrical equipment and conductive materials required by Section 250.4. These fittings should be made to be electrically continuous to maintain safety. Manufacturers of expansion, expansion-deflection, and deflection fittings could produce such fittings with integral bonding means. This would make installing an external bonding jumper unnecessary, as the bonding process is completed during the installation of such fittings. If the fittings do not include an integral bonding means, then an appropriately sized bonding jumper with listed connection means must be provided to maintain effective continuity and conductivity across such connections.

Change Summary

- The words "expansion-deflection, or deflection" have been incorporated into this section.
- Bonding requirements in this section now apply to expansion deflection, and deflection fittings, as well as telescoping expansion fittings.
- Some fittings have integral bonding jumpers, others do not, and bonding jumpers must be installed.

FR: 7990
SR: None

250.104(A)(B)(C)(D)

Article 250 Grounding and Bonding

Part V Bonding

Bonding of Piping Systems and Exposed Structural Metal

Code Language

250.104 Bonding of Piping Systems and Exposed Structural Metal. (See *NEC* text) The bonding jumper(s) shall be sized in accordance with Table 250.102(C)(1) except that it shall not be required to be larger than 3/0 copper or 250 kcmil aluminum or copper-clad aluminum and except as permitted in 250.104(A)(2) and 250.104(A)(3).

Informational Note No. 2: Additional information for gas piping systems can be found in NFPA 54-2018, National Fuel Gas *Code*, and NFPA 780-2017, Standard for the Installation of Lightning Protection Systems.

(See NEC for actual text)

Change Summary

- The words "except that it shall not be required to be larger than 3/0 copper or 250 kcmil aluminum or copper-clad aluminum" have been restored within this section.
- Bonding jumper sizes do not have to exceed 3/0 copper or 250 aluminum as appeared in the 2014 *NEC* and prior.
- Informational note references to *NFPA 54* and *NFPA 780* have been updated.

Significance of the Change

Code Panel 5 has reversed a 2017 *NEC* change in sizing requirements for bonding conductors installed for structural metal, and metal water piping systems. The change that was made as a result of changing a reference from Table 250.66 to Table 250.102(C)(1) in the 2017 cycle resulted in an inadvertent increase in the bonding conductor size. No Tentative Interim Amendment to the 2017 *NEC* was ever submitted to restore the original sizing requirement. The result in the 2020 *NEC* is that Section 250.104 has been revised to include language indicating that the bonding jumpers referenced in this section, "shall not be required to be larger than 3/0 copper or 250 aluminum or copper-clad aluminum."

The Informational Note has been simplified to reference *NFPA 54-2018, National Fuel Gas Code*. Adding the reference to *NFPA 780* provides further guidance on protection of CSST systems. Adding bonding of CSST in the *NEC* to protect against lightning events has been rejected by CMP 5 for multiple *NEC* development cycles. The *NEC* Correlating Committee and the Standards Council have affirmed that this issue is outside the scope of the *NEC*. Protection of CSST from the effects of lighting is more properly found in *NFPA 780: Standard for the Installation of Lightning Protection Systems*.

FRs: 8031, 8033, 8034, 8035
SR: 7795

Multiconductor Cable Reidentified

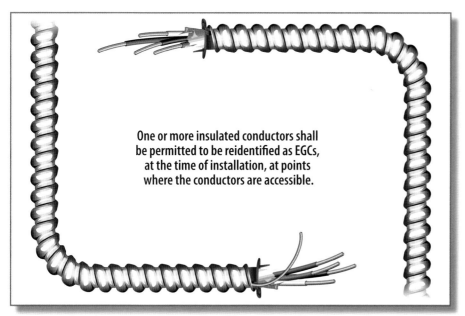

One or more insulated conductors shall be permitted to be reidentified as EGCs, at the time of installation, at points where the conductors are accessible.

Code Language

(B) Multiconductor Cable. One or more insulated conductors in a multiconductor cable, at the time of installation, shall be permitted to be permanently identified as equipment grounding conductors at each end and at every point where the conductors are accessible by one of the following means:

(1) Stripping the insulation from the entire exposed length.

(2) Coloring the exposed insulation green.

(See NEC for actual text)

Significance of the Change

Action by CMP-5 removes overly restrictive text related to reidentification of permanently identified equipment grounding conductors addressed by this section. There is no other requirement similar to "Where the conditions of maintenance and supervision ensure that only qualified persons service the installation" to perform such identification. As such, this phrase has been removed from this section. As indicated in the substantiation to Public Input 2784, there is no logical reason why the requirement "Where the conditions of maintenance and supervision ensure that only qualified persons service the installation" exists for reidentifying conductors of a multi-conductor cable. No such requirement exists for reidentifying conductors sized 6 AWG or smaller in 200.6(A) or for conductors sized 4 AWG or larger in 200.6(B). No such requirement exists in 200.6(D) for reidentifying conductors of different systems that are installed in a raceway, cable, box, auxiliary gutter, or other type of enclosure. Action by Code Panel 5 removes this text, and restores the consistency between other sections of the *Code* that address the same identification issue. At some point, the term *permanently* should be addressed within this and multiple other sections that address "reidentification of conductor" allowances, for conductors that are already permanently identified.

Change Summary

- This section provides allowances for reidentifying equipment grounding conductors.
- The words "Where the conditions of maintenance and supervision ensure that only qualified persons service the installation" have been removed from this section.
- No other such restrictions exist that deal with reidentification of conductors.

FR: 8043
SR: None

Metal Frame of Building or Structure

Code Language

250.121 Restricted Use of Equipment Grounding Conductors.

(A) (See *NEC* Text)

(B) Metal Frame of Building or Structure. The structural metal frame of a building or structure shall not be used as an equipment grounding conductor.

(See NEC for actual text)

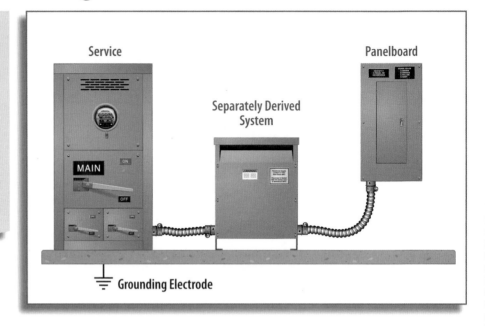

Change Summary

- The word "restricted" has been added to the title of this section.
- Added text in (B) restricts structural metal building frames from use as equipment grounding conductors.
- The revision provides consistency with the provisions of 250.136(A).

Significance of the Change

Section 250.121 is fairly new to the *NEC* and addresses restricted use of equipment grounding conductors, as both a grounding electrode conductor, and an equipment grounding conductor by exception only. The exception indicates that "a wire-type equipment grounding conductor installed in compliance with 250.6(A), and the applicable requirements for both the equipment grounding conductor and the grounding electrode conductor in Parts II, III, and VI of this article, shall be permitted to serve as both an equipment grounding conductor and a grounding electrode conductor." Action by *Code* Panel 5 on FR 7544 and SR 7757 results in the change in the title of 250.121. The word "restricted" has been added to the title of this section, to appropriately reflect the context of this rule, which generally prohibits an equipment grounding conductor used as both an equipment grounding conductor and a grounding electrode conductor simultaneously. This section has also been reorganized into two subdivisions, and to include the concepts in the existing last sentence of 250.136(A), resulting in consistency with that section. Added text in subdivision (B) restricts structural metal building frames from use as equipment grounding conductors.

FR: 7544
SR: 7757

Size of Equipment Grounding Conductors

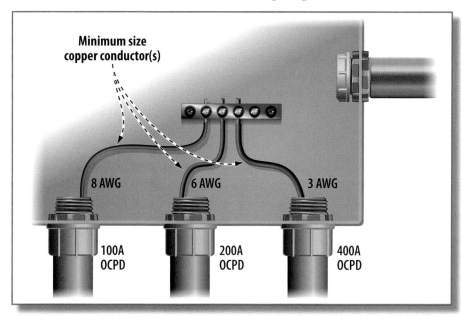

Minimum size copper conductor(s)

8 AWG — 100A OCPD
6 AWG — 200A OCPD
3 AWG — 400A OCPD

Code Language

250.122 Size of Equipment Grounding Conductors.

(A) General. (See *NEC* text)

(B) Increased in Size. If ungrounded conductors are increased in size for any reason other than as required in 310.15(B) or 310.15(C), wire-type equipment grounding conductors, if installed, shall be increased in size proportionately to the increase in circular mil area of the ungrounded conductors.

Exception: Equipment grounding conductors shall be permitted to be sized by a qualified person to provide an effective ground fault current path in accordance with 250.4(A)(5) or (B)(4).

(See NEC for actual text)

Significance of the Change

A significant effort was made to change the format of Table 250.122 and how equipment grounding conductors are sized. The idea proposed was that the EGC would be based on the size of the largest ungrounded conductor of the circuit. This effort was not successful, as it introduced far too many challenges and conflicts that could not be addressed in the 2020 *NEC* development cycle. As a result, Table 250.122 remains as it appeared in the previous edition of the *Code*, and slight technical changes were made in this section. Specifically, there has been no test data to confirm the determined sizes will not jeopardize the ability of the conductor to safely carry potential fault current. The panel has requested a research project be initiated to fully investigate this type of change in sizing methods for EGCs. Sizes for aluminum and copper-clad aluminum, for overcurrent devices, rated 5000 and 6000 amperes, are revised in Table 250.122 to correlate with sizes identified in Chapter 9, Table 8. Revisions in subdivision (B) clarify that adjustment and/or correction factors do not require an increase in the size of the EGC. The exception was added to allow the EGC to be sized by a qualified person, provided an effective ground fault current path can be established.

Change Summary

- Subdivision (B) is revised to clarify that adjustment and/or correction factors do not require an increase in the size of the EGC.
- The new exception to (B) indicates qualified persons shall be permitted to size equipment grounding conductors to provide an effective ground-fault current path.
- EGC sizes for 5000 and 6000 amperes are revised to correlate with Table 8, Chapter 9.

FR: 8114
SR: 7760

Connections to an Equipment Grounding Conductor

Code Language

250.134 Equipment Fastened in Place or Connected by Permanent Wiring Methods (Fixed). Unless connected to the grounded circuit conductor... (See *NEC* text) ... shall be connected to an equipment grounding conductor by one of the following methods:

(1) By connecting to any of the equipment grounding conductors permitted by 250.118(2) through (14)

(2) By connecting to an equipment grounding conductor of the wire type that is contained within the same raceway, contained within the same cable, or otherwise run with the circuit conductors

(See NEC for actual text)

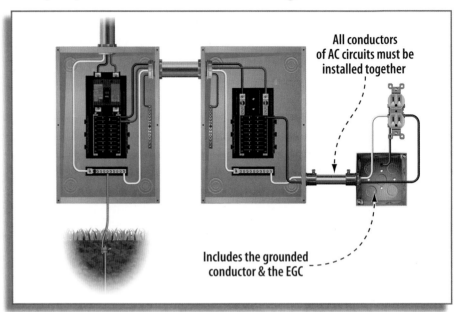

All conductors of AC circuits must be installed together

Includes the grounded conductor & the EGC

Change Summary

- This section has been rearranged into a list format in accordance with the *NEC Style Manual*.

- Revisions in (2) include the words "of the wire type" and "contained within the same" for clarification.

- Informational Note No. 2 now includes both flexible cords and flexible cables.

Significance of the Change

This section has been rearranged into a list format in accordance with the *NEC Style Manual*. List item (2) has been revised to include the words "of the wire type" and "contained within the same" for clarification. Section 300.3(B) requires that all conductors of the same circuit and, where used, the grounded conductor and all equipment grounding conductors and bonding conductors, shall be contained within the same raceway, auxiliary gutter, cable tray, cablebus assembly, trench, cable, or cord, unless otherwise permitted in accordance with 300.3(B)(1) through (B)(4). Substantiation indicated that, as written, this section could have been misinterpreted to allow the wire-type EGC to be installed in a manner that is separate from the contained circuit conductors of the applicable wiring method. The revision in (2), former subdivision (B), provides the clarification needed and correlates more directly with the requirements in 300.3(B). The requirement to run the EGC with the circuit conductors is now clear, that it must be contained within the wiring method with which it is installed, unless specifically allowed to be run externally by other *NEC* provisions, such as in Exception No.1 in this section. Informational Note No. 2 has been revised to include reference to both flexible cords and flexible cables.

FR: 7441
SR: None

Equipment Secured to Grounded Metal Supports

Code Language

250.136 Equipment Secured to Grounded Metal Supports. Electrical equipment secured to and in electrical contact with a metal rack or structure provided for its support shall be permitted to be considered as being connected to an equipment grounding conductor if the metal rack or structure is connected to an equipment grounding conductor by one of the means indicated in 250.134.

(See NEC for actual text)

Significance of the Change

This section is revised for clarity and shortened considerably to remove redundancy in the *NEC*. The title of this section has been revised to "Equipment Secured to Grounded Metal Supports." This more accurately reflects the text in this section which relates specifically to equipment that is grounded by connection to a metal rack or frame, that is also grounded through a connection to the equipment grounding conductor of the branch circuit supplying the equipment that is mounted to it. This section still mandates that in order for the equipment to be considered grounded, there must be electrical contact between the supported equipment and the rack or support frame. This could involve removal of paint or other coatings, in accordance with 250.12, to ensure such connection is established. Action by CMP-5 on FR 7544 relocates the sentence that prohibits the use of the metal frame of a building as an equipment grounding conductor. This text is now located in Section 250.121. Existing subdivision (B) has been deleted because the connection of the elevator equipment to the equipment grounding conductor is covered in Part IX of Article 620. The requirements in Article 620 amend those of Article 250 as directed by 90.3.

Change Summary

- The title of this section has been revised to "Equipment Secured to Grounded Metal Supports."
- Text was added to clarify that the metal rack or structure must be connected to an equipment grounding conductor of the circuit.
- Former Subdivision (B) has been deleted as it is redundant to the equipment grounding conductor requirements in Part IX of Article 620 covering elevators.

FRs: 7542, 7544
SR: None

Line- and Load-Side Equipment Grounding

Code Language

(A) Supply-Side Equipment. A grounded circuit conductor shall be permitted to be connected to non–current-carrying metal parts of equipment, raceways, and other enclosures under any of the following conditions:

(1) (See *NEC* text)

(2) (See *NEC* text)

(3) (See *NEC* text)

(4) On the supply side or within the enclosure of a supply-side disconnect(s)

(See NEC for actual text)

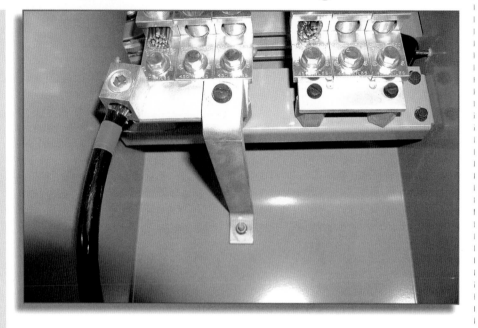

Change Summary

- This section has been revised to be consistent with the use of defined *grounding* and *bonding* terms.
- A new item has been added to (A), which recognizes the grounded conductor for grounding in a supply-side disconnect application that is not at the service.
- Exception No. 3 to 250.142(B) has been removed.

Significance of the Change

Section 250.142 provides requirements and restrictions for using the grounded conductor, for grounding on the supply side, covered in subdivision (A), and on the load side covered in subdivision (B), of the service disconnecting means. This revision is made to be consistent with the language used elsewhere in Article 250, with specific regard to the phrase "to be connected to," which replaces the word "ground" which is defined as "the earth." The revised language also expands the application regardless of purpose. Equipment on the supply side of the service disconnecting means is permitted to be connected to the grounded conductor as stated in 250.142(A). Exception No. 3 has been deleted from this section, because 250.164 does not specifically address making a grounded conductor connection on the load side of the disconnecting means. Additional edits are made for clarity and accuracy. The term *supply-side disconnect* was added to the list of items permitted 250.142 to be grounded by the grounded conductor. This clarifies that the allowance for use of the grounded conductor for grounding is permitted on the supply side of equipment supplied by a source other than a service such as generators, wind turbines, PV systems, energy storage systems, and so forth.

FRs: 7545, 7548

SR: 7845

Receptacle Grounding Connections to Grounded Boxes

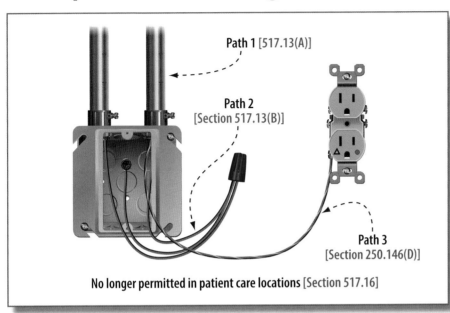

Path 1 [517.13(A)]

Path 2 [Section 517.13(B)]

Path 3 [Section 250.146(D)]

No longer permitted in patient care locations [Section 517.16]

Code Language

250.146 Connecting Receptacle Grounding Terminal to an Equipment Grounding Conductor. An equipment bonding jumper shall be used to connect the grounding terminal of a grounding-type receptacle to a metal box that is connected to an equipment grounding conductor, except as permitted in 250.146(A) through (D). The equipment bonding jumper shall be sized in accordance with Table 250.122.

(See NEC for actual text)

Significance of the Change

The phrase "the provisions of" has been removed as part of a global revision in the *NEC*. The title of Section 250.146 has been changed to remove the word "box" and replace it with the term *equipment grounding conductor*. The language in the first sentence was changed to be consistent with 406.3(D). Deleting that language would be inconsistent with 406.3(D) and could create confusion. Edits have also been made in terminology to improve readability and provide consistency with other parts of the *Code*, and to account for nonmetallic boxes. The last phrase of 250.146 that reads "based on the overcurrent device protecting the circuit conductors" has been removed as unnecessary wording that is redundant and covered in the text of 250.122. In subdivision (D) the term *electrical noise* has been replaced with the term *electromagnetic interference* because it is a better-understood term and is more technically accurate. This change is also consistent with actions in Article 406 such as in 406.3(D). The Informational Note has been editorially revised to be consistent with the language used elsewhere in Article 250 with specific regard to the phrase "to be connected to," which replaces the defined word *grounded*.

Change Summary

- The phrase "the provisions of" has been removed as part of a global revision in the *NEC*.
- The title of Section 250.146 has been changed to remove the word "box" and replace it with the term *equipment grounding conductor*.
- The revised text provides clarification about the metal box that is connected to an EGC.

FR: 7654
SR: 7844

Continuity of EGCs and Attachment in Metal Boxes

Code Language

250.148 Continuity of Equipment Grounding Conductors and Attachment in Boxes. If circuit conductors are spliced within a box or terminated on equipment within or supported by a box, all wire-type equipment grounding conductor(s) associated with any of those circuit conductors shall be connected within the box or to the box in accordance with 250.8 and 250.148(A) through (D).

(See NEC for actual text)

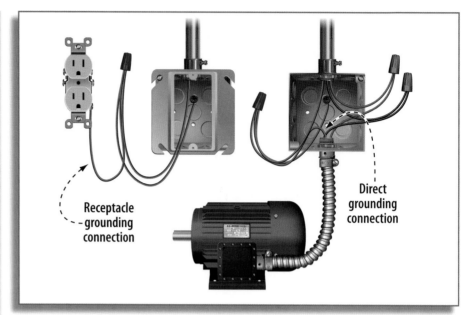

Receptacle grounding connection

Direct grounding connection

Change Summary

- The title of this section has been revised by replacing the word "to" with the word "in."
- This section has been revised to restore the words "associated with any of those circuit conductors" that appeared in the 2014 *NEC*.
- Subdivision (E) has been deleted as the restrictions related to soldered connections is covered in 250.8.

Significance of the Change

Editorial changes are made to improve readability and to clarify when equipment grounding conductors within a box are intended to be connected together and bonded to a metal box or device. The title of this section has been revised by replacing the word "to" with the word "in." The significance of this revision is the title previously implied that the EGC had to always be connected to the box. The idea here is that the EGC maintain continuity to devices and pass through wiring, whether through a conductive box or not, such as when installed in a nonmetallic box. This section has been revised to restore the words "associated with any of those circuit conductors" that appeared in the 2014 *NEC*. This revision relaxes the requirement for connecting together all EGCs contained in the box, which is unnecessary to achieve the objective of this requirement. EGC continuity can be effectively accomplished through a conductive metal box. In the 2017 *NEC* this section mandated connecting all EGCs together, which in some wiring circumstances is impractical and unnecessary. Subdivision (E) has been deleted as the restrictions related to soldered connections is covered in 250.8(B).

FR: 8415
SR: 7846

250.184(A)(1) & (C) Exception

Multipoint Grounded Neutral Systems

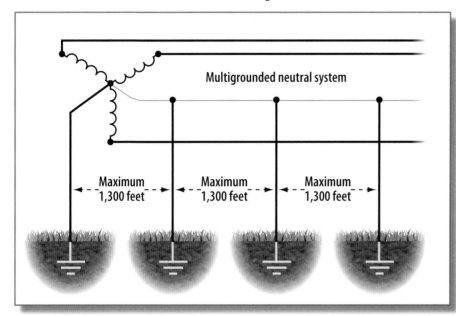

Multigrounded neutral system

Maximum 1,300 feet   Maximum 1,300 feet   Maximum 1,300 feet

Significance of the Change

Exception No. 1 to 250.184(A)(1) has been revised. The exception does not apply to single-point grounded systems since bare underground neutral conductors would be inherently grounded (connected to earth) at multiple locations along the entire run. A new exception to Section 250.184(C) has been added and relaxes the requirement to make a connection to a grounding electrode at intervals not exceeding 1300 ft. The revision brings the *NEC* in alignment with the NESC rules addressing this same type of installation. Recently the NESC committees revised their Code to allow long cable runs such as those for wind farms and solar farms to still be considered multipoint grounded, but not held to the 400 m (1300 ft) maximum length between bonding of the neutral conductor to a grounding electrode. The reason is that removing the cable jacket only to create a point for bonding creates a less desirable condition than allowing further distance between the grounding connections. Removing the jacket creates a weak spot that could lead to premature cable failure. In addition, bonding to the shielding material could potentially affect the shielding of the cables and could result in undesirable EMF occurring at the point where the cable jacket is removed and the connection to the shield is made.

Code Language

(A) Neutral Conductor.

(1) Insulation Level. The minimum insulation level for neutral conductors of solidly grounded systems shall be 600 volts.

Exception No. 1: For multigrounded neutral systems as permitted in 250.184(C), bare copper conductors shall be permitted to be used for the neutral conductor of the following:

(1) (See *NEC* text)

(2) (See *NEC* text)

(3) (See *NEC* text)

(5) (See *NEC* text)

Exception: In a multipoint grounded system, a grounding electrode shall not be required to bond the neutral conductor in an uninterrupted conductor exceeding 400 m (1300 ft) if the only purpose for removing the cable jacket is for bonding the neutral conductor to a grounding electrode.

(See NEC for actual text)

Change Summary

• Exception No. 1 to 250.184(A)(1) has been revised to remove the word "bare" and add the text "For multigrounded neutral systems as permitted in 250.184(C), bare..." (See *NEC* text).

• A new exception to 250.184(C) relaxes the distance requirement if the only purpose is to remove the cable sheath to make a grounding electrode connection.

FRs: 8415, 7819

SR: None

Chapter 3

Articles 300–396
Wiring Methods and Materials

Conductors, Paralleled Installations

Code Language

300.3 Conductors

(B) Conductors of the Same Circuit

(1) Paralleled Installations. ... (See *NEC* text) Connections, taps, or extensions made from paralleled conductors shall connect to all conductors of the paralleled set, grounded and ungrounded, as applicable... (See *NEC* text)

(See NEC for actual text)

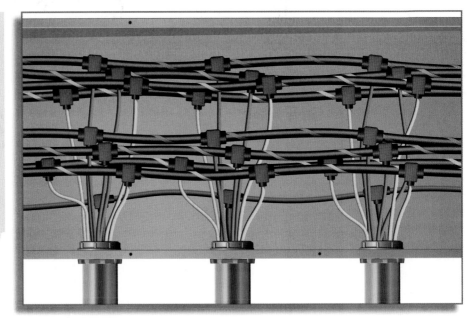

Change Summary

- 300.3(B)(1) is modified to require connections, taps or extensions from paralleled conductors be made in a manner to equalize the current.

- This revision attempts to provide additional clarity for the termination of and tapping from paralleled conductors.

- 310.10(H) does not address potential misapplication of connections to paralleled conductors.

Significance of the Change

General requirements for the installation of parallel conductors are found in 300.3(B)(1). This requirement mandates that parallel conductors be installed in accordance with 310.10(G), previously 310.10(H). Each portion of the parallel installation must be installed in the same raceway, gutter, cable tray, etc. A new sentence is added to provide clarity to eliminate potential confusion. Connections, taps or extensions made from paralleled conductors are now required to connect to all conductors of the paralleled set. This includes all grounded and ungrounded conductors as applicable. This revision is safety driven and should illuminate potential misapplication. The requirements of 310.10(G) [previously 310.10(H)] do not address how to connect to the conductors of the paralleled set. This revision addresses a fairly common *Code* violation. For example, consider a paralleled 800-amp feeder consisting of two 500-kcmil copper conductors per phase and grounded conductor.

Further, consider six sets of tap conductors to supply air handling units rated at a lower value. This revision now clarifies that each set of tap conductors must connect to all conductors of the paralleled set. Based upon our example, in the past, some installers would have connected three sets of tap conductors to half of the parallel feeder and the remainder to the other half of the paralleled feeder.

FR: None
SR: 7849

Protection Against Physical Damage, Fittings

Code Language

300.4(G) Fittings. ... (See *NEC* text) raceways contain 4 AWG or larger... (See *NEC* text) in accordance with any of the following:

(1) ... (See *NEC* text) smoothly rounded insulating surface

(2) ... (See *NEC* text) listed metal fitting that has smoothly rounded edges

(3) Separation... (See *NEC* text) insulating material... (See *NEC* text)

(4) Threaded hubs or bosses... (See *NEC* text) smoothly rounded or flared entry for conductors.

(See NEC for actual text)

Significance of the Change

The title of 300.4(G) in the 2017 *NEC* was *Insulated Fittings*. The title is revised by deleting the word "Insulated." This requirement applies to raceways that contain insulated circuit conductors that are 4 AWG or larger. The previous general requirement for raceways that entered a cabinet, box, or enclosure was to provide an identified fitting with a smoothly rounded insulating surface unless the conductors were separated from the fitting or raceway by an identified insulating material that was securely fastened in place. By requiring a "smoothly rounded insulating surface," the general requirement did not allow metal fittings with smoothly rounded edges. The previous exception did permit threaded hubs or bosses that were an integral part of a cabinet, box, enclosure or raceway provided there was a smoothly rounded or flared entry for conductors. The revised text in list item (1) still permits an identified fitting with a smoothly rounded insulated surface and provides three additional options to meet this requirement. They include (2) listed metal fittings with smoothly rounded edges, (3) separation from the fitting or raceway through an identified insulating material that is securely fastened in place, and (4) threaded hubs or bosses that are an integral part of a cabinet, box, enclosure, or raceway with a smoothly rounded or flared entry for conductors. The last two sentences of the previous requirement are retained. Conduit bushings made completely of insulating material cannot be used to secure a fitting or raceway. Insulated fittings or the insulating material must have a temperature rating not less than the insulation temperature rating of the installed conductors.

Change Summary

- 300.4(G) is modified to recognize multiple methods for fittings to provide protection in positive text.
- Physical protection is required, not insulation. New list items are added.
- The exception is deleted and rolled into new list item (3).

FR: 8667
SR: 7865

Raceways Exposed... Temperatures, Sealing

Code Language

300.7(A) Sealing. ...(See *NEC* text) Sealants shall be identified for use with cable insulation, conductor insulation, a bare conductor, a shield, or other components... (See *NEC* text)

(See NEC for actual text)

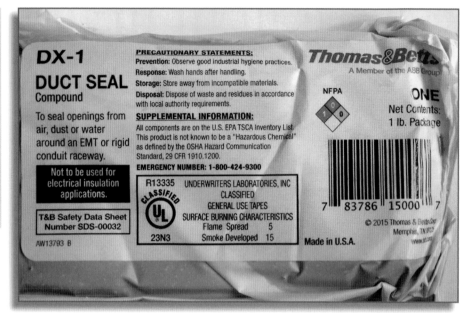

Courtesy of ABB

Change Summary

- 300.7(A) is revised to correlate with 225.27.
- Products used to seal raceways or sleeves must be identified for the use.
- Compatibility with the cable/ conductor insulation, bare conductor, shield or other component is required.

Significance of the Change

Section 300.7 provides requirements for raceways exposed to different temperatures. 300.7(A) requires portions of a raceway or sleeve that are known to be subjected to different temperatures be sealed to prevent the circulation of warm air to a colder part of the raceway or sleeve. This is required where condensation is known to be a problem, such as in cold storage areas of a building or where passing from the interior to the exterior of the building. The previous requirement for the material used to prevent the passage of air was that it be "approved." The term *approved* is defined in Article 100 as acceptable to the authority having jurisdiction (AHJ). That means that if the inspector liked it, it was approved. This text is revised to correlate with a similar requirement in 225.27. This revision requires that sealants must now be identified for use with the cable installation, conductor insulation, bare conductors, shields or other components. The term *identified* is also defined in Article 100. While there are multiple ways to ensure that a product is identified for a specific purpose, it is likely an AHJ will require listed or labeled products where sealing is required.

FR: 8684

SR: None

Exit Enclosures (Stair Towers)

Code Language

300.25 Exit Enclosures (Stair Towers). Where an exit enclosure is required to be separated from the building, only electrical wiring methods serving equipment permitted by the authority having jurisdiction in the exit enclosure shall be installed within the exit enclosure.

Informational Note: For more information, refer to NFPA 101-2018, *Life Safety Code*, 7.1.3.2.1(10)(b).

(See NEC for actual text)

Significance of the Change

NFPA 101: Life Safety Code permits conduits and cable assemblies to enter into an exit enclosure or stair tower where they serve equipment essential for egress. All other wiring methods are prohibited from entering the exit enclosure or stair tower. This means that stair towers, for example, cannot be used as a convenient chase to get a few conduits from one floor to another. This revision provides the authority having jurisdiction (AHJ) with the final say on what can and cannot be installed in an exit in enclosure or stair tower. The fact that this requirement is literally based upon the opinion of an AHJ, the electrical installer must work with each different AHJ to determine what will be permitted and what will not be permitted in the exit enclosure or stairway. The requirements that the AHJ should base permission on are found in *NFPA 101*. Examples of equipment found within exit enclosures and stair towers that may be supplied with cable assemblies and raceways through the fire-rated wall into the exit enclosure or stair tower include, but are not limited to: egress lighting, fire alarm devices, such as flow and tamper switches and associated wiring, purge fans, security systems, public address systems, and firefighter communication systems.

Change Summary

- New section 300.25 addresses the installation of wiring methods in stair towers.
- Only wiring methods serving equipment permitted by the AHJ are permitted.
- This new section correlates with existing requirements in *NFPA 101, the Life Safety Code.*

FR: 8742
SR: 7888

Article Scope and Conductors

Code Language

310.1 Scope. ... (See *NEC* text) rated up to and including 2000 volts... (See *NEC* text)

310.3(A) Minimum Size of Conductors. ...(See *NEC* text) Up to and including 2000 volts...(See *NEC* text) 14 AWG copper or 12 AWG aluminum or copper clad aluminum...(See *NEC* text)

310.3(B) Conductor Material. ... (See *NEC* text) shall be made AA-8000 series electrical grade aluminum alloy....(See *NEC* text)

(See NEC for actual text)

Courtesy of Copperweld Bimetallics LLC

Change Summary

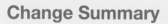

- The scope of article 310 is now limited to not more than 2000 volts.

- Requirements and ampacity tables for conductors over 2000 volts are relocated into new Article 311.

- Copper clad aluminum (CCA) conductors must meet the material requirements of the definition in Article 100.

FR: 8030

SR: None

Significance of the Change

Article 310 contains general requirements for conductors. This article has been significantly revised. The scope of this Article in 310.1 is modified to include general requirements for conductors rated up to and including 2000 volts. All of the requirements and ampacity tables for conductors rated at or above 2000 volts are deleted from Article 310. These requirements are relocated in new Article 311 titled *Medium Voltage Cable*. A definition in 311.2 relocated from Article 328 clarifies that medium voltage cable is rated 2001 up to, and including, 35,000 volts nominal. The majority of installations will be covered in Article 310, and separating the medium voltage requirements from Article 310 into a new article provides clarity and usability. 310.3(A) provides clarity on minimum size conductors, and 310.3(B) contains requirements for conductor material.

During the revision process, a new last paragraph was added to 310.3(B) to require that in all CCA conductors, the copper must form a minimum of 10% of the cross-sectional area of solid conductors in each strand of stranded conductors. This text was deleted due to floor actions at the NFPA Annual meeting. This failed action relocated construction requirements here from the previous definition of CCA conductors in Article 100. Definitions are not permitted to contain requirements per the *NEC Style Manual*.

Requirements for solid aluminum conductors to be made from AA-8000 series electrical grade aluminum alloy are relocated from 310.106(B) to 310.3(B).

Single-Phase Dwelling Services and Feeders

Code Language

310.12 Single-Phase Dwelling Services and Feeders.

(A) Services and (B) Feeders. ... (See *NEC* text) If no adjustment or correction factors are required, Table 310.12 shall be permitted to be applied.

Table 310.12 Single-Phase Dwelling Services and Feeders

(See NEC for actual text)

Significance of the Change

Requirements for sizing single-phase dwelling services and feeders are relocated from 310.15(B)(7) into a new section 310.12. This requirement has seen multiple modifications over the last several *NEC* cycles. In the 2011 *NEC*, this requirement permitted the conductor types and sizes for 120/240 volt, 3-wire, single phase services, or feeders as listed in Table 310.15(B)(7). In the 2014 *NEC*, this requirement was modified by deleting the table and adding a requirement for these conductors to have an ampacity of not less than 83% of the service or feeder rating. Additionally, an informational note was added to remind the *Code* user that other correction or adjustment factors applicable to the given installation may impact the final conductor ampacity. In the 2017 *NEC*, the table deleted in 2014 was added back into Annex D, Example D7 for usability and the requirement in 310.15(B)(7) was modified to include two ungrounded conductors and the neutral conductor from a 208Y/120-volt system.

This revision relocates the requirement into a new section 310.12 and relocates the table from Annex D into 310.12. The requirement is separated into four first-level subdivisions for clarity. The requirements in 310.12(A) for *Services* and (B) for *Feeders* still permit an ampacity not less than 83% of the service or feeder rating. A new sentence is added to each of these requirements permitting Table 310.12 to be applied where no ampacity adjustment or correction factors are required.

Change Summary

- Previous requirements of 310.15(B)(7) are relocated into new section 310.12.
- The existing table in Annex D, previously located in 310.15(B)(7) is reinserted as Table 310.12.
- Table 310.12 is permitted to be applied where no ampacity adjustment or correction factors are required.

FR: 8030
SR: 7638

Ampacity Tables

Code Language

310.14 Ampacities for Conductors Rated 0 Volts 0-2000 Volts.

310.15 Ampacity Tables.

(A) General. ... (See *NEC* text) Under engineering supervision, ampacities of sizes not shown in ampacity tables for conductors meeting the general wiring requirements shall be permitted to be determined by interpolation of the adjacent conductors based on the conductors area.

Informational Note 2... see Chapter 9 Table 8...

Informational Note 3... ampacities...400.5...402.5

(See NEC for actual text)

Change Summary

- Previous requirements in 310.15(A)(1) through (A)(3) are relocated into new 310.14.

- Under engineering supervision interpolation of the conductor, ampacities are permitted.

- 310.15(A) is modified to require that conductor ampacity complies with 310.15(A) through (F) and 310.12.

Significance of the Change

The title of 310.15 is modified to *Ampacity Tables*, and the requirements of previous 310.15 (B) are now located in 310.15(A) *General*. The previous requirements of 310.15(A), which addressed *Tables or Engineering Supervision*, selection of ampacity, and the temperature limitation of conductors are relocated into new Section 310.14 *Ampacities for Conductors Rated 0 Volts 0-2000 Volts*. First level subdivision 310.15(A) is modified to require that conductor ampacity complies with first-level subdivisions 310.15(A) through (F) and 310.12. Additionally, 310.15(A) now permits under engineering supervision, sizes not shown in the ampacity tables, for conductors meeting the general requirements to be determined by interpolation of the adjacent conductors based on the conductor's area. Interpolation means that an engineer will utilize mathematical and statistical tools to determine the ampacity of a non-standard size conductor size by using the existing ampacity values for a smaller and a larger conductor based upon the conductor area. A new Informational Note No.2 is added to send the *Code* user to Chapter 9 Table 8 for conductor area and to explain that interpolation is based on the conductor area, and not the conductor's overall area. An additional Informational Note No.3 is added to send the *Code* user to 400.5 and 402.5 for the ampacities of flexible cords/cables and fixture wires.

FR: 8030

SR: 7650

NEW
REVISION
RELOCATE

310.15(B) & (C)
Article 310 Conductors for General Wiring
Part III Installation

Ambient Temperature Correction/Adjustment Factors

Code Language

300.15(B) Ambient Temperature Correction Factors
(1) General
(2) Rooftop

310.15(C) Adjustment Factors
(1) More Than Three Current Carrying Conductors
(2) Raceway Spacing
(D) Bare or Covered Conductors
(E) Neutral Conductor
(F) Grounding or Bonding Conductor

(See NEC for actual text)

Significance of the Change

Requirements for ambient temperature correction factors are relocated from 310.15(B)(2) to 310.15(B). The ambient temperature correction factor tables are retitled as 310.15(B)(1) and (B)(2). Ambient temperature correction requirements for raceways or cables exposed to direct sunlight on or above rooftops are relocated to 310.15(B)(2). The requirement to install raceways or cables a minimum distance above the roof to the bottom of the raceway or cable is deleted. The correction factors for raceways or cables installed less than $^7/_8$-inch above the roof remain unchanged. Ampacity correction factor requirements in 310.15(C)(1) for more than three current carrying conductors in raceways or cables are modified to clarify that the ampacity of each conductor must be reduced where correction factors are applicable.

Six new sections are added to correlate with each of the remaining ampacity tables. Each of these new sections contains prescriptive conditions for the application of each associated table. These conditions include conductor voltage ranges, conductor temperature ratings, ambient temperature, and the number of current carrying conductors in raceway or cable. These ampacity tables are

- 310.16 for *Insulated Conductors in Raceway, Cable or Earth (Directly Buried)*
- 310.17 *Single Insulated Conductors in Free Air*
- 310.18 *Insulated Conductors in Raceway or Cable*
- 310.19 *Single Insulated Conductors in Free Air*
- 310.20 *Conductors Supported on a Messenger*
- 310.21 *Bare or Covered Conductors in Free Air*

Change Summary

- Requirements for ambient temperature correction factors are completely reorganized.
- Six new sections are added to correlate with remaining ampacity tables.
- Revised structure increases clarity and usability.

FR: 8030
SRs: 7650, 7651

NEW

Article 311 Medium Voltage Conductors and Cable

Code Language

Article 311 Medium Voltage Conductors and Cable

Part I General

Part II Construction Specifications

Part III Installation

Part IV Ampacities

(See NEC for actual text)

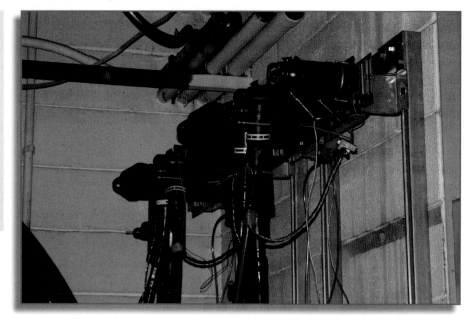

Change Summary

- New Article 311 is added to cover the use, installation, construction specifications, and ampacities for Type MV medium voltage conductors and cable.

- Article 328 for MV cable is deleted.

- Requirements for conductors rated over 2000 volts are removed from Article 310 into 311.

Significance of the Change

A new Article 311 *Medium Voltage Conductors and Cable*, is added to cover the use, installation, construction specifications, and ampacities for Type MV medium voltage conductors and cable. This is a combination of existing Articles 328 *Medium Voltage Cable* and requirements from Article 310 *Conductors for General Wiring* that addressed conductors rated over 2000 volts. This revision significantly increases clarity and usability in Article 310, by relocating requirements for conductors rated over 2000 volts. Additionally, the *Code* user can now go to a single article for requirements that pertain to medium voltage conductors and cable. This article is logically separated into four parts as follows:

- Part I General
- Part II Construction Specifications
- Part III Installation
- Part IV Ampacities

FR: 8030
SRs: 7577, 7574, 7576, 7578, 7579

Power Monitoring or Energy Management Equipment

Courtesy of Eaton

Code Language

312.8(B) Power Monitoring or Energy Management Equipment

(3) Conductors. Conductors used exclusively for control or instrumentation circuits shall comply with either 312.8(B)(3)(a) or (B)(3)(b).

(a) Conductors shall comply with 725.49.

(b) Conductors smaller than 18 AWG, but not smaller than 22 AWG for a single conductor and 26 AWG for a multiconductor cable, shall be permitted to be used where the conductors and cable assemblies meet all of the following conditions... (See *NEC* text)

(See NEC for actual text)

Significance of the Change

Section 312.8 contains requirements for wiring space within enclosures for switches and overcurrent devices. 312.8(B) previously addressed only power monitoring equipment and is now modified to also include energy management equipment. Editorially, this requirement is separated into second-level subdivisions with new (3) *Conductors* to address conductors used exclusively for control or instrumentation. These conductors must comply with either 312.8(B)(3)(a) or (B)(3)(b). The first option requires compliance with 725.49, which permits conductor sizes 18 AWG and 16 AWG provided they supply loads that do not exceed ampacities given in 402.5 and are installed in a raceway or an approved enclosure or a listed cable. Permitted insulation types for these conductors are listed in 725.49(B). The second option permits conductors smaller than 18 AWG but not smaller than 22 AWG for single conductors and 26 AWG for multiconductor cable, provided they meet all of the following conditions:

(1) Are enclosed within raceways or routed along one or more walls of the enclosure and secured at intervals that do not exceed 250 mm (10 in.)

(2) Are secured within 250 mm (10 in.) of terminations

(3) Are secured to prevent contact with current-carrying components within the enclosure

(4) Are rated for the system voltage and not less than 600 volts

(5) Have a minimum insulation temperature rating of 90°C

Change Summary

- 312.8(B) now addresses both power monitoring and energy management systems.
- New requirements are added for conductors used exclusively for control or instrumentation circuits.
- Existing requirements are separated into subdivisions for clarity.

FR: 7539
SR: 8161

Number of Conductors...Box Volume/Fill

Code Language

314.16 Number of Conductors in Outlet, Device, and Junction Boxes and Conduit Bodies.
(A) Box Volume Calculations

Table 314.16(A) Metal Boxes
(B) Box Fill Calculations
(B)(5) Equipment Grounding Conductor Fill. Where up to four equipment grounding conductors... (See *NEC* text) a single volume... (See *NEC* text) A $\frac{1}{4}$ volume allowance... (See *NEC* text) for each additional equipment grounding conductor... (See *NEC* text)

(See NEC for actual text)

Change Summary

- The single volume allowance for EGCs and EBJs is limited to four of these conductors.
- A ¼ volume allowance based upon the largest EGC or EBJ in the box is added for each EGC or EBJ over four.
- Editorial revisions are made in the parent text and Table 314.16(A).

Significance of the Change

A new sentence is added to the parent text of 314.16 to emphasize that outlet and device boxes must also comply with 314.24. Table 314.16(A) is modified to add "gang" after each use of masonry box and FS/FD boxes. The use of the word "gang" is correct and was inadvertently removed in the 2017 revision cycle. 314.16(B)(5) previously required that where one or more equipment grounding conductors (EGCs) or equipment bonding jumpers (EBJs) enter a box, a single volume allowance must be made based on the largest EGC or EBJ in the box. This revision now requires a single volume allowance in accordance with Table 314.16(B) where up to four EGCs or EBJs enter a box based upon the largest conductor. Where more than four EGCs or EBJs enter a box, a $\frac{1}{4}$ volume allowance must be made for each additional EGC or EBJ based on the largest EGC or EBJ in the box. This revision now eliminates the need to specifically address the equipment grounding conductors permitted by 250.146(D).

FRs: 7540, 7543, 7531
SR: None

Conductors Entering Boxes, Conduit Bodies, or Fittings

Significance of the Change

First level subdivision 314.17(A) provides requirements for openings in boxes, conduit bodies, or fittings that must be closed. Openings through which conductors enter must now be closed in a manner *identified* for the application. The previous text only required that it be *approved*. 314.17(B) is retitled as *Boxes and Conduit Bodies* and is separated into four second-level subdivisions as follows:

- 314.17(B)(1) *Conductors Entering Through Individual Holes or Through Flexible Tubing* relocates the previous requirement in 314.17(B) with editorial revisions.
- 314.17(B)(2) *Conductors Entering Through Cable Clamps* requires cable assemblies with nonmetallic sheaths to extend not less than $1/4$ inch inside the box and beyond any cable clamp.
- New 314.17(B)(3) *Conductors Entering Through Raceways* permits individual conductors or nonmetallic cable assemblies installed in a complete raceway without being additionally secured.
- New 314.17(B)(4) *Temperature Limitation* requires that nonmetallic boxes and conduit bodies be suitable for the lowest temperature rated conductor that enters the box or conduit body.

Both second-level subdivision 314.17(B)(2) and (3) do not require the additional securement where raceways enclose cable assemblies to protect them from physical damage, as required in 300.15(C).

Code Language

314.17 Conductors Entering Boxes, Conduit Bodies, or Fittings.

(A) Openings to Be Closed. Openings ... (See *NEC* text) in a manner identified for the application.

(B) Boxes and Conduit Bodies.

(3) Conductors Entering Through Raceways ... (See *NEC* text) the conductors or cable assemblies shall not be required to be additionally secured. ... (See *NEC* text) 300.15(C)... (See *NEC* text) not be required to be additionally secured within the box or conduit body.

(4) Temperature Limitation. Nonmetallic boxes and conduit bodies shall be suitable for the lowest temperature-rated conductor... (See *NEC* text)

(See NEC for actual text)

Change Summary

- Openings through which conductors enter must now be closed in a manner *identified* for the application.
- 314.17(B) is retitled as *Boxes and Conduit Bodies* and is separated into four second-level subdivisions.
- 314.17(B)(4) *Temperature Limitation* requires nonmetallic boxes/conduit bodies to be suitable for the lowest temperature rated conductor.

FRs: 7546, 7557

SR: None

Boxes at Ceiling-Suspended (Paddle) Fan Outlets

Code Language

314.27(C) Boxes at Ceiling-Suspended (Paddle) Fan Outlets... Outlet boxes mounted in the ceilings of habitable rooms of dwelling occupancies in a location acceptable for the installation of a ceiling-suspended (paddle) fan shall comply with one of the following:

(1) Listed for the sole support of ceiling-suspended (paddle) fans

(2) An outlet box complying with the applicable requirements of 314.27 and providing access to structural framing capable of supporting of a ceiling-suspended (paddle) fan bracket or equivalent

(See NEC for actual text)

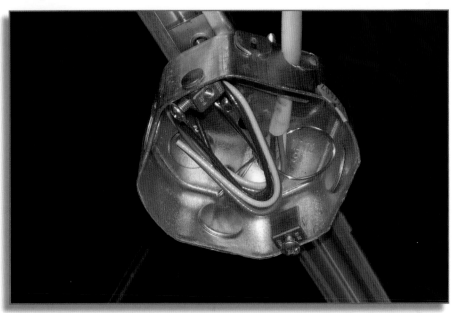

Change Summary

- The limitation of this requirement to "where spare, separately switched, ungrounded conductors, are provided to a ceiling-mounted outlet box" is deleted.

- Boxes listed for the sole support of ceiling suspended fans and those providing access to structural framing capable of supporting a ceiling-suspended fan bracket, or equivalent are permitted.

Significance of the Change

First level subdivision 314.27(C), which provides requirements for boxes at ceiling-suspended fan outlets, is modified to recognize new technology to reference "habitable rooms." The existing first paragraph remains unchanged. This revision recognizes that ceiling-suspended (paddle) fans can now be installed on outlet boxes with two current-carrying conductors that are remote-controlled fans. Therefore, this revision deletes the limitation of this requirement to "where spare, separately switched, ungrounded conductors, are provided to a ceiling-mounted outlet box." This text is replaced with "outlet boxes mounted in the ceilings of *habitable rooms* of dwelling occupancies in a location acceptable for the installation of a ceiling-suspended fan." Article 100 now contains the definition of a habitable room as follows:

Habitable Room. A room in a building for living, sleeping, eating, or cooking, but excluding bathrooms, toilet rooms, closets, hallways, storage or utility spaces, and similar areas.

Two options exist: (1) boxes listed for the sole support ceiling suspended fans and (2) boxes complying with 314.27 and providing access to *structural framing capable of supporting a ceiling-suspended fan bracket or equivalent*. This recognizes the practice of supporting a ceiling-suspended (paddle) fan by the structural framing, and independent of the outlet box.

FR: 7563
SR: 8163

Ampacity

Code Language

320.80(A), 330.80(C) and 338.10(B)(4)(2). Where more than two Type MC cables containing two or more current-carrying conductors in each cable are installed in contact with thermal insulation, caulk, or sealing foam without maintaining spacing between cables, the ampacity of each conductor shall be adjusted in accordance with Table 310.15(C)(1).

(See NEC for actual text)

Significance of the Change

New text is added to 320.80(A), a new list item in 338.10(B)(4)(2) and a new first-level subdivision 330.80(C) titled *Thermal Insulation* is added to address heating concerns where these cables are installed in direct contact with thermal insulation. This new requirement applies where more than two cables containing two or more current-carrying conductors in each cable are installed in direct contact with thermal insulation, caulk, or sealing foam without maintaining the spacing between cables. Where this occurs, the ampacity of each conductor must be adjusted in accordance with Table 310.15(C)(1). This revision is based upon data supplied to the technical committee on testing performed on Type SE cable installed in direct contact with thermal insulation without maintaining spacing between cables. This revision is similar to 334.80, which requires more than two NM cables containing two or more current-carrying conductors installed, without maintaining spacing between the cables, through the same opening in wood framing that is to be sealed with thermal insulation, caulk, or sealing foam.

The ampacity table references in 330.80(B)(2) are editorially revised to refer to new Article 311 for medium voltage cables and conductors.

Change Summary

- New text in 320.80(A), 330.80(C) and 338.10(B)(4) are added to address the installation of more than two cables in thermal insulation.
- Where space is not maintained between cables that are in contact with thermal insulation, caulk, or sealing that foam, capacity must be adjusted in accordance with Table 310.15(C)(1).
- Editorial revisions are made in 330.80(B) to reference tables in new Article 311 MV Conductors and Cables.

FR: 7959, 7961, 7955

SR: None

Hazardous (Classified) Locations

Code Language

330.130 Hazardous (Classified) Locations. Where required to be marked MC-HL, the cable shall be listed and shall have a gas/vapor tight continuous corrugated metallic sheath, an overall jacket of suitable polymeric material, and a separate equipment grounding conductor.

(See NEC for actual text)

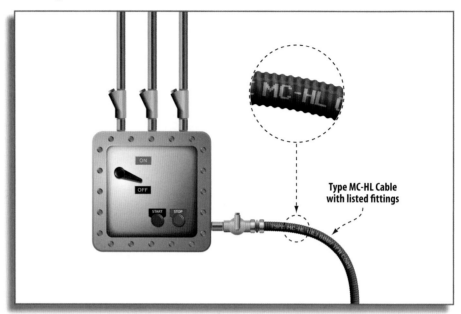

Type MC-HL Cable with listed fittings

Change Summary

- New 330.130 provides construction requirements for type MC-HL cable.
- Type MC-HL cable is built to the UL Product Category, *Cable for Use in Hazardous Locations, PJPP*.
- Type MC-HL cable is recognized for use in some hazardous location applications.

FR: 7883
CC: 7590
SCR: 47

Significance of the Change

The potential use of metal clad cable in hazardous (Classified) locations has seen a significant amount of discussion and debate over the last few *NEC* revision cycles. The debate involved two committees, one with purview over Type MC cable, and one with purview over hazardous locations.

A new section 330.130 is added in Part III of Article 330, which covers Construction Specifications. This new section is titled *Hazardous (Classified) Locations* and provides construction requirements for type MC-HL cable. The construction requirement in 330.130 mandates that where required to be marked MC-HL, the cable shall be listed and shall have a gas/vapor tight continuous corrugated metallic sheath, an overall jacket of suitable polymeric material, and a separate equipment grounding conductor.

This requirement correlates with the UL Product Category, *Cable for Use in Hazardous Locations, PJPP* as follows:

Type MC-HL cable consists of two or more insulated conductors, one or more grounding conductors, and an overall gas/vapor tight continuous corrugated metallic sheath. A nonmetallic jacket is provided over the metal sheath. The equipment grounding conductor required within Type MC-HL cable may be insulated or bare and may be sectioned. Any additional grounding conductors have green insulation.

See 501.10(A)(1)(3) for an example of where type MC-HL cable is permitted for use in a hazardous location.

Conductors

Courtesy of Copperweld Bimetallics LLC

Code Language

330.104 For ungrounded, grounded, and equipment grounding conductors, the minimum conductor sizes shall be 14 AWG copper, nickel, or nickel-coated copper and 12 AWG aluminum or copper-clad aluminum.

For control and signal conductors minimum conductor sizes shall be 18 AWG copper, nickel, or nickel-coated copper, or 14 AWG copper-clad aluminum, and 12 AWG aluminum.

Similar revisions in 336.104

(See NEC for actual text)

Significance of the Change

Sections 330.104 and 336.104 have been revised to address minimum sizes of different types of conductors. The key revision here is new text to recognize the minimum size of copper-clad aluminum conductors as 14 AWG for control and signal use based on data submitted to the technical committee. The public input that was behind this revision sought to recognize a 10-amp general ampacity rating for 14 AWG copper-clad aluminum conductor with a 60°C rating. However, the test data provided addressed temperature considerations only, and the revision was limited to copper clad aluminum for controlling signals only. It is important to recognize that if 14 AWG copper-clad aluminum conductors were recognized, with a general ampacity of 10 amps, the provisions of 240.4(B) would apply, allowing these conductors to be protected at 15 amps.

Change Summary

- To address minimum conductor sizes for control and signal conductors, the following revisions are implemented.
- 18 AWG copper, nickel, or nickel-coated copper, 14 AWG copper clad aluminum, and 12 AWG aluminum.
- 14 AWG copper clad aluminum is permitted for only controlling signal conductors.

FR: None
SRs: 7736, 7739

334.30

Article 334 Nonmetallic Sheathed Cable: Types NM and NMC
Part II Installation

Securing and Supporting

Code Language

334.30 Securing and Supporting … (See *NEC* text) shall be supported and secured by staples, … (See *NEC* text) at intervals not exceeding (4½ ft) and within (12 in.) of every cable entry into enclosures such as outlet boxes, junction boxes, cabinets, or fittings. The cable length between the cable entry and the closest cable support shall not exceed 450 mm (18 in.) … (See *NEC* text)

(See NEC for actual text)

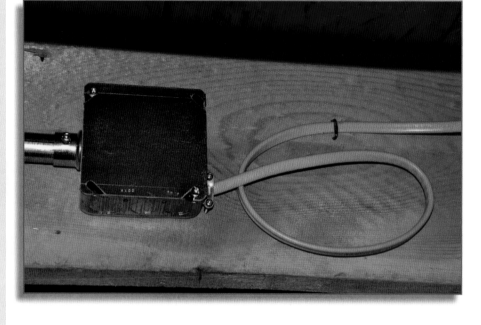

Change Summary

- New text in 334.30 mandates that the cable length between the cable entry and the closest cable support shall not exceed 18 inches.
- This is necessary where loops are left for future modifications.
- All references to, and requirements for, Type NMS cable are deleted throughout Article 334.

Significance of the Change

All references to, and requirements for, Type NMS cable are deleted. Type NMS cable is no longer manufactured.

Section 334.30 provides requirements for securing and supporting nonmetallic sheathed cable. Staples, cable ties listed and identified for securement and support, straps, hangers or similar fittings are required to be installed at intervals not exceeding 4½ feet and within twelve inches of every cable entry into an enclosure, such as an outlet box, junction box, cabinet or fitting. New text is added to clarify the maximum length of cable between the last support and the cable entry. This new text addresses a common installation technique to leave a small loop of conductor to allow for future modifications or renovations. This new text mandates that the cable length between the cable entry and the closest cable support shall not exceed 18 inches.

A new list item (11) was added to 334.12 for *uses not permitted*, prohibiting the use of Type NM and NMC cable from being installed where subject to physical damage. This was done in the comment stage without public review and was rejected as new material.

FRs: 8005, 8049
SR: 7728

Type TC Cable, Uses Permitted

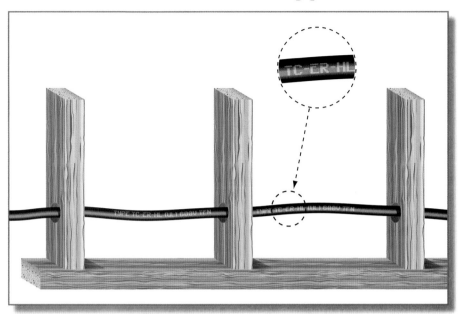

Code Language

336.10 Uses Permitted. Type TC cable shall be permitted to be used as follows:

(9) In one- and two-family dwelling units, Type TC-ER-JP cable containing both power and control conductors ... (See *NEC* text) shall be permitted for branch circuits and feeders... (See *NEC* text) where installed as exterior wiring shall be installed per the requirements of Part II of Article 340.

(11) In hazardous (classified) locations where specifically permitted by other articles in this *Code*.

(See NEC for actual text)

Significance of the Change

Section 336.10 for permitted use of TC cable is revised to clarify that only Type TC-ER-JP cable containing both power and control conductors is permitted in one- and two-family dwelling units as branch circuits and feeders. Where it is installed as exterior wiring, Type TC cable must be installed in accordance with Part II of Article 340. The suffix JP means that the Type TC-ER-JP cable is suitable for pulling through structural members. The suffix ER means that the Type TC-ER-JP meets the crush and impact tests of Type MC cable. Informational Note No. 1 is deleted because the general rule now requires these cables to be marked JP. A new list item (11) now permits Type TC cable to be installed in hazardous (classified locations) where specifically permitted by other Articles in this *Code*. This is a significant revision, as it expands the use of Type TC cable in hazardous locations.

Change Summary

- Only Type TC-ER-JP cable containing both power and control conductors is permitted in one- and two-family dwelling units.

- Type TC-ER-JP cable installed on the exterior of a dwelling unit must comply with Part II of Article 340.

- Type TC cable is now permitted in hazardous locations where specifically referenced elsewhere in the *Code*.

FR: 8032
SR: 7689

Hazardous (Classified) Location Cable

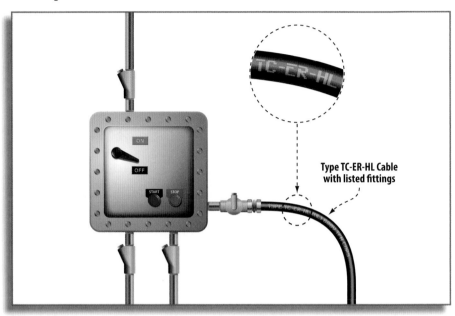

Type TC-ER-HL Cable with listed fittings

Code Language

336.130 Hazardous (Classified) Location Cable. Cable listed and marked Type TC-ER-HL shall comply with the following:

(1) The overall nonmetallic jacket shall be suitable for the environment.

(2) The overall cable construction shall be essentially circular in cross-section.

(3) The overall nonmetallic jacket shall be continuous and gas/vapor tight.

(4) For construction greater than 25.4 mm (1 in.) in diameter, the following shall apply:

(a) The equipment grounding conductor shall be bare.

(b) A metallic shield shall be included over all conductors under the outer jacket.

(See NEC for actual text)

Change Summary

- New construction requirements for Type TC-ER-HL are added to correlate with 336.10(11).
- The use of Type TC-ER-HL in hazardous locations has been expanded.
- TC-ER-HL cable larger than 1 inch in diameter must meet additional requirements.

Significance of the Change

The 2020 revision cycle of the *NEC* significantly expands the use of Type TC-ER-HL cable in hazardous locations. The use of this type of cable, its construction, and permitted use in hazardous locations have been debated for several *NEC* cycles. Ultimately, actions by the *NEC* correlating committee and the floor of the NFPA annual meeting pushed these revisions out until the 2020 *NEC* revision cycle. Section 336.10 list item (11) now permits Type TC-ER-HL to be installed in hazardous locations where specifically permitted in other articles of this *Code*. Chapter 5 articles that deal with hazardous locations now include permission for the use of Type TC-ER-HL cable. This new section 336.130, provides minimum requirements for the construction of Type TC-ER-HL cable. The outer nonmetallic jacket must be suitable for the environment, which means an evaluation must be performed to determine potential contaminants. Larger cables tend to be elliptical in shape and this section requires that they be essentially circular in cross-section. The outer nonmetallic jacket must be continuous and gas/vapor tight.

Where Type TC-ER-HL cables are larger than one inch in diameter, the equipment grounding conductor must be bare, and a metallic shield must be included over all conductors and under the outer jacket.

FR: 7647
SR: 7674

Type P Cable

Code Language

337.10 Uses Permitted. Type P cable shall be permitted to be used:

(1) Under engineering supervision in industrial locations where conditions of maintenance and supervision ensure that only qualified persons monitor and service the system.

(2) In hazardous (classified) locations where specifically permitted by other articles in this code.

(See NEC for actual text)

Significance of the Change

A new Article 337 *Type P Cable* (marine shipboard cable) is added to recognize this rugged wiring method which is commonly used in land-based oil and gas well drilling rigs. Type P cable is resistant to petroleum-based additives, abrasives, and various chemicals. This cable is suitable for environments in which there is significant vibration, shaking, extreme cold conditions, and where the potential for physical damage exists. Type P cable has been used for more than four decades in these adverse conditions and is now added to the *NEC*. Section 337.10 limits the application of this cable to industrial installations where conditions of maintenance and supervision ensure that only qualified persons monitor and service the system and in hazardous locations were specifically permitted elsewhere in this code. The scope of this article limits the installation of this cable type to a maximum of 2000 volts. The inclusion of Type P cable in the *NEC* is part of a much larger discussion on wiring methods in hazardous locations. This involves the expanded use of Type TC-ER-HL cable. As previously mentioned, Type P cable has a long history of successful use in land-based oil and gas rigs. These environments are continuously moving from site to site and do not lend themselves well to the use of rigid conduit and Type TC-ER-HL cable. This is just another example of recognizing a practice or wiring method that has been successfully used for a long period of time into the *NEC*.

Change Summary

- New Article 337 now permits the installation of Type P cable (marine shipboard cable).
- Type P cable has been used in land-based oil and gas rigs for over four decades.
- Type P cable is limited to industrial installations and hazardous locations.

FR: 8036
SR: 7729

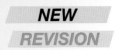
Service Entrance Conductor Assembly

Code Language

338.2 Service-Entrance Conductor Assembly. Multiple single-insulated conductors twisted together without an overall covering, other than an optional binder intended only to keep the conductors together.

(See NEC for actual text)

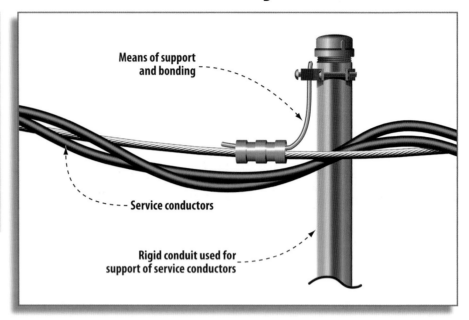

Means of support and bonding

Service conductors

Rigid conduit used for support of service conductors

Change Summary

- A new definition of "Service Entrance Conductor Assembly" is added to 338.2.
- This definition is necessary to address assemblies of single insulated USE conductors.
- Construction requirements are modified to recognize service entrance conductor assemblies.

Significance of the Change

Article 338 contains requirements for service entrance cable, which includes Types SE and USE. Type SE cable is typically two insulated conductors with a bare concentric conductor and an overall outer jacket. Type SER cable is three insulated conductors with a bare concentric conductor and an overall outer jacket. Type USE is typically a single insulated conductor but can be more than one with an outer jacket. However, Type USE is available in an assembly of single insulated conductors. A new definition is added in 338.2 to recognize these assemblies. Multiple single insulated Type USE conductors do not have an overall outer covering, but an optional binder to hold them together is permitted.

The addition of this new definition required the construction requirements in section 338.100 be revised. This section is now separated into two first-level subdivisions. 338.100(A) permits cable assemblies of multiple single conductor Type USE, with all conductors insulated for direct burial. 338.100(B) permits Type SE or USE cable with an overall covering containing two or more conductors to have one conductor uninsulated.

FRs: 7953, 7950
SR: 7680

Physical Damage and Severe Physical Damage

Code Language

342.10/344.10(E) Severe Physical Damage. IMC/RMC shall be permitted to be installed where subject to severe physical damage.

358.10(E) Physical Damage. Steel and stainless steel EMT shall be permitted to be installed where subject to physical damage.

(See NEC for actual text)

Significance of the Change

New first-level subdivisions have been added into the XXX.10(E) sections of Articles 342 *Intermediate Metal Conduit: Type IMC*, 344 *Rigid Metal Conduit: Type RMC* and 358 *Electrical Metallic Tubing: Type EMT*, to address physical damage capabilities. Type IMC and RMC are now permitted to be installed where subject to severe physical damage, and Type EMT is permitted to be installed where subject to physical damage. There is a long history in the *NEC* development process on the debate between physical damage and severe physical damage. Many attempts to define these terms have been submitted, but none were successful. The determination that the potential for physical damage exists and the level of potential (for example, severe physical damage) damage must be made on a case-by-case basis by the installer and the AHJ. There is no easy button to press to make this determination. One example is to look at an individual in a grocery store with a metal shopping cart. They are capable of inflicting physical damage to any exposed wiring method. When they load groceries into a vehicle and drive out of the parking lot, they are now capable of inflicting severe physical damage to any exposed wiring method.

Change Summary

- Physical damage is now specifically addressed in the XXX.10(E) sections for IMC, RMC, and EMT.
- IMC and RMC are permitted to be installed in areas subject to severe physical damage.
- EMT is permitted to be installed in areas subject to physical damage.

FRs: 8023, 7994, 8084
SR: None

Dissimilar Metals

Code Language

342/344/358.14 Dissimilar Metals... (See *NEC* text) Stainless steel and aluminum fittings and enclosures shall be permitted to be used with galvanized steel IMC/RMC/EMT where not subject to severe corrosive influences...(See *NEC* text) Stainless steel IMC/RMC/EMT shall only be used with the following:

(1) Stainless steel fittings

(2) Stainless steel boxes and enclosures

(3) Steel (galvanized, painted, powder or PVC coated, and so forth) boxes and enclosures when not subject to severe corrosive influences

(4) Stainless steel, nonmetallic, or approved accessories

(See NEC for actual text)

Change Summary

- Galvanized IMC/RMC/EMT are permitted to be used with stainless steel and aluminum fittings where not subject to severe corrosive influences.

- Stainless steel IMC/RMC/EMT must be installed with stainless fittings, boxes and enclosures.

- Steel boxes and enclosures are permitted where not subject to corrosive influences.

Significance of the Change

Revisions are made to the XXX.14 sections with requirements for dissimilar metals of Articles 342 *Intermediate Metal Conduit: Type IMC*, 344 *Rigid Metal Conduit: Type RMC*, and 358 *Electrical Metallic Tubing: Type EMT*, to address the compatibility of metal fitting types. Stainless steel and aluminum fittings are permitted to be used with galvanized IMC, RMC, and EMT. Stainless steel IMC, RMC, and EMT are only permitted to be used with stainless steel fittings, stainless steel boxes and enclosures, steel boxes and enclosures when not subject to severe corrosive influences, and stainless steel non-metallic or approved accessories.

The requirements in these sections address corrosion that can occur when two different metals are in contact. Accelerated galvanic corrosion may occur on one metal surface, while the other metal may remain galvanically protected. This revision is based on installations where extreme corrosion occurred due to dissimilar metals.

FRs: 7986, 8025, 8085
SR: None

Securing/Supporting and Expansion Splice Plates

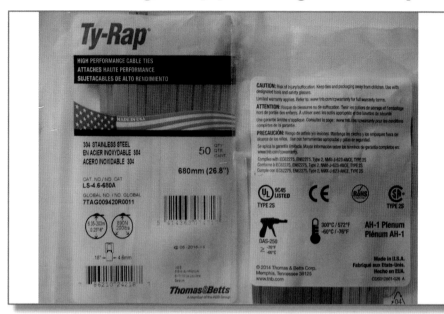

Courtesy of ABB

Code Language

392.30(B) Cables and Conductors... (See *NEC* text)

(4) Cable ties shall be listed and identified for the application and for securement and support.

392.44 Expansion Splice Plates. Expansion splice plates for cable trays shall be provided where necessary to compensate for thermal expansion and contraction.

(See NEC for actual text)

Significance of the Change

Where cable ties are used to secure and/or support cables and conductors in cable tray, the cable ties must be listed and identified for the application and for securement and support. The only type of cable ties permitted for securing and supporting are listed cable ties identified as Type 2S or 21S. The "S" suffix for these cable ties means they are recognized for *securement and support*. This requirement correlates with similar securing and supporting requirements for cable assemblies, flexible conduit and flexible tubing added in the 2017 *NEC* revision cycle.

A new Section 392.44 titled *Expansion Splice Plates* is added to require that cable tray be provided with expansion splice plates where necessary to compensate for thermal expansion and contraction. The length of straight cable tray in a run and the temperature differential based upon the installation will govern the number of expansions splice plates necessary. An example is provided in NEMA VE-2, Cable Tray Installation Guidelines, Table 3-2, and an example in Figure 3-38.

Change Summary

- Cable ties used in cable tray must be listed and identified for the application and for securement and support.
- Cable ties for securement and support must have the suffix S, 2S or 21S.
- Expansion splice plates for cable trays are required where necessary, to compensate for thermal expansion and contraction.

FRs: 8010, 7964
SRs: 7540, 7543

Bushed Conduit and Tubing, Flanged Connections

Code Language

392.46 Bushed Conduit and Tubing.

(A) Through Bushed Conduit or Tubing. Individual conductors or multiconductor cables with entirely nonmetallic sheaths shall be permitted to enter enclosures where they are terminated through nonflexible bushed conduit or tubing... (See *NEC* text)

(B) Flanged Connections... (See *NEC* text) permitted to enter enclosures through openings associated with flanges from cable trays where the cable tray is attached to the flange and the flange is mounted directly to the equipment.

(See NEC for actual text)

Courtesy of Mark Hilbert

Change Summary

- 392.46 is separated into first-level subdivisions for clarity.
- Only nonmetallic cables or conductors are permitted to transition through bushed conduit, tubing or flanged connections.
- Conduits, tubing, and flanged connections must be protected from the abrasion and sealed to prevent debris from entering.

Significance of the Change

Section 392.46 in the 2017 *NEC* permits cables or conductors to leave cable tray without a box and transition into bushed conduit/tubing. A flanged connection is not recognized in 2017. The section is separated into two first-level subdivisions for clarity to address requirements for transition through bushed conduit and tubing in (A) and transition through flanged connections in (B). New requirements are added mandating that the conductors or cables are secured at the point of transition from the tray, sealing of openings, and protection from abrasion. This permission is now limited to conductors and cables with entirely nonmetallic sheaths. 392.46(A) permits individual conductors or multiconductor cable with nonmetallic sheaths to enter enclosures through non-flexible bushed conduit or tubing provided the conductors are cables are secured at the point of transition from the cable tray, and the conduit or tubing is sealed to prevent debris from entering through the conduit or tubing. 392.46(B) permits individual conductors or multiconductor cable with nonmetallic sheaths to enter enclosures through flanged connections where the cable tray is attached to the flange, and the flange is mounted directly to the equipment. These openings must be protected from abrasion and sealed to prevent debris from entering the enclosure.

FR: 8013
SR: 7544

Reproduction of NFPA's Standards Development Process Flow Chart

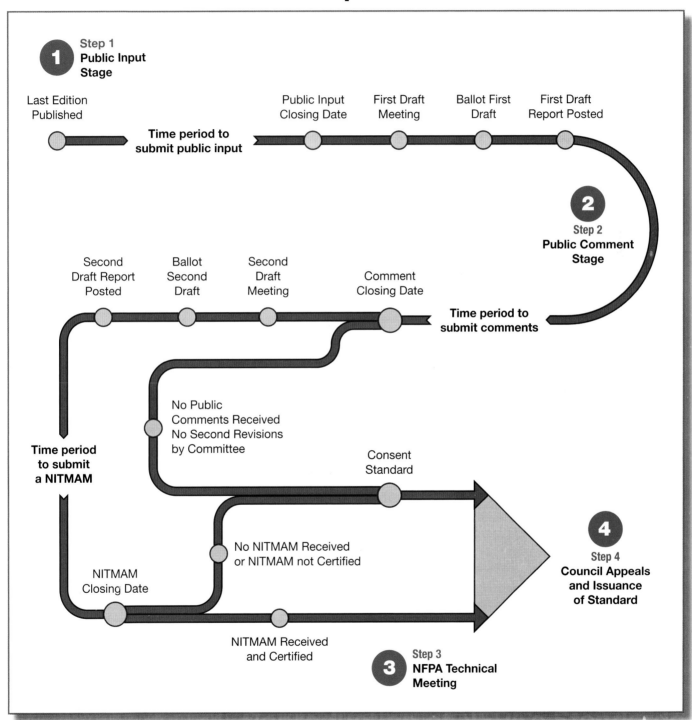

Chapter 4

Articles 400–490
Equipment for General Use

Uses Not Permitted

Code Language

400.12 Uses Not Permitted. Unless specifically permitted in 400.10, flexible cords, flexible cables, cord sets, and power supply cords shall not be used for the following:

(4) Where attached to building surfaces

Exception to (4): ... and 590.4.

(5) Where concealed by walls, floors, or ceilings or located above suspended or dropped ceilings

Exception to (5): Flexible cords, flexible cables, and power supply cords ... (See NEC text)

(See NEC for actual text)

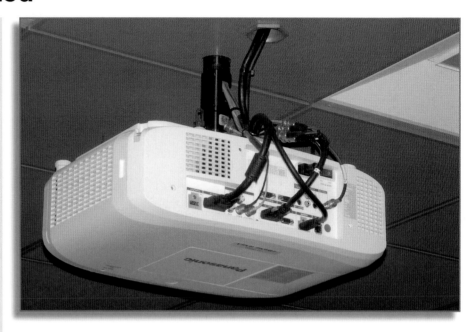

Change Summary

- The application of 400.12 is clarified to include flexible cords, flexible cables, cord sets, and power supply cords.
- The reference to 590.4 is reinserted into list item (5) Exception.
- A new IN is added to reference UL 817 for cord sets, power supply cords, and UL 62 for flexible cords and cables.

Significance of the Change

Article 400 is titled flexible cords and flexible cables. However, this article covers flexible cords, flexible cables, cord sets, and power supply cords. Section 400.12 contains requirements for uses not permitted. The parent text of this section is modified for clarity to include flexible cords, which was omitted in a previous cycle. For example, the prohibition in 400.12 list item (2), which prohibits running through holes in walls, structural ceilings, suspended ceilings, drop ceilings or floors, applies to flexible cords, flexible cables, cord sets, and power supply cords. List item (4) prohibits attachment to building surfaces. The existing exception, which permits flexible cord or flexible cable to be attached to the building in accordance with 368.56(B), is expanded to include 590.4 for temporary wiring. List item (5) prohibits concealment by walls, floors, or ceilings or located above suspended or dropped ceilings. The existing exception permits concealment if contained within an enclosure for use in other spaces for environmental air. This exception is expanded to include power supply cords. A new informational note is added to identify applicable product standards as follows:

Informational Note: For proper application, see UL 817, *Cord Sets and Power-Supply Cords*, and UL 62, *Flexible Cords and Cables*.

FR: 7907
SR: 7732

Rating and Use of Switches

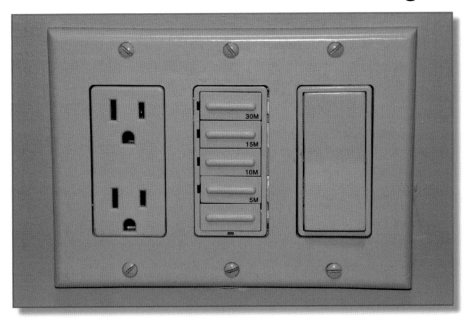

Significance of the Change

Section 404.14 *Rating and Use of Switches* now requires all switches to be listed and used within their ratings. 404.14(A)(3) is revised to specifically permit electric discharge lamp loads controlled by ac general use snap switches. Both 404.14(A) (ac general use snap switch) and (B) (ac or dc general use snap switch) are revised to permit electronic ballasts, self-ballasted lamps, compact fluorescent lamps, and LED lamp loads with associated drivers. AC general use snap switches rated for 347 volts [404.14(D)] are now required to not be readily interchangeable in box mounting with switches covered in 404.14(A) and (B), which cover ac and ac/dc general use snap switches. A new 404.14(D)(3) provides requirements for lighting loads controlled by general use snap switches rated for 347 volts. This includes electronic ballast, self-ballasted lamps, compact fluorescent lamps, and LED light lamp loads with associated drivers. 404.14(E) is revised to recognize other electronic controls including, but not limited to, timing switches and occupancy sensors used to control permanently connected loads.

Code Language

404.14 Rating and Use of Switches. Switches shall be listed and used within their ratings. Switches of the types covered in 404.14(A) through (E) shall be limited to the control of loads as specified accordingly. Switches used to control cord-and-plug-connected loads shall be limited as covered in 404.14(F).

(E) Dimmer and Electronic Control Switches. ...(See *NEC* text) Other electronic control switches, such as timing switches and occupancy sensors, shall be used to control permanently connected loads. They shall be marked by their manufacturer with their current and voltage ratings and used for loads that do not exceed their ampere rating at the voltage applied.

(See NEC for actual text)

Change Summary

- 406.14 now requires all switches to be listed and used within their ratings.
- Permitted loads are clarified in subdivisions (A) through (E).
- Electronic control switches are permitted to control permanently connected loads applied within their ratings.

FR: 7674
SR: 8170

Receptacle Replacements

Code Language

406.4(D)(3) GFCI Protection

406.4(D)(4) AFCI Protection

~~Exception No. 1: AFCI protection shall not be required where all of the following apply:~~

406.4(D)(7) Controlled Receptacles. Automatically controlled receptacles shall be replaced with equivalently controlled receptacles. If automatic control is no longer required, the receptacle and any associated receptacles marked in accordance with 406.3(E) shall be replaced with a receptacle and faceplate not marked in accordance with 406.3(E).

(See NEC for actual text)

Courtesy of Legrand

Change Summary

- The exception in 406.4(D)(3) for GFCI is modified to remove ambiguity.

- The exception in 406.4(D)(4) for AFCI is removed because devices are commercially available. Guest rooms/suites and patient sleeping rooms in nursing homes and limited care facilities are added.

- New 406.4(D)(7) requires that where automatically controlled receptacles are replaced, the replacement must be a controlled receptacle if control is still required.

FRs: 8302, 8319
SRs: 8204, 8211

Significance of the Change

Where receptacles are replaced, Section 406.4(D) applies. This requires AFCI or GFCI type replacement devices be readily accessible. 406.4(D)(3) requires a replacement receptacle be GFCI protected where required elsewhere in this *Code*. The existing exception is modified to remove ambiguous text and now only applies where the outlet box will not physically permit the installation of a GFCI type receptacle. 406.4(D)(4) requires a replacement receptacle be AFCI protected in areas identified in 210.12(A), (B) or (C). This replacement requirement is expanded with a reference to 210.12(C). The existing exception in 406.4(D)(4) is deleted. This deletion is necessary because listed combination type AFCI/GFCI circuit breakers and GFCI/AFCI dual function receptacles are now commercially available. A new second level subdivision 406.4(D)(7) is added to address the replacement of controlled receptacles. Where automatically controlled receptacles are replaced, they must now be replaced with equivalently controlled receptacles that are marked in accordance with 406.3(E). Where a controlled receptacle is replaced, and automatic control is no longer required, the receptacle is not required to meet the requirements of 406.3(E).

There have been significant revisions for receptacle replacements over the last several cycles. It is extremely important to note that any device that acts on ground fault, such as a GFCI or an AFCI with a GFP component will open where neutral conductors are combined downstream, such as in older homes with knob and tube wiring.

406.5(G) & 406.9(C)

Article 406 Receptacles, Cord Connectors, and Attachment Plugs (Caps)

Part N/A

Receptacle Orientation and Location

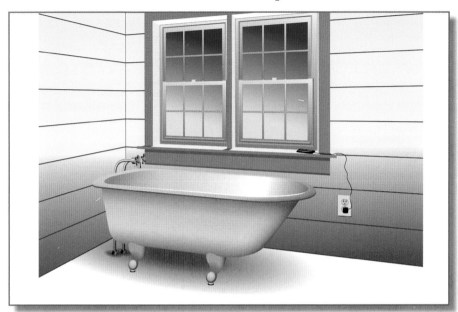

Code Language

406.5(G)(2) Under Sinks. Receptacles shall not be installed in a face-up position in the area below a sink.

406.9(C) Bathtub and Shower Space. Receptacles shall not be installed... (See *NEC* text) (3 ft) horizontally and.. (8 ft) vertically from the top of the bathtub rim or shower stall threshold. ... (See *NEC* text) shall include the space directly over the tub or shower stall.

Exception: In bathrooms with less than the required zone ... (See NEC text) installed opposite the bathtub rim or shower stall threshold on the farthest wall within the room.

(See NEC for actual text)

Significance of the Change

Section 406.5 addresses *Receptacle Mounting* and (G) provides requirements for receptacle orientation. 406.5(G) is separated into two second-level subdivisions. Requirements for receptacles in countertops and work surfaces are addressed in 406.5(G)(1) and are not permitted to be installed in the face opposition unless listed for that application. A new second-level subdivision 406.5(G)(2) is added to prohibit receptacles from being installed in the face-up position in the area below a sink.

In the 2017 *NEC*, 406.9(C) prohibited a receptacle from being installed within or directly over a bathtub or shower stall. That text literally permitted a receptacle to be installed within inches of the edge of the tub. This requirement is revised, and receptacles are now prohibited within the zone measured 3 feet horizontally and 8 feet vertically from the top of a bathtub rim or shower stall threshold. Additionally, new text clarifies that this zone is all-encompassing and includes the space directly over a tub or shower stall. The dimensions in this zone for bathtub and shower areas are not new to the *NEC*. Luminaires are prohibited to be located within the zone measured 3 feet horizontally and 8 feet vertically from the top of a bathtub rim or shower stall threshold.

Change Summary

- 406.5(G) prohibits receptacles installed in the face-up position below a sink.
- A prescriptive zone is added to prohibit receptacles near bathtub or shower spaces.
- An exception is added for bathrooms with less than the required zone permitting a receptacle on the farthest wall within the room.

FRs: 8336, 8350

SR: 8214

Single-Pole Separable-Connector Type Receptacles

Code Language

406.13 Single-Pole Separable-Connector Type. Single-pole separable connectors shall be listed and labeled and shall comply with 406.13(A) through (D).

(A) Locking or Latching Type.

(B) Identification.

(C) Interchangeability.

(D) Connecting and Disconnecting.

(1) … (See *NEC* text) interlocked… not possible to connect or disconnect connectors when the supply is energized.

(2) … (See *NEC* text) sequence…

(3) … (See *NEC* text) caution notice…

(a) EGC connectors

(b) grounded conductors

(c) ungrounded conductors

(See NEC for actual text)

Change Summary

- New 406.13 contains requirements for single-pole separable connector type receptacles, commonly called camlock.
- These devices must be listed and of the locking or latching type.
- Prescriptive steps for connecting and disconnecting are provided and must be provided on the equipment.

FR: 8378

SR: None

Significance of the Change

New section 406.13 contains requirements for single-pole separable connector type receptacles. These devices have been used successfully for decades and are now recognized in the *NEC*. In the field, these single-pole separable connectors are more commonly known by the tradename *camlock*. These devices are commonly used in emergency temporary power applications, carnivals, concerts, fairs, motion picture/TV studios, convention centers, and theaters. Single-pole separable connectors are required by 406.13(A) to be listed and be of either the locking or latching type, marked with the manufacturer's name or identification, and marked with voltage/amp ratings. 406.13(B) requires that connectors for grounded conductors be identified with white-colored housing and connectors for the EGC be identified with a green-colored housing. 406.13(C) permits single-pole separable connectors to be used for ac or dc or for different current ratings or voltages on the same premises, as long as they are listed for that use and marked in a suitable manner. 406.13(D) requires that single-pole separable connectors be used only by a qualified person and comply with one of three methods for connection and disconnection: (D)(1), Where connection and disconnection is only possible where the connectors are interlocked to the source, and it is not possible to connect or disconnect while energized. (D)(2), connected in the following sequence, 1st EGC, 2nd grounded conductor, 3rd ungrounded conductors. (D)(3), a caution notice must be provided on the equipment indicating the connection sequence (above) and disconnection in reverse order.

Connections, Switchboards, and Switchgear

Courtesy of Eaton

Code Language

408.18(C) Connections. Each section of equipment that requires rear or side access to make field connections shall be so marked by the manufacturer on the front. Section openings requiring rear or side access shall comply with 110.26. Load terminals for field wiring shall comply with 408.18(C)(1) or, (C)(2), or (C)(3) as applicable.

(C)(1) EGCs

(C)(2) Grounded Circuit Conductors

(C)(3) Ungrounded Circuit Conductors

(See NEC for actual text)

Significance of the Change

Second level subdivision 408.3(2) is deleted, and barrier requirements to protect from inadvertent contact for service supplied panelboards, switchboards, and switchgear are relocated to 230.62(C). This requirement is relocated to Article 230 and revised to require barriers be placed to prevent inadvertent contact by persons or maintenance equipment while servicing load terminations in all *service supplied equipment*.

Requirements for access to load terminals in switchboards and switchgear are relocated from 408.3(D) to 408.18(C). Panelboards are removed from this requirement, as it does not apply. New requirements are added in 408.18(C) for switchboards and switchgear requiring that each section of the equipment that needs rear or side access to make field connections be marked by the manufacturer on the front of the equipment. Additionally, section openings requiring rear or side access are required to comply with workspace clearance requirements in 110.26. Load terminals in this equipment must comply with 408.18(C)(1) for EGCs, (C)(2) for grounded conductors, and (C)(3) for ungrounded conductors. These revisions will drive manufacturers to produce equipment that reduces exposure to energize conductors or circuit parts. All of these revisions are safety-driven with the intent of reducing exposure to electrical hazards in switchboards and switchgear. Each of these second-level subdivisions requires that load terminals be located so that field wiring can be accomplished without reaching across an ungrounded bus to make connections.

Change Summary

- Requirements for barriers to prevent inadvertent contact are relocated to 230.62(C).
- New 408.18(C) includes previous requirements in 408.3(D), providing prescriptive requirements for load side connections.
- Switchboard and switchgear sections requiring rear or side access must be marked as such on the front of the equipment and must comply with 110.26.

FRs: 7655, 7764, 7675

SR: 8180

Short-Circuit Current Rating and Directories

Code Language

408.4(A) Circuit Directory... (See *NEC* text) or in an approved location adjacent to... (See *NEC* text)

408.6 Short-Circuit Current Rating. Switchboards, switchgear, and panelboards shall have a short-circuit current rating not less than the available fault current. In other than one- and two-family dwelling units, the available fault current and the date the calculation was performed shall be field marked on the enclosure at the point of supply. The marking shall comply with 110.21(B)(3).

(See NEC for actual text)

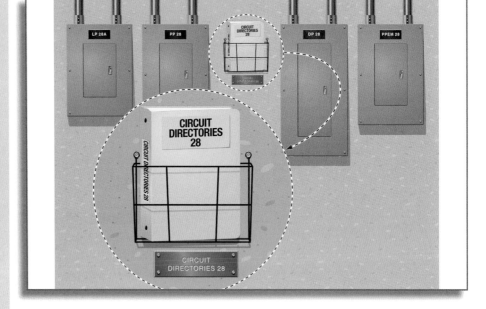

Change Summary

- New text in 408.4(A) permits the circuit directory in an approved location adjacent to equipment.
- New 408.6 requires switchboards, switchgear, and panelboards to have a short circuit current rating not less than the available fault current.
- 408.6 also requires available fault current, and the date the calculation was performed to be field marked on the enclosures at the point of supply.

FRs: 7661, 7663
SR: 8171

Significance of the Change

Circuit directories or circuit identification is required in 408.4(A) for panelboards and at each switch or circuit breaker in a switchboard for switchgear. This requirement is revised to permit this information in *an approved location adjacent to* the equipment. This will permit the installer to provide significantly more detail in the circuit directory. For example, a prominently labeled notebook of circuit directories for adjacent panelboards could be provided.

New Section 408.6 now requires switchboards, switchgear, and panelboards to have an equipment short-circuit current rating not less than the available fault current. This new requirement also mandates that in other than one- and two-family dwelling units, the available fault current and the date the calculation was performed must be field marked on the enclosure at the point of supply. These field markings must comply with 110.21(B)(3). This requirement is long-overdue in Article 408 and will now correlate with multiple other requirements throughout the *NEC*. Switchboards, switchgear, and panelboards used as service equipment are required to be marked in this manner in accordance with 110.24(A). Section 110.3 requires that all listed and labeled equipment be installed in accordance with the listing labeling and manufacturing instructions. Clarifying that switchboards, switchgear, and panelboards must have an equipment short-circuit current rating not less than the available fault current and mandating the marking of available full current will ensure this equipment is installed properly.

Reconditioning of Equipment

Courtesy of Eaton

Significance of the Change

New Section 408.8 specifically addresses reconditioning of panelboards, switchboards, and switchgear. This new requirement is significantly different from other requirements that address the reconditioning of equipment. The parent text requires that the reconditioning process, use *design qualified parts* verified under applicable standards and be performed in accordance with manufacturer instructions. Additionally, this requirement mandates that equipment damaged by fire, products of combustion, or water, be specifically evaluated by the manufacturer or a qualified testing laboratory. 408.8(A) prohibits the reconditioning of panelboards. The replacement of a panelboard within an existing enclosure is permitted. Where the replacement panelboard has not been listed for the specific cabinet/enclosure and the available fault current is greater than 10,000 amps, the assembly must be field labeled, and any previously applied listing marks on the cabinet containing the panelboard must be removed. 408.8(B) permits the reconditioning of switchboards and switchgear. Reconditioned switchgear must be listed or field labeled as reconditioned, and previously applied listing marks must be removed. The term *reconditioned* means that electromechanical systems, equipment, apparatus, or components are restored to operating conditions. It is imperative to note that some equipment lends itself very well to the reconditioning process, and other equipment cannot be reconditioned. This process (reconditioning) is significantly different from normal servicing of equipment that remains within a facility. See the "NEMA Policy on Reconditioned Electrical Equipment" for more information.

Code Language

408.8 Reconditioning of Equipment. Reconditioning of equipment within the scope of this article shall be limited as described in 408.8(A) and (B). The reconditioning process shall use design qualified parts verified under applicable standards and be performed in accordance with any instructions provided by the manufacturer. If equipment has been damaged by fire, products of combustion, or water, it shall be specifically evaluated by its manufacturer or a qualified testing laboratory prior to being returned to service.

(A) Panelboards.

(B) Switchboards and Switchgear.

(See NEC for actual text)

Change Summary

- New 408.8 provides requirements for reconditioning of panelboards, switchboards, and switchgear.
- Equipment damaged by fire or water must be specifically evaluated by the original manufacturer or a qualified testing laboratory.
- In general, switchboards and switchgear are permitted to be reconditioned; panelboards are not permitted to be reconditioned.

FR: None
SR: 8172

Panelboard Orientation

Code Language

408.43 Panelboard Orientation. Panelboards shall not be installed in the face-up position.

240.33 Vertical Position. Enclosures for overcurrent devices shall be mounted in a vertical position... (See *NEC* text)

(See NEC for actual text)

Courtesy of Eaton

Change Summary

- New 408.43 prohibits panelboards from being installed in the face-up position.
- Section 240.33 is revised to require enclosures for overcurrent devices to be mounted in a vertical position.

Significance of the Change

A new Section 408.43 *Panelboard Orientation* is added to prohibit panelboards from being installed in the face-up position. There are multiple venues, including laundromats, that attempt to save space by mounting panelboards in the face-up position on top of equipment. This increases the likelihood that contaminants will accumulate on the panelboard and the circuit breakers enclosed. This also creates a significant hazard and challenges with respect to workspace requirements. It is interesting to note that the committee statement behind this revision clarifies that this new limitation does not prohibit the mounting of the panelboard in a horizontal face-down position.

This revision correlates with changes in Section 240.33 *Vertical Position*, which provides requirements for enclosures containing overcurrent devices. This section is revised to require that all overcurrent devices be mounted in a vertical position. Previous text permitted otherwise, where it was *shown to be impracticable* and is deleted. During the first draft stage of this cycle, Section 240.33 was separated into three first-level subdivisions with one of those prohibiting panelboards from being installed in the face-up position.

This safety-driven revision will prevent significant hazards from being created where a person may need to troubleshoot a panelboard installed in the face-up position.

FR: 8669
CCN: 67
SR: 8340

Reconditioned Equipment, Luminaires

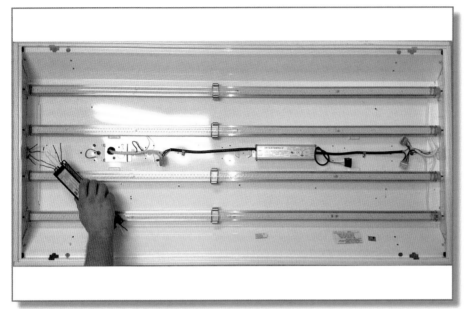

Courtesy of Independence LED Lighting, LLC

Code Language

410.7 Reconditioned Equipment. Luminaires, lampholders, and retrofit kits shall not be permitted to be reconditioned. If a retrofit kit is installed in a luminaire in accordance with the installation instructions, the retrofitted luminaire shall not be considered reconditioned.

(See NEC for actual text)

Significance of the Change

New Section 410.7 provides requirements for reconditioned equipment. In general, luminaires, lampholders, and retrofit kits are not permitted to be reconditioned. Additional text clarifies that if a retrofit kit is installed in a luminaire in accordance with the installation instructions, the retrofitted luminaire is not to be considered reconditioned. It is important to note that 410.6 requires all luminaires, lampholders, and retrofit kits be listed. While this requirement, in general, prohibits luminaires, lampholders, and retrofit kits from being reconditioned, a listed retrofit kit is permitted to be installed in a luminaire in accordance with the installation instructions. In this case, the retrofitted luminaire is not considered to be reconditioned.

The term *reconditioned* means that electromechanical systems, equipment, apparatus, or components are restored to operating condition. It is imperative to note that some equipment lends itself very well to the reconditioning process, and other equipment cannot be reconditioned. This process (reconditioning) is significantly different from normal servicing of equipment that remains within a facility. Additionally, it is important to note replacement of listed equipment on a one-to-one basis does not constitute "reconditioned equipment." Additional terms to describe this process include: *rebuilt*, *refurbished*, or *remanufactured*. See the "NEMA Policy on Reconditioned Electrical Equipment" for more information.

Change Summary

- New 410.7 provides requirements for reconditioned equipment.
- Luminaires, lampholders, and retrofit kits are in general, not permitted to be reconditioned.
- Where a listed retrofit kit is installed in a luminaire in accordance with installation instructions, the retrofitted luminaire is not considered to be reconditioned.

FR: None
SR: 8162

Luminaires Supported by Outlet Boxes

Code Language

410.36(A) Luminaires Supported By Outlet Boxes. Luminaires shall be permitted to be supported by outlet boxes or fittings installed as required by 314.23. The installation shall comply with the following requirements:

(1) The outlet boxes or fittings shall comply with 314.27(A)(1) and 314.27(A)(2)

(2) Luminaires shall be permitted to be supported in accordance with 314.27(E)

(3) Outlet boxes complying with 314.27(E) shall be considered lighting outlets as required by 210.70(A), (B), and (C).

(See NEC for actual text)

Change Summary

- 410.36(A) is modified for clarity and restructured into list items.
- New text specifically permits luminaires to be supported by separable attachment fittings, 314.27(E).
- New text clarifies that outlets complying with 314.27(E) are considered lighting outlets.

Courtesy of Sky Technologies (formerly Safety Quick Lighting & Fans)

Significance of the Change

Requirements for boxes supporting luminaires at outlets are located in 314.27(A). Prescriptive requirements are provided for luminaires installed in vertical surface outlets in 314.27(A)(1), and ceiling outlets in 314.27(A)(2). Previous requirements for the support of luminaires in 410.36(A) only referenced 314.27(A)(1) and 314.27(A)(2) for support of luminaires. First level subdivision 410.36(A) is modified for clarity and restructured into list items. The parent text continues to permit luminaires to be supported by outlet boxes or fittings installed as required by 314.23. New list item 410.36(A)(1), continues to permit outlet boxes or fittings that comply with 314.27(A)(1) and 314.27(A)(2). New list item 410.36(A)(2), now permits luminaires to be supported in accordance with 314.27(E), which contains requirements for separable attachment fittings. These devices include a listed locking support and mounting receptacle that is used in combination with compatible attachment fittings. A separable attachment fitting is by definition, a receptacle, and is referenced in the Article 100 definition of *receptacle* as "a device for the direct connection of electrical utilization equipment designed to meet with the corresponding contact device." New list item 410.36(A)(3) clarifies that outlet boxes complying with 314.27(E) are considered as lighting outlets required by 210.70(A), (B), and (C). This is necessary to clarify that a *separable attachment fitting* installed for lighting, is a lighting outlet and not a receptacle outlet.

FR: 8418
SR: 8169

Identification of Control Conductor Insulation

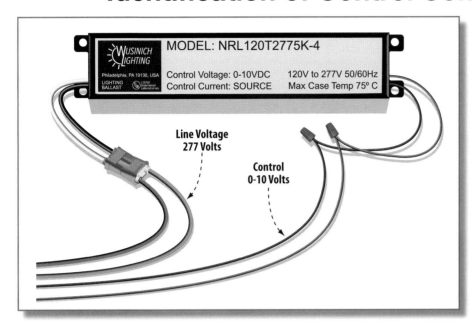

MODEL: NRL120T2775K-4

WUSINICH LIGHTING
Philadelphia, PA 19130, USA
LIGHTING BALLAST

Control Voltage: 0-10VDC
Control Current: SOURCE

120V to 277V 50/60Hz
Max Case Temp 75° C

Line Voltage
277 Volts

Control
0-10 Volts

Significance of the Change

New Section 410.69 is titled *Identification of Control Conductor Insulation*. This new requirement mandates that where control conductors are spliced, terminated, or connected in the same luminaire or enclosure as branch circuit conductors, the field connected control conductor shall not be of a color reserved for grounded conductors in 200.6. This revision will have a significant impact on a large number of controls, drivers, and ballasts that have integral control conductors and for that reason, this requirement is delayed and becomes effective on January 1, 2022. In order to aid in the transition of identification of control conductors, and to allow for the use of existing stock, an exception is added. This exception will permit field connected gray-colored control conductors where they are permanently re-identified by marking tape, painting, or other effective means at each termination and each location where the conductor is visible and accessible. This revision is based upon multiple shock incidents that have occurred. One common control conductor scheme is to use "purple and gray" colored control conductors. The shock incidents occurred where "gray control" conductors were inadvertently spliced to the grounded conductor. These lighting control conductors are not limited to control of a single branch circuit; they can control multiple branch circuits. This sets up a scenario where employees are working on a branch circuit that has been placed into an electrically safe work condition, but an inadvertently spliced common control conductor in a luminaire becomes energized when a completely different branch circuit is energized.

Code Language

410.69 Identification of Control Conductor Insulation. Where control conductors are spliced, terminated, or connected in the same luminaire or enclosure as the branch-circuit conductors, the field-connected control conductor shall not be of a color reserved for the grounded branch-circuit conductor or the equipment grounding conductor. This requirement shall become effective January 1, 2022.

Exception: A field-connected gray-colored control conductor shall be permitted if the insulation is permanently re-identified by marking tape, painting, or other effective means at its termination and at each location where the conductor is visible and accessible. Identification shall encircle the insulation and shall be a color other than white, gray, or green.

(See NEC for actual text)

Change Summary

- New 410.69 provides requirements on how to identify control conductors.
- Shock incidents have occurred where gray control conductors were inadvertently spliced to a grounded conductor.
- This requirement becomes effective January 1, 2022.

FR: 8512
SR: 8179

Installation in Fire-Resistant Construction

Code Language

410.116(C) Installation in Fire-Resistant Construction. Luminaires marked "FOR USE IN NON-FIRE-RATED INSTALLATIONS" shall not be used in fire-rated installations. Where a luminaire is recessed in fire-resistant material in a building of fire-resistant construction, the recessed luminaire shall satisfy one of the following:

(1)... (See *NEC* text) be listed for use in a fire resistance–rated construction.

(2)... (See *NEC* text) be installed in or used with a luminaire enclosure that is listed for use in a fire resistance–rated construction.

(3)... (See *NEC* text) be listed and shall be installed in accordance with a tested fire resistance–rated assembly... (See *NEC* text) a recessed LED luminaire of comparable construction shall be permitted.

(See NEC for actual text)

Change Summary

- Requirements for fire-resistant construction are modified and moved from 410.115(B) to new 410.116(C).
- Luminaires marked "for use in non-fire rated installations" or prohibited in fire rated installations.
- Three permitted methods are provided in 410.116(C).

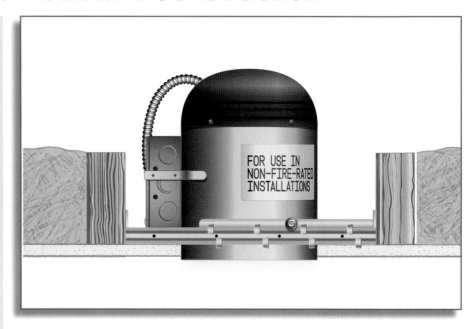

Significance of the Change

Requirements for recessed luminaires in fire-resistant material in a building of fire-resistant construction previously existed in 410.115(B). This requirement contained only references to temperature and contained no means of verification that the luminaire was suitable for use. First level subdivision 410.115(B) has been deleted, and a new 410.116(C) *Installation in Fire-Resistant Construction* is added with prescriptive requirements for luminaires that are recessed in fire-resistant material in buildings of fire-resistant construction. This new requirement clarifies that luminaires marked "FOR USE IN NON-FIRE RATED INSTALLATIONS" are prohibited in fire-rated installations. Three list items are added to clarify requirements for luminaires that are recessed in fire-resistant material in buildings of fire-resistant construction. They include (1) luminaires listed for use in fire-resistance-rated construction, (2) luminaires installed in or used with enclosures listed for use in fire-resistance-rated construction and, (3) listed luminaires installed in accordance with a tested fire-resistance-rated assembly. List item (3) clarifies that when a tested fire-resistance-rated assembly allows the installation of a recessed fluorescent luminaire, a recessed LED luminaire of comparable construction is permitted. This revision provides significant clarity for the installer and the electrical inspector in the field.

FR: 8515
SR: None

Access to Other Boxes

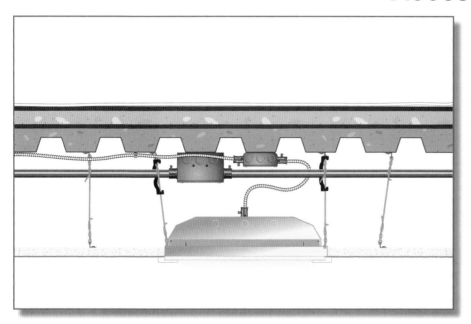

Code Language

410.118 Access to Other Boxes. Luminaires recessed in ceilings, floors, or walls shall not be used to access outlet, pull, or junction boxes or conduit bodies, unless the box or conduit body is an integral part of the listed luminaire.

(See NEC for actual text)

Significance of the Change

Part X of Article 410 contains special provisions for flush and recessed luminaires. A new Section 410.118 is added to address access to other boxes through luminaires. This requirement impacts all luminaires that are flush-mounted or recessed in ceilings, floors, or walls. They shall not be used to access outlet, pull, or junction boxes, or conduit bodies unless the box or conduit body is an integral part of the luminaire. Where finished ceilings are inaccessible, such as a drywall ceiling, installers must locate outlet, pull, or junction boxes in areas where they can be accessed. In most cases, this requires the installer to add access panels or doors. In some cases, installers have placed junction boxes behind flush or recessed luminaires. This creates multiple problems. Where junction boxes are installed behind luminaires, they are inaccessible to maintenance personnel as they have no idea where they are located. Access to such boxes requires removal and potential damage to the luminaire and the building finish.

This new requirement prohibits the common practice of hiding junction boxes behind luminaires.

Change Summary

- New Section 410.118 is added to address access to other boxes behind a luminaire.
- This new requirement clarifies that luminaires are not permitted to be used to access outlet, pull, or junction boxes or conduit bodies.
- Access panels, doors, or other means of access must be provided where necessary.

FR: 8412

SR: None

Special Provisions for Horticultural Lighting Equipment

Code Language

410.170 General. Luminaires complying with Parts, I. II, III, IV, V, VI, VII, IX, X, XI, and XII of this article shall be permitted to be used for horticultural lighting. Part XVI shall additionally apply to lighting equipment specifically identified for horticultural use.

Informational Note: Lighting equipment identified for horticultural use is designed to provide a spectral characteristic needed for the growth of plants and can also provide supplemental general illumination within the growing environment.

(See NEC for actual text)

Courtesy of MedPharm Holdings, member of American Trade Assn of Cannabis and Hemp

Change Summary

- A new part XVI is added to Article 410 with special provisions for horticultural lighting equipment.
- These new requirements will impact the rapidly increasing industry of indoor plant growing facilities.
- These installations are subject to increased temperatures, humidity, and water spray, and require unique support and flexibility.

Significance of the Change

A new Part XVI Is added in Article 410 to address the installation of indoor horticultural lighting equipment. This revision is necessary to address the significant number of indoor plant growing facilities installed for farming and the cannabis industry. These facilities require horticultural lighting equipment that provides a wavelength of light necessary for plant growth. These installations need to be portable and adjustable to accommodate seasonal plant growth and diversity. Luminaires in compliance with the remainder of Article 410 are permitted to be used for horticultural lighting with the additional requirements of Part XVI. Horticultural lighting equipment is required to be listed and installed and used in accordance with manufacturer's instructions. Horticultural lighting is not permitted for general illumination unless indicated in the manufacturer's instructions and is not permitted where subject to physical damage or concealed. Flexible cord is permitted to connect these luminaires to each other, to a branch circuit outlet or remote power source. Luminaires identified for horticultural use with flexible cords with one or more connectors must be GFCI protected.

FR: 8537
SR: 8167

422.5

Article 422 Appliances

Part I General

GFCI Protection for Personnel

Significance of the Change

Section 422.5 provides requirements for GFCI protection for personnel using appliances. This requirement supplements the general GFCI requirements located in 210.8. An appliance by definition is utilization equipment other than industrial, normally built-in standardized sizes or types to perform one or more functions, such as clothes washing, air-conditioning, food mixing, deep-frying, and more. The requirements of 210.8(A) and (B) are designed to provide GFCI protection where most appliances are used, and anything connected to the receptacle outlets identified, such as tools. There have been many attempts to correlate and/or consolidate the requirements in these two sections. This revision provides clarity by identifying appliances rated 150 volts or less to ground and 60 amps or less single- or 3-phase. This provides a correlation with the parent text in 210.8(B) but differs significantly because this requirement is not limited to receptacles. The parent text is also modified to require Class A GFCI protection. While this is not necessary because the defined term *ground fault circuit interrupter* clarifies that it is a Class A device, this new text eliminates confusion with special-purpose ground fault circuit interrupter protection for personnel (SPGFCI). Sump pumps are added to the list of appliances requiring GFCI protection as they may be handled while wet. 210.8(D) previously required GFCI protection for outlets supplying dishwashers in dwelling unit locations. This first level subdivision has been deleted, and dishwashers are added to the list in 422.5(A). This is a significant revision as GFCI protection of dishwashers is no longer limited to dwelling unit locations.

Code Language

422.5(A) General. Appliances identified in 422.5(A)(1) through (A)(7) rated 150 volts or less to ground and 60 amperes or less, single- or 3-phase, shall be provided with Class A GFCI protection for personnel. Multiple Class A GFCI protective devices shall be permitted but shall not be required.

(1) Automotive vacuum machines

(2) Drinking water coolers and bottle fill stations

(3) Cord-and-plug-connected high-pressure spray washing machines

(4) Tire inflation machines

(5) Vending machines

(6) Sump pumps

(7) Dishwashers

Informational Note: Section 210.8 specifies requirements for GFCI protection for the branch-circuit outlet where the covered location warrants such protection.

(See NEC for actual text)

Change Summary

- The parent text in 422.5(A) is modified to include appliances rated 150 volts or less to ground and 60 amps or less, single- or 3-phase and is not limited to receptacles.
- Sump pumps and dishwashers are added to the list.
- A new informational note sends *Code* users to 210.8 for additional GFCI requirements.

FRs: 8143, 8164
SR: 8124

Utilizing Separable Attachment Fittings

Code Language

422.22 Utilizing Separable Attachment Fittings. Appliances shall be permitted to utilize listed locking support and mounting receptacles in combination with compatible attachment fittings utilized within their ratings and used in accordance with 314.27(E).

(See NEC for actual text)

Courtesy of Sky Technologies (formerly Safety Quick Lighting & Fans)

Change Summary

- New Section 422.22 is added to specifically recognize the use of separable attachment fittings to supply appliances.
- Article 100 now contains a definition of "attachment fitting."
- This new permissive requirement provides installers and inspectors with prescriptive permission to use these devices.

Significance of the Change

New Section 422.22 is added to specifically permit appliances to be installed using separable attachment fittings. This requirement permits listed locking support and mounting receptacles in combination with compatible attachment fittings used in accordance with 314.27(E). Appliances such as, but not limited to, a ceiling paddle fan may be installed using a separable attachment fitting. A separable attachment fitting is referenced in the definition of *receptacle* in Article 100 for "the direct connection of electrical utilization equipment designed to meet with the corresponding contact device." These devices are a combination of a receptacle and an *attachment fitting*, which is now defined in Article 100 as follows: A device that by insertion into a locking support and mounting receptacle, establishes a connection between the conductors of the attached utilization equipment and the branch circuit conductors connected to the locking support and mounting receptacle.

This new section is required to provide installers and inspectors with specific permission allowing the installation of separable attachment fittings to supply appliances.

FR: 8237
SR: None

Electronically Protected Motors

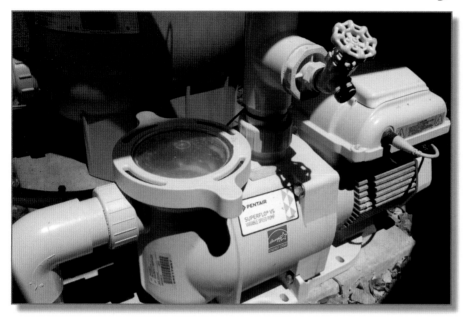

Significance of the Change

A new definition, *Electronically Protected (as applied to motors)* is added in 430.2 to define electronic protection against overload for motors. Electronically protected motors have been listed for approximately 10 years. These motors are commonly used for HVAC systems, pool pumps, refrigeration, and many other uses. These motors are also becoming popular as stand-alone motors that are not part of an assembly. The overload protection in an electronically protected motor is not adjustable. For that reason, requirements for electronically protected motors are added to the same sections that reference thermally protected motors in 430.32(A)(2) and (B)(2). Electronically protected motors prevent dangerous overheating due to the failure of the electronic control itself, overload, or failure of the motor to start.

New text is added into 430.32(A)(2) and (B)(2) to permit electronically protected motors. Electronically protected motors are approved for use on the basis that the electronic protection will prevent dangerous overheating due to the failure of the electronic control, overload, or failure to start the motor.

Code Language

430.2 Definitions

Electronically Protected (as applied to motors). A motor that is provided with electronic control that is an integral part of the motor and protects the motor against dangerous overheating due to failure of the electronic control, overload and failure to start.

430.32(A)(2) *and* **(B)(2)**... (See *NEC* text) An electronically protected motor shall be approved for use on the basis that it will prevent dangerous overheating due to the failure of the electronic control, overload, or failure to start the motor... (See *NEC* text)

(See NEC for actual text)

Change Summary

- 430.32(A)(2) and (B)(2) are modified to permit electronically protected motors.
- The electronic protection prevents dangerous overheating from failure of the electronic control, overload, or failure to start.
- A new definition is added in 430.2 to define this electronic protection.

FRs: 8022, 8027, 8028

SR: 7542

Conductors, Minimum Size and Ampacity

Code Language

430.122(A) Branch/Feeder Circuit Conductors.

Informational Note No. 2: Circuit conductors on the output of an adjustable-speed drive system are susceptible to breakdown under certain conditions due to the characteristics of the output waveform of the drive. Factors affecting the conductors include but are not limited to the output voltage, frequency, and current, the length of the conductors, the spacing between the conductors, and the dielectric strength of the conductor insulation. Methods to mitigate breakdown include consideration of one or more of these factors.

(B) Output Conductors... (See *NEC* text)

(D) Several Motors or a Motor and Other Loads... (See *NEC* text)

(See NEC for actual text)

Change Summary

- A new informational note is added in 430.122(A) to explain that the characteristics of the output waveform of the drive can breakdown circuit conductors.

- New 430.122(B) provides requirements for the ampacity of output conductors.

- New 430.122(D) provides requirements for conductors supplying several motors or a motor and other loads.

Courtesy of Eaton

Significance of the Change

Section 430.122(A) requires that branch circuit conductors supplying power conversion equipment included as part of an adjustable speed drive system have an ampacity of not less than 125% of the rated input current to the power conversion equipment. An informational note is added following 430.122(A) to explain that circuit conductors on the output of an adjustable speed drive system are susceptible to breakdown under certain conditions due to the characteristics of the output waveform of the drive. New 430.122(B) requires output conductors between the power conversion equipment and motor to have an ampacity not less than 125% of the motor full load current. An exception addresses equipment marked as *suitable for output motor conductor protection* with two options for sizing conductors. The options are

(1) 125% of the motor full-load current as determined by 430.6(A) or (B), and

(2) the ampacity of the minimum conductor size marked on the power conversion equipment.

A new 430.122(D) requires conductors supplying several motors or a motor and other loads, including power conversion equipment, to have an ampacity in accordance with 430.24 using the rated input current of the power conversion equipment for purposes of calculating ampacity.

FRs: 7989, 8000
SRs: 7597, 7641, 7688

C, SC, GF Protection Power Conversion Equipment

Significance of the Change

Section 430.130 provides requirements for branch circuit, short-circuit, and ground fault protection for single motor circuits containing power conversion equipment. The parent text in 430.130(A) is modified to now clearly require that circuits containing power conversion equipment be protected by all four list items provided. List item 430.130(A)(1) is modified to refer to 430.6(A) and (B) for full load current rating of the motor. This requires that the rating and type of protection be determined by 430.52(C)(1), (C)(3), (C)(5), or (C)(6), using the full-load current rating of the motor load as determined by 430.6(A) or (B). A new exception is added to 430.130(A)(1) for power conversion equipment that is listed and marked *suitable for output motor conductor protection*. This permits the rating and type of protection to be determined by Table 430.52 using the power conversion equipment rated input current. A new Informational Note No. 2 explains that a motor branch circuit using power conversion equipment, including equipment listed and marked *suitable for output motor conductor protection* includes the input circuit to the power conversion equipment. Adjustable speed drive system technology is capable of providing output conductor branch circuit, short-circuit, and ground fault protection.

Code Language

430.132 (A) Circuits Containing Power Conversion Equipment.

Exception to 1: The rating and type of protection shall be permitted to be determined by Table 430.52 using the power conversion equipment's rated input current where the power conversion equipment is listed and marked "Suitable for Output Motor Conductor Protection."

Informational Note No. 2: A motor branch circuit using power conversion equipment, including equipment listed and marked "Suitable for Output Motor Conductor Protection," includes the input circuit to the power conversion equipment.

(See NEC for actual text)

Change Summary

- An exception is added to permit an alternate method to determine BC, SC, GF protection for motors supplied by power conversion equipment.
- Where power conversion equipment is listed and marked *suitable for output motor conductor protection*, the equipment rated input current and Table 430.52 may be used.

FR: 7999
SR: 7677

Grounding and Bonding

Code Language

440.9 Grounding and Bonding. Where equipment is installed outdoors on a roof, an equipment grounding conductor of the wire type shall be installed in outdoor portions of metallic raceway systems that use compression type fittings.

(See NEC for actual text)

iStock Photo Courtesy of NECA

Change Summary

- 440.9 now applies only where compression type fittings are used.
- This does not permit set screw type fittings without an equipment grounding conductor.
- The raceway XXX.42 sections require that in wet locations Section 314.15 applies to couplings and connectors.

Significance of the Change

Section 440.9 is modified to provide clarity. This requirement now mandates that where *equipment* (the reference to multimotor and combination load is deleted) is installed outdoors on a roof, an equipment grounding conductor of the wire type must be installed in all outdoor portions of metallic raceway systems that use *compression type fittings*. The previous text required an equipment grounding conductor where non-threaded fittings were used. This created some confusion in the field due to the fact that even a compression type fitting has threads. In the previous text, the reference to threads was intended to include threads on rigid and intermediate metal conduits.

At first glance, the user of the *Code* may look at this revision and think that set screw type couplings and connectors are permitted. They are not. See the XXX.42 sections for EMT, RMC, and IMC. Each of these sections requires that where couplings and connectors without *running threads* are installed in wet locations, they must comply with 314.15, which requires fittings installed in wet locations to be listed for use in wet locations.

FR: 3582
SR: None

Listing of Generators

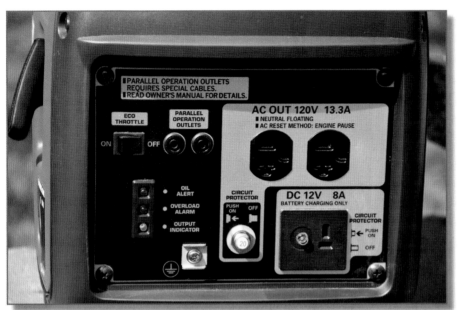

Code Language

445.6 Listing. Stationary generators 600 volts and less shall be listed.

Exception: One of a kind or custom manufactured generators shall be permitted to be field labeled by a field evaluation body.

Informational Note: For additional information, see UL 2200, *Standard for Stationary Engine Generator Assemblies.*

(See NEC for actual text)

Significance of the Change

New Section 445.6 *Listing* requires all stationery generators rated at 600 V and less to be listed. An exception is included for one-of-a-kind or custom manufactured generators. These generators are permitted to be *field labeled* by a *field evaluation* body. This ensures that one-of-a-kind or custom manufactured generators comply with the same requirements as listed generators. The term *field labeled* is defined in Article 100 as Equipment or materials to which has been attached a label, symbol, or other identifying mark of a field evaluation body (FEB) indicating the equipment or materials were evaluated and found to comply with requirements as described in an accompanying field evaluation report. A FEB is an organization or part of an organization that performs field evaluations of electrical or other equipment. An informational note is included with 445.6 to reference UL 2200, the *Standard for Stationary Engine Generator Assemblies*, which addresses safety concerns for both the electrical and fuel control for electrical generating equipment. Engine-driven generators are not inherently safe and are unique hybrid products that include numerous hazards; hazardous voltages, high energy AC and DC circuits, low voltage limited energy and communications circuits, mechanical hazards, highly flammable fuels, high temperatures, and poisonous exhaust gasses.

Change Summary

- New 445.6 *Listing* requires all stationery generators rated at 600 V and less to be listed.
- One-of-a-kind or custom manufactured generators are permitted to be *field labeled* by a *field evaluation* body.
- UL 2200 the *Standard for Stationary Engine Generator Assemblies* addresses safety concerns for the electrical and other hazards associated with generators.

FR: None

SR: 7639

Emergency Shutdown in 1 and 2 Family Dwelling Units

Code Language

445.18 Disconnecting Means and Emergency Shutdown

(B) Emergency Shutdown of Prime Mover

(C) Remote Emergency Shutdown

(D) Emergency Shutdown in One- and Two-Family Dwelling Units. For other than cord-and-plug-connected portable generators, an emergency shutdown device shall be located outside the dwelling unit at a readily accessible location.

(See NEC for actual text)

Change Summary

- New 445.18(D) requires an emergency shutdown device located outside of one- and two-family dwellings for other than cord and plug connected portable generators.

- The emergency shutdown device is required at a readily accessible location.

- Editorial revisions are included to clarify emergency shutdown.

Significance of the Change

New 445.18(D) is added to require an emergency shutdown device be located outside of one- and two-family dwelling units. This requirement does not apply to cord and plug connected portable generators, as they can be easily identified and disconnected at the generator. This new first-level subdivision is added to provide the fire service and other first responders with the capability to remove power from a dwelling unit during an emergency. Together, with new requirements for readily accessible emergency disconnecting means in one- and two-family dwelling units for services in Section 230.85, storage batteries in 480.7(B), energy storage systems in 706.15(A), and in wind electric systems in 694.22(C)(1), these requirements will provide first responders with the ability to quickly and safely remove power from dwelling units during an emergency.

The title of this section is modified to clarify that these are requirements for disconnects and emergency *shutdown*. The title of 445.18(B) is revised to clarify that the requirements within address *emergency* shutdown of the prime mover. The last paragraph of existing 445.18(B) is editorially relocated into a new 445.18(C) *Remote Emergency Shutdown*. This requirement is clarified with new text to better explain the intent of this requirement, which is to mandate that generators with greater than 15 kW rating be provided with a *remote emergency stop switch*.

FRs: 8874, 7770, 7846

SR: 7645

Ventilation

Code Language

450.9 Ventilation. The ventilation shall dispose of the transformer full-load heat losses without creating a temperature rise that is in excess of the transformer rating... (See *NEC* text)

Transformers with ventilating openings shall be installed so that the ventilating openings are not blocked by walls or other obstructions. The required clearances shall be clearly marked on the transformer. Transformer top surfaces that are horizontal and readily accessible shall be marked to prohibit storage.

(See NEC for actual text)

Significance of the Change

Section 450.9 contains requirements that ensure transformers are able to dispose of heat without creating a temperature rise that is in excess of the transformer rating. Transformers with ventilating openings must be installed so that the ventilating openings are not blocked by walls or other obstructions. The required clearances must be clearly marked on the transformer. A new last sentence is added in Section 450.9 to require that the top surface of transformers that are horizontal and readily accessible be marked to prohibit storage.

It is very common to find unqualified persons using electrical equipment rooms to store materials. Section 110.26 provides requirements for workspace clearances. Where materials are stored on top of transformers, the resulting heat rise created by insulating the top of the transformer may damage the transformer. Additionally, the heat created could be a fire concern. This new requirement does not provide the exact text to be placed on top of the transformer enclosure. An example marking would be " WARNING, DO NOT PLACE OR STORE MATERIALS."

Change Summary

- A new last sentence in 450.9 requires the top of transformers that are horizontal and readily accessible be marked to prohibit storage.

- The intent is to eliminate hazards created by storing material on top of transformers.

FR: 7774
SR: 8197

Safe Zone, Protective Devices Rated or Adjusted

Code Language

460.2 Safe Zone. Low probability of damage other than a slight swelling of the capacitor case, as identified by the case rupture curve of the capacitor.

460.25(D) Protective Devices Rated or Adjusted. Protective devices for capacitors or capacitor equipment shall be rated or adjusted to operate within the limits of the safe zone for individual capacitors.

(See NEC for actual text)

Courtesy of Eaton

Change Summary

- New definition of *Safety Zone* is added into 460.2.
- The safety zone is plotted on a chart similar to a time-current curve for fuses.
- In order to protect the capacitor from rupturing, the overcurrent protective device must clear in the safe zone.

Significance of the Change

A new definition of *Safe Zone* is added into 460.2. Section 460.25 addresses overcurrent protection requirements for capacitors. 460.25(A) requires a means be provided to detect and interrupt fault current likely to cause dangerous pressure within an individual capacitor. 460.25(D) requires protective devices for capacitors or capacitor equipment be rated or adjusted to operate within the limits of the *safe zone* for individual capacitors. Previous text that addressed limits outside of the *safe zone*, including Zone 1 and Zone 2 is deleted. The existing informational note is also deleted, as the referenced standard did not contain definitions of *Safe Zone*, *Zone 1*, and *Zone 2*. The *NEC* now defines 460.2 *Safe Zone* as the low probability of damage other than a slight swelling of the capacitor case, as identified by the case rupture curve of the capacitor.

Protection zones for capacitors look similar to a time-current curve for fuses. The safe zone is to the left of the rupture curves. Protection within the safe zone could result in a slight swelling of the capacitor shell with no severe damage. If available fault current gets into Zone 1, there may be a slight rupture and fluid may leak from the capacitor. If available fault current gets into Zone 2, there may be a violent rupture of the shell. If available fault current gets into the Hazardous Zone, there may be a violent rupture with a blast, which may damage adjacent equipment.

FRs: 7909, 7913

SR: None

Storage Batteries

Courtesy of Tesla Energy

Code Language

480.1 Scope. This article applies to all stationary installations of storage batteries.

480.2 Storage Battery (Battery). A single or group of rechargeable cells connected together electrically in series, in parallel, or a combination of both, and comprised of lead-acid, nickel-cadmium, or other rechargeable electrochemical types.

(See NEC for actual text)

Significance of the Change

Article 706 *Energy Storage Systems* was added in the 2017 *NEC* revision cycle. Batteries are used for energy storage, but they are not the only method of energy storage. The scope of Article 480 is clear; it applies to all installations of *Storage Batteries*.

In the 2017 *NEC*, there was significant overlap between Articles 480 *Storage Batteries* and 706 *Energy Storage Systems*. This revision relocates multiple sections from Article 706 that pertain to batteries into Article 480, and multiple sections in Article 706 are deleted, as they are redundant. Section 480.2 is modified to clarify that the definitions contained, apply only within Article 480. The defined term *battery* is deleted from Article 706. The defined term *storage battery* is modified to correlate with a similar definition in *NFPA 855*. A *storage battery* is a single or group of rechargeable cells connected together electrically in series, in parallel, or a combination of both, and comprised of lead-acid, nickel-cadmium, or other rechargeable electrochemical types.

Accessibility requirements for storage batteries are located in 480.4(D) and redundant text is deleted in 480.9. Requirements for the disconnection of battery circuits connected in series is deleted in 706.30(B) and is located in 480.7(B), which deals strictly with batteries. Requirements for battery interconnections are deleted in 706.32 and relocated into 480.12, as they deal strictly with batteries. Ground fault protection requirements for batteries are relocated from 706.30(D) to 480.13.

Change Summary

- This revision correlates Article 706 for Energy Storage Systems with Article 480.
- Requirements pertaining to storage batteries are relocated into 480.
- The definition of battery is deleted, as it is redundant. The definition of storage battery is modified to correlate with *NFPA 855*.

FRs: 8979, 8875, 8979
SRs: 7708, 7553, 7555

Emergency Disconnect, Batteries

Code Language

480.7(B) Emergency Disconnect. For one-family and two-family dwellings, a disconnecting means or its remote control for a stationary battery system shall be located at a readily accessible location outside the building for emergency use. The disconnect shall be labeled "EMERGENCY DISCONNECT".

(See NEC for actual text)

Courtesy of Tesla Energy

Change Summary

- New 480.7(B) requires an emergency disconnect or its remote control for storage batteries in one- and two-family dwellings.
- The emergency disconnect must be readily accessible.
- The emergency disconnect must be labeled "EMERGENCY DISCONNECT".

Significance of the Change

A new first-level subdivision 480.7(B) requires an *Emergency Disconnect* or its remote control for storage batteries in one- and two-family dwellings. The emergency disconnect must be located at a readily accessible location outside the building for emergency use. The disconnect is required to be labeled "EMERGENCY DISCONNECT". This emergency disconnect will allow first responders to quickly and safely remove all power from a dwelling unit in an emergency.

Together with new requirements for readily accessible emergency disconnecting means in one- and two-family dwelling units for services in section 230.85, generators in 445.18(D), energy storage systems in 706.15(A) and in wind electric systems in 694.22(C)(1), these requirements will provide first responders with the ability to quickly and safely remove power from dwelling units during an emergency.

FR: 8089
SR: 7721

Notification, DC Disconnect Methods

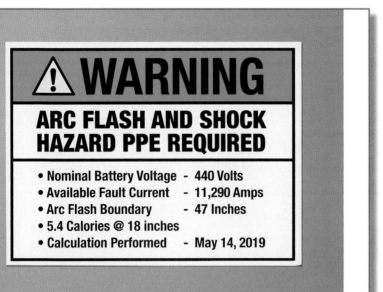

Significance of the Change

Section 480.7 provides requirements for *DC Disconnect Methods*. New first-level subdivision 480.7(F) *Notification* requires that the disconnecting means be legibly marked in the field. A label is required and must be of sufficient durability to withstand the environment. The required information is modified to include an arc flash label in accordance with the acceptable industry practice. The label requirements are: (1) nominal battery voltage, (2) available fault current derived from the stationary battery system (An IN explains that the equipment suppliers can provide available fault current on any battery), (3) an arc flash label in accordance with acceptable industry practice (An IN is added to clarify that *NFPA 70E* is an acceptable industry practice and provides assistance in determining the severity of potential exposure, planning safe work practices, arc flash labeling, and selecting personal protective equipment), (4) the date calculation was performed.

This labeling requirement differs from the arc flash labeling requirements found in 110.16(B). This labeling requirement refers directly to an arc flash label in accordance with acceptable industry practice. This will require labeling in accordance with section 130.5 in *NFPA 70E*. The arc flash label may include incident energy at the working distance or it may be labeled with an arc flash PPE category and the arc flash boundary.

Code Language

480.7(F) Notification… (See *NEC* text) and shall include the following:

(1) Nominal battery voltage

(2) Available fault current derived from the stationary battery system

Informational Note: Battery equipment suppliers can provide information about available fault current on any particular battery model.

(3) An arc flash label in accordance with acceptable industry practice

Informational Note: *NFPA 70E-2018, Standard for Electrical Safety in the Workplace*, … (See *NEC* text)

(4) Date the calculation was performed

Exception: List items (2), (3), and (4) shall not apply to one- and two-family dwellings.

(See NEC for actual text)

Change Summary

- 480.7(F) now requires labeling with an arc flash label applied in accordance with acceptable industry practice.
- A new informational note identifies *NFPA 70E* as the acceptable industry practice.
- The reference to 110.16 is deleted, as it is unnecessary.

FR: 8089
SR: 7721

Identification of Power Sources

Code Language

480.7(G) Identification of Power Sources. Battery systems shall be indicated by 480.7(G)(1) and (G)(2).

(1) Facilities with Utility Services and Battery Systems. Plaques or directories shall be installed in accordance with 705.10 and 712.10.

Exception: This requirement does not apply where a disconnect in 480.7(A) is not required.

(2) Facilities with Stand-Alone Systems. A permanent plaque or directory shall be installed in accordance with 710.10.

(See NEC for actual text)

Courtesy of Tesla Energy

Change Summary

- A new first-level subdivision 480.7(G) is added to require permanent plaques or directories for identification of power sources.
- 480.7(G)(1) applies to *Facilities with Utility Services and Battery Systems.*
- 480.7(G)(2) applies to *Facilities with Stand-Alone Systems.*

Significance of the Change

A new first-level subdivision 480.7(G) is added to require permanent plaques or directories for *Identification of Power Sources*.

480.7(G)(1) applies to facilities with utility services and battery systems and requires compliance with 705.10 and 712.10. This requires a permanent plaque or directory to be installed at each service equipment location or approved readily visible location listing each power source disconnecting means for the building or structure. The plaque or directory must be marked CAUTION MULTIPLE SOURCES OF POWER. An additional permanent directory must list all dc electric power sources. A building supplied by a dc micro grid system must have a permanent plaque or directory installed outside the building at each service equipment location or another approved readily visible location.

480.7(G)(2) applies to facilities with stand-alone systems. This requires a permanent plaque or directory to be installed in accordance with 710.10. This permanent plaque or directory must be installed at a building supplied by a stand-alone system at each service equipment location or approved readily visible location. The plaque must provide the location of each power source disconnecting means for the building or be grouped with other plaques or directories. Where multiple sources supply the building, the plaque or directory shall be marked with the words CAUTION MULTIPLE SOURCES OF POWER.

FR: 8089
SR: 7721

490.21(A)(5) & 490.21(E)

Article 490 Equipment Over 1000 Volts, Nominal
Part II Equipment—Specific Provisions

Retrofit Trip Units and Load Interrupters

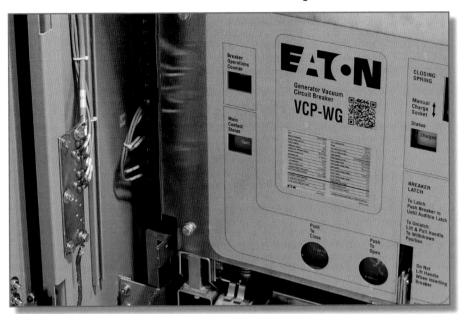

Courtesy of Eaton

Code Language

490.21(A) Circuit Breakers

(5) Retrofit Trip Units. Retrofit trip units shall be listed for use with the specific circuit breaker with which it is installed.

490.21(E) Load Interrupters... (See *NEC* text) Where more than one switch is installed with interconnected load terminals to provide for alternate connection to different supply conductors, each switch shall be provided with a warning sign identifying the presence of more than one source. Each warning sign or label shall comply with 110.21.

(See NEC for actual text)

Significance of the Change

Section 490.21 provides requirements for *Circuit-Interrupting Devices* over 1000 volts. 490.21(A) *Circuit Breakers* includes five-second level subdivisions with requirements for circuit breakers. A new 490.21(A)(5) is added to address *retrofit trip units*. This revision mandates that retrofit trip units for circuit breakers be listed for use with the specific circuit breaker in which it is installed. Circuit breaker trip units are critical to the proper operation of all circuit breakers. Where a retrofit circuit breaker trip unit is not evaluated on a specific type or brand of circuit breaker, there could be significant unintended effects on the clearing times of the device. This can have significant implications with respect to device coordination arc flash studies, and more. Retrofit trip units must be listed for use with the specific circuit breaker on which it is installed.

The requirements of 490.21(E) *Load Interrupters* are modified for clarity. Previous text required that where more than one switch is installed with interconnected load terminals to provide for alternate connection to supply different conductors, each switch had to be provided with a *conspicuous sign identifying this hazard*. The hazard inferred is the presence of more than one source. The second paragraph is modified to make it obvious what the warning sign is all about. Each switch must now be provided with a warning sign identifying the *presence of more than one source*. A new last sentence requires that this warning sign or label comply with 110.21(B).

Change Summary

- New 490.21(A)(5) requires that retrofit trip units be listed for use with the specific circuit breaker in which it is installed.
- The warning sign required in 490.21(E) is modified to identify the hazard, which is the *presence of more than one source*.

FRs: 7827, 7805
SR: 8219

Accessibility of Energized Parts, Control Equipment

Code Language

(B) Control Equipment... (See *NEC* text) shall not be installed in compartments with exposed high-voltage energized parts or high-voltage wiring, unless either of the following conditions is met:

(1) ... (See *NEC* text) access means is interlocked ... (See *NEC* text) when the high-voltage switch is in the closed position or a withdrawable disconnecting means is in the connected position, and

(2) All high-voltage parts or high-voltage wiring in the compartment that remain energized when a fixed mounted high-voltage switch is in the open position or a withdrawable disconnecting means is in the isolating (fully withdrawn) position are protected by insulating or grounded metal barriers to prevent accidental contact with energized high-voltage parts or wiring.

(See NEC for actual text)

Change Summary

- The conditions for accessing control equipment operating 1000 volts normal or less are modified.
- 490.35(B)(1) addresses interlocking with the high-voltage switch or withdrawable disconnecting means.
- 490.35(B)(2) addresses insulating and guarding.

Courtesy of Eaton

Significance of the Change

Section 490.35 provides requirements for *Accessibility of Energized Parts* over 1000 volts. The intent of 490.35(B) *Control Equipment* is to prevent exposure to energized conductors and circuit parts operating at 1000 volts or more, where compartments containing low voltage control equipment are accessed. The existing two conditions are modified for clarity and to more clearly convey the intent of this requirement.

The general rule of 490.35(B) prohibits control equipment, relays, motors, etc. operating at 1000 volts or less from being installed in compartment with high-voltage parts or high voltage wiring, unless the following two conditions are met: (1) access to the control equipment is interlocked with the high-voltage switch or disconnecting means to prevent access when the high-voltage switch is in the closed position, or withdrawable disconnecting means, is in the connected position, and (2) all high-voltage parts or wiring in the compartment that remain energized when fixed switches are in the open position or a withdrawable disconnect is in the isolating position (fully withdrawn), are protected by insulating or grounded metal barriers to prevent accidental contact.

FR: 7811
SR: None

Reconditioned Switchgear

Courtesy of Eaton

Code Language

490.49 Reconditioned Switchgear. Switchgear, or sections of switchgear, within the scope of this article shall be permitted to be reconditioned. The reconditioning process shall use design qualified parts verified under applicable standards and be performed in accordance with any instructions provided by the manufacturer. Reconditioned switchgear shall be listed or field labeled as *reconditioned*, and previously applied listing marks, if any, within the portions reconditioned shall be removed. If equipment has been damaged by fire, products of combustion, or water, it shall be specifically evaluated by its manufacturer or a qualified testing laboratory prior to being returned to service.

(See NEC for actual text)

Significance of the Change

A new Section 490.49 specifically addresses reconditioning of medium voltage switchgear. This new requirement is significantly different from other requirements that address the reconditioning of equipment. The parent text requires that the reconditioning process use *design qualified parts*, verified under applicable standards, and performed in accordance with manufacturer instructions. Reconditioned medium voltage switchgear is required to be listed or field labeled as *reconditioned* and previously applied listing marks within the reconditioned equipment must be removed. Additionally, this requirement mandates that equipment damaged by fire, products of combustion, or water, be specifically evaluated by the manufacturer or a qualified testing laboratory.

Medium voltage switchgear, if reconditioned is likely to be reconditioned in place and a field evaluation can be performed.

See 408.8, which contains requirements for reconditioning of panelboards, switchboards, and switchgear.

The term *reconditioned* means that electromechanical systems, equipment, apparatus, or components are restored to operating conditions. It is imperative to note that some equipment lends itself very well to the reconditioning process and other equipment cannot be reconditioned. This process (reconditioning) is significantly different from normal servicing of equipment that remains within a facility. See the "NEMA Policy on Reconditioned Electrical Equipment" for more information.

Change Summary

- 490.49 provides requirements for reconditioning medium voltage switchgear.
- Reconditioned switchgear must be listed, or field labeled as reconditioned and previous listing marks removed.
- Equipment damaged by fire, products of combustion, or water, must be specifically evaluated by the manufacturer or a qualified testing laboratory.

FR: None
SR: 8222

Chapter 5

Articles 500–590
Special Occupancies

Significant Changes
TO THE NEC 2020

Relocation of Hazardous (Classified) Locations

Code Language

Article 100 Definitions

Part III Hazardous (Classified) Locations. (CMP-14)

Aircraft Paint Hangar. An aircraft hangar constructed for the express purpose of spray/coating/dipping applications and provided with dedicated ventilation supply and exhaust.

Associated Apparatus. Apparatus in which the circuits are not necessarily intrinsically safe themselves but that affects the energy in the intrinsically safe circuits and is relied on to maintain intrinsic safety. Such apparatus is one of the following:

(1) Electrical apparatus that has an alternative type of protection for use in the appropriate hazardous (classified) location

(2) Electrical apparatus not so protected that shall not be used within a hazardous (classified) location... (See *NEC* text)...

(See NEC for actual text)

Change Summary

- All definitions previously located in the .2 sections of the hazardous (classified) locations articles in Chapter 5 have been relocated to Article 100 Part III.
- All Article 100 hazardous (classified) locations definitions in the previous edition of the *NEC* have been incorporated into the new Part III.

Significance of the Change

Action by CMP-14 on FR 7761 relocates all of the hazardous location definitions in the Chapter 5 Hazardous (Classified) Locations articles to a new Part III of Article 100 titled "Hazardous (Classified) Locations." All Article 100 hazardous (classified) locations definitions in the previous edition of the *NEC* have been incorporated into the new Part III. The scope of Article 100 has also been revised to include a new last sentence that indicates Part III of Article 100 contains definitions applicable to hazardous (classified) locations. This revision is a significant enhancement in the usability of the *Code* while reducing confusion. The relocation also brings the *NEC* more in compliance with the *NEC Style Manual* relative to duplicate definitions in Chapter 5 of the *NEC* that previously appeared in more than two of the Chapter 5 articles. The defined words and terms included in Part III remain under the technical responsibility of CMP-14. Locating all of the hazardous location definitions in a new Part III of Article 100 titled "Hazardous (Classified) Locations" improves the usability of the *Code*, eliminates confusion, and enhances safety.

FR: 7789
FCR: 269
SR: Global 8123

Remove the Term "Class I" from Zones 0, 1, and 2

Significance of the Change

The term *Class I* has been removed from preceding Zone 0, Zone 1, and Zone 2 as provided within this article. The term *Class I* has also been removed from preceding Zone 0, Zone 1, and Zone 2 in Articles 511, 513, 514, 515, and 516. This revision aligns the *NEC* with proper terminology used for classification of hazardous locations under the Zone system of classification. As indicated by *Code*-Panel 14, Zone 0, Zone 1, and Zone 2 only apply to flammable gases, vapors, or liquids so the "Class I" prefix is redundant and has been deleted, except for text that is extracted from other documents or to remain consistent throughout an article.

The new informational note in the .3 Sections of each article recognizes that extract material in the *NEC* may continue to contain the term *Class I* in transition for the coming development cycle(s). To meet the requirements in the *NEC Style Manual*, extract material has to remain as it appears in the standard from which the extract is taken. The text has been added to explain the application of what was the "Class I" prefix to Zones 0, 1, and 2. This occurs in each of the articles where Zone 0, 1, and 2 hazardous (classified) locations are mentioned.

Code Language

505.3 Other Articles...(See *NEC* text)...

Where the term "Class I" is used with respect to Zone classifications within other articles of the *Code*, it shall apply to Zone 0, Zone 1, and Zone 2 designations.

Informational Note: The term "Class I" was originally included as a prefix to Zone 0, Zone 1, and Zone 2 locations and references as an identifier for flammable gases, vapors, or liquids to differentiate from Class II and Class III locations. Zone 0, Zone 1, and Zone 2 only apply to flammable gases, vapors, or liquids so the "Class I" prefix is redundant and has been deleted, except for text that is extracted from other documents or to remain consistent throughout an article.

(See NEC for actual text)

Change Summary

- The term *Class I* has been removed from preceding Zone 0, Zone 1, and Zone 2 as provided within this article.
- The term *Class I* has also been removed from preceding Zone 0, Zone 1, and Zone 2 in Articles 511, 513, 514, 515, and 516.
- An informational note in the .3 Sections of each article recognizes that extract material in the *NEC* may continue to contain "Class I" in transition for coming development cycle(s).

FR: 7789

FCR: 269

SR: Global 8123

Normal and Abnormal Operation

Code Language

(1) Class II, Division 1. A Class II, Division 1 location is a location:

(1) In which combustible dust is in the air under normal operating conditions... (See *NEC* text)... or

(2) Where mechanical failure or abnormal operation of machinery or equipment might cause such explosive or ignitible mixtures to be produced... (See *NEC* text)...or

(3) In which Group E combustible dusts may be present in quantities sufficient to be hazardous in normal or abnormal operating conditions.

(See NEC for actual text)

Change Summary

- The words "in normal or abnormal operating conditions" have been added to 500.5(C)(1)(3).
- The revision clarifies that the classification of the area applies regardless of operating condition.
- Equipment and wiring within such locations must meet the applicable rules in Article 502 for Class II locations.

Significance of the Change

List item (3) has been revised to clarify that the classification of the location applies in normal and abnormal operating conditions. The additional text clarifies that due to the potential high hazard of Group E (metallic) dust materials, a Division 2 classification is not warranted or permissible. Substantiation with Public Input 219 indicated that in facilities or processes handling metal dusts, Group E combustible dusts may be present in quantities sufficient to be hazardous due to abnormal operations. This occurs typically tightly around dust-generating machines or tools. In these cases, the requirement should be for the equipment operated in this location to be dust ignitionproof (Group E) during normal operation (Division 2). As an example, there are often situations where Group E combustible dusts are present in quantities sufficient to be hazardous and present around dust collectors used to collect metal dusts produced during sanding of metal frames in automotive body workshops. As Article 500 describes Class II hazardous locations, owners sometimes consider their whole facility as non-hazardous when Group E combustible dusts may be present only directly around dust generating machines or tools and will not use dust ignitionproof equipment in this particular area. This helps clarify where Division 1 Class II Group E location exists and thus requires use of hazardous (classified) location certified equipment and wiring methods.

FR: 7522

SR: NA

REVISION

500.7(K)(1) through (4)
Article 500 Hazardous (Classified) Locations, Classes I, II, III, Divisions 1 & 2
Part NA

Combustible Gas Detection System

Code Language

(K) Combustible Gas Detection System. A combustible gas detection system shall be permitted as a means of protection in industrial establishments with restricted public access and where the conditions of maintenance and supervision ensure that only qualified persons service the installation.

(1) General. ... (See *NEC* Text)...

(2) Inadequate Ventilation. ... (See *NEC* text)...

(3) Interior of a Building or Enclosed Space. ... (See *NEC* text)...

(4) Interior of a Control Panel. ... (See *NEC* text)...

(See NEC for actual text)

Significance of the Change

Section 500.7(K) covers combustible gas detection systems as a protection technique limited to use in industrial establishments with restricted access and under conditions, maintenance, and supervision by qualified persons. Substantiation indicated this section previously did not provide sufficient detail to install and operate the gas detection system as an equipment protection technique for electrical equipment that would not otherwise be suitable for the hazardous location. Section 500.7(K)(1) now prohibits use of temporary wiring methods and both transportable and portable equipment. The gas detectors must only point-type detectors and are permitted to be augmented with open-path (line of sight) type detectors. Additionally, the listing of equipment, installation location, alarm and shutdown criteria, and calibrated frequency must be documented. Item (2) covering inadequate ventilation has been revised to permit classification of the area as Class I, Division 2, provided a combustible gas detection system is used, and also to include alarms when the lower flammable limit has exceeded 40%. Item (3) now includes criteria to consider the interior of any building or enclosed space as unclassified. Item (4) covers the interior of control panels and continues to allow classification of Class I, Division 2 as before, but an alarm (audible or visual or both) shall be activated at gas concentrations that exceed 40% of the lower flammable limit.

Change Summary

- Section 500.7(K) has been expanded to provide additional restrictions on the use of combustible gas detection systems.

- The driving text has been renumbered as list item (1) and includes restrictions on portable and temporary wiring methods, the type of detection equipment to be used, and documentation that is required.

- List items (2) through (4) have been expanded to provide more details on their requirements.

FR: 7723
SR: 8082

Optical Radiation

Code Language

500.7 Protection Techniques. The following protection techniques shall be acceptable for electrical and electronic equipment in hazardous (classified) locations... (See *NEC* text)...

(L) Inherently Safe Optical Radiation "op is." ...(See *NEC* text)...

(M) Protected Optical Radiation "op pr." ...(See *NEC* text)...

(N) Optical System With Interlock "op sh." ...(See *NEC* text)...

(See NEC for actual text)

Change Summary

- Three new protection techniques have been incorporated into Section 500.7.

- Each protection technique is directly related to optical radiation, which can, in some instances, be a source of ignition for explosive atmospheres.

- A reference to ANSI/UL 60079-28 has been added where additional information about protection from optical radiation can be obtained.

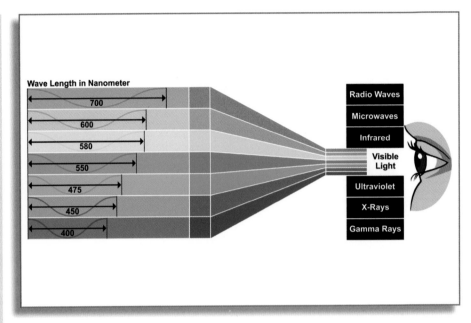

Significance of the Change

Section 500.7 provides a list of protection techniques acceptable for electrical and electronic equipment in hazardous (classified) locations. Three new protection techniques in subdivisions (L) through (N) have been incorporated to address optical radiation as an ignition source.

The Inherently Safe Optical Radiation protection technique shall be permitted for equipment in Class I or II, Division 1 or 2 locations for which the equipment is identified.

The Protected Optical Radiation protection technique shall be permitted for equipment in Class I or II, Division 2 locations for which the equipment is identified.

The Optical System With Interlock protection technique shall be permitted for equipment in Class I or II, Division 1 or 2 locations for which the equipment is identified.

For each of the above protection techniques, the identified class and division depends on the intended explosive atmosphere and the number of faults applied as part of the protection technique evaluation. These types of protection for optical radiation are based on ANSI/UL 60079-28:2017. Optical radiation as a potential "non-electrical" risk of ignition in a hazardous (classified) location is largely generated by electrical means. Although most optical radiation is not a source of ignition, this standard allows determination of those that are a source of ignition.

FR: 7867
SR: None

Equipment Involving Optical Radiation

Significance of the Change

Optical radiation as a potential "non-electrical" risk of ignition in a hazardous (classified) location is largely generated by electrical means. A new subdivision (G) titled "Equipment Involving Optical Radiation" has been added to Section 500.8. This new subdivision indicates that there is a risk of ignition of explosive atmospheres, such as combustible dusts or gases, where exposed to wave forms within the range of 380 nanometers to 10 micrometers. The problems are not with the equipment producing the wave forms, which are typically located outside the hazardous (classified) location; it is when the omitted optical radiation enters such atmospheres. A new informational note provides a valuable reference to a standard having information on types of protection that can be applied to minimize the risk of ignition in explosive atmospheres from optical radiation, see ANSI/UL 60079-28-2017, which is titled "Explosive Atmospheres — Part 28: Protection of Equipment and Transmission Systems Using Optical Radiation." Although most optical radiation is not a source of ignition, this standard facilitates the determination of those that are a source of ignition. The exception in this new subdivision relaxes the requirement for luminaires (fixed, portable, or transportable) and hand lights intended to be supplied by mains (with or without galvanic isolation) or powered by batteries, with any continuous divergent light source, including LEDs.

Code Language

(G) Equipment Involving Optical Radiation. For equipment involving sources of optical radiation (such as laser or LED sources) in the wavelength range from 380 nm to 10 μm, the risk of ignition from optical radiation shall be considered for all electrical parts and circuits that may be exposed to the radiation, both inside and outside the optical equipment… (See *NEC* text)…

Exception: All luminaires (fixed, portable, or transportable) and hand lights intended to be supplied by mains (with or without galvanic isolation) or powered by batteries, with any continuous divergent light source, including LEDs, shall be excluded from this requirement.

(See NEC for actual text)

Change Summary

- A new subdivision (G) titled "Equipment Involving Optical Radiation" has been incorporated into Section 500.8.
- The new rules describe sources of optical radiation such as lasers or LED sources.
- Wavelengths ranging from 380 nanometers (nm) to 10 micrometers (μm), present a risk of ignition from optical radiation and shall be considered for all electrical parts and circuits that may be exposed to it.

FR: 7869
SR: 7918

New Wiring Methods

Code Language

501.10(A)(1) General. ... (See *NEC* text)...

(6) In industrial establishments with restricted public access, where the conditions of maintenance and supervision ensure that only qualified persons service the installation, for applications limited to 600 volts nominal or less, and where the cable is not subject to physical damage, and terminated with fittings listed for the location, Type TC-ER-HL cable... (See *NEC* text)...

(7) In industrial establishments with restricted public access, where the conditions of maintenance and supervision ensure that only qualified persons service the installation, listed Type P cable with metal braid armor, with an overall jacket, terminated with fittings listed for the location, and installed in accordance with 337.10.

(See NEC for actual text)

Change Summary

- Two new list items and wiring methods have been incorporated into Section 501.10(A)(1).
- List item (6) addresses Type TC-ER-HL and (7) addresses Type P Cable.
- Both are limited to use in industrial establishments with other specific restrictions that must be met.

Significance of the Change

Section 501.10(A)(1) provides a list of wiring methods acceptable for use in Class I, Division 1 locations. Two new wiring methods have been added to this section, and each has restrictive conditions that must be met. List item (6) covers Type TC-ER-HL cable if the cable is not subject to physical damage and is terminated in fittings listed for the location. The use is also limited to applications of 600 volts or less, in industrial establishments only, and there must be conditions of maintenance and supervisions that ensure only qualified persons service the installation. A new Informational Note No. 1 references ANSI/UL 2225 Cables and Cable Fittings for Use in hazardous (classified) locations. A new list item (7) addresses a new Type P cable that has similar installation restrictions, and it must be installed in accordance with the requirements in 337.10 a new article covering Type P Cable. Type P cable is also required to be terminated using fittings listed for the location. Type P cable is a fairly robust product and has been used for years in the marine applications and is commonly referred to as shipboard cable. A new informational note references ANSI/UL 1309, which is titled "Marine Shipboard Cable."

FR: 7609
SR: 7962

Equipment Grounding Conductor Plus Drain Wire

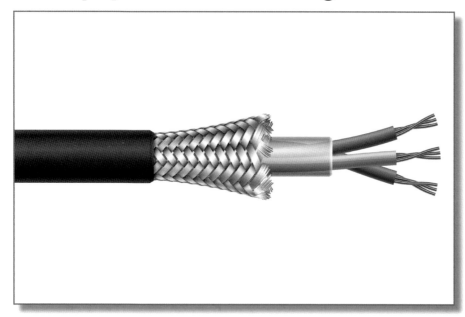

Significance of the Change

The phrase "include an equipment grounding conductor in addition to a drain wire" has been added in list items (3), (4), and (5).

Type PLTC-ER and Type ITC-ER product standards do not specifically require an equipment grounding conductor and furthermore, when present, may allow the drain wire to serve as the equipment grounding conductor. Any exposed run cable of this type should include an equipment grounding conductor for grounding. Substantiation indicated that the drain wire is typically not connected at both ends, thus rendering it ineffective as an equipment grounding conductor. Drain wires should not be used for this purpose. This revision clarifies that for Types PLTC-ER, ITC-ER, and TC-ER, an equipment grounding conductor must be included in the cable just as the TC-ER is required to have. List item (6) in this section has been expanded to include PVC-coated rigid metal conduit (RMC), elbows and fittings, in addition to PVC-coated intermediate metal conduit (IMC), elbows and fittings as wiring methods for locations where corrosion exists, and metal conduit alone does not provide sufficient corrosion resistance.

Code Language

501.10(B)(1) General. ... (See *NEC* text)

(3) Types PLTC and PLTC-ER cable in ... (See *NEC* text)... The cable shall be terminated with listed fittings. Type PLTC-ER cable shall include an equipment grounding conductor in addition to a drain wire that might be present.

(4) Types ITC and ITC-ER cable as permitted in 727.4 and terminated with listed fittings. Type ITC-ER cable shall include an equipment grounding conductor in addition to a drain wire.

(5) Type MC, MV, TC, or TC-ER cable, including installation in cable tray systems. Type TC-ER cable shall include an equipment grounding conductor in addition to a drain wire that might be present...(See *NEC* text)...

(6)...(See *NEC* text)...

(See NEC for actual text)

Change Summary

- The phrase "include an equipment grounding conductor in addition to a drain wire" has been added in items (3), (4), and (5).

- Equipment grounding conductors are required to be connected at both ends; some drain wires are not.

- List item (6) now includes PVC-coated rigid and IMC for use in areas where corrosion is a concern.

FR: 7620
SR: 8007

NEW

Type "P" Cable

Code Language

(9) In industrial establishments with restricted public access, where the conditions of maintenance and supervision ensure that only qualified persons service the installation, listed Type P cable with or without metal braid armor, with an overall jacket, terminated with fittings listed for the location, and installed in accordance with 337.10.

Informational Note No. 1: For information on construction, testing, and marking of Type P cable, see ANSI/UL 1309-2017, Marine Shipboard Cable.

Informational Note No. 2 For information on construction, test, and marking of cable fittings...(See *NEC* text)...

(See NEC for actual text)

Change Summary

- A new list item (9) has been added to 501.10(B)(1) and addresses Type P cables.
- Type P cable is also covered in Chapter 3 in a new Article 337, which includes uses permitted and uses not permitted.
- Type P cable is known as shipboard cable, and informational notes reference ANSI/UL 1309 titled "Marine Shipboard Cable."

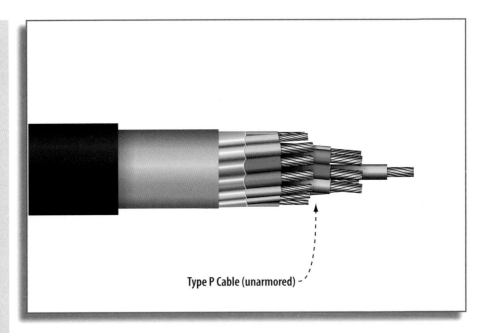

Type P Cable (unarmored)

Significance of the Change

A new list item (9) has been added to 501.10(B)(1) and addresses Type P cables installed as a wiring method in Class I, Division 2 locations under restrictive conditions. In industrial establishments with restricted public access, where the conditions of maintenance and supervision ensure that only qualified persons service the installation, listed Type P cable with or without metal braid armor, with an overall jacket is permitted, and it must be terminated with fittings listed for the location. Type P cable is covered in Chapter 3 in a new Article 337, which includes three parts. Part I has general requirements, Part II includes installation rules, and Part III provides construction specifications for Type P cable. This cable is suitable for use in voltages up to 2,000 volts (armored and unarmored). By definition, Type P cable is a factory assembly of one or more insulated flexible tinned copper conductors, with associated equipment grounding conductors, with or without a braided metallic armor, and with an overall nonmetallic jacket. Type P cables and associated fittings are required to be listed. Type P cable is not permitted to be installed or used where it will be exposed to physical damage. Type P cable is known as shipboard cable. Informational Note No. 1 references ANSI/UL 1309 titled "Marine Shipboard Cable."

FR: 7620
SR: 8007

Type TC-ER-HL and Type P Cables Added

Significance of the Change

Section 502.10(A)(1) provides a list of wiring methods acceptable for use in Class II, Division 1 locations. Two new wiring methods have been added to this section, and each has restrictive conditions that must be met. List item (6) covers Type TC-ER-HL cable, if the cable is not subject to physical damage, and is terminated in fittings listed for the location. The use is also limited to applications of 600 volts or less, in industrial establishments only, and there must be conditions of maintenance and supervisions that ensure only qualified persons service the installation. A new informational note references ANSI/UL 2225 Cables and Cable Fittings for Use in Hazardous (Classified) Locations. A new list item (7) addresses a new Type P cable that has similar installation restrictions, and it must be installed in accordance with the requirements in 337.10. Type P cable is also required to be listed and terminated using fittings listed for the location. Type P cable is a fairly robust product and has been used for years in the marine applications and is commonly referred to as shipboard cable. A new informational note references ANSI/UL 1309, which is titled "Marine Shipboard Cable."

Code Language

502.10(A)(1) General.

(6) In industrial establishments with restricted public access, where the conditions of maintenance and supervision ensure that only qualified persons service the installation, for applications limited to 600 volts nominal or less, and where the cable is not subject to physical damage, and terminated with fittings listed for the location, listed Type TC-ER-HL cable...(See *NEC* text)...

(7) In industrial establishments with restricted public access, where the conditions of maintenance and supervision ensure that only qualified persons service the installation, listed Type P cable with metal braid armor, with an overall jacket, terminated with fittings listed for the location and installed in accordance with Article 337...(See *NEC* text)...

(See NEC for actual text)

Change Summary

- Two new list items and wiring methods have been incorporated into Section 502.10(A)(1).
- List item (6) addresses Type TC-ER-HL, and (7) addresses Type P Cable.
- Both are limited to use in industrial establishments with other specific restrictions that must be met.

FR: 7645
SCR: 37

Type TC-ER-HL and Type P Cables Added

Code Language

502.10(A)(2) Flexible Connections.
...(See *NEC* text)...

(7) In industrial establishments with restricted public access, where the conditions of maintenance and supervision ensure that only qualified persons service the installation, for applications limited to 600 volts nominal or less, and where the cable is not subject to physical damage, and terminated with fittings listed for the location, listed Type TC-ER-HL cable. Type TC-ER-HL cable shall be installed in accordance with 336.10.

(8) In industrial establishments with restricted public access, where the conditions of maintenance and supervision ensure that only qualified persons service the installation, listed Type P cable with metal braid armor, with an overall jacket, terminated with fittings listed for the location, and installed in accordance with 337.10.

(See NEC for actual text)

Change Summary

- Two new list items and wiring methods have been incorporated into Section 502.10(A)(2).
- List item (7) addresses Type TC-ER-HL and (8) addresses Type P Cable.
- Both are limited to use in industrial establishments with other specific restrictions that must be met.

Significance of the Change

Section 502.10(A)(2) provides a list of flexible wiring methods acceptable for use in Class II, Division 1 locations. Two new wiring methods have been added to this section, and each has restrictive conditions that must be met. List item (7) covers Type TC-ER-HL cable if the cable is not subject to physical damage and is terminated in fittings listed for the location. The use is also limited to applications of 600 volts or less, in industrial establishments only, and there must be conditions of maintenance and supervisions that ensure only qualified persons service the installation. A new informational note references ANSI/UL 2225 Cables and Cable Fittings for Use in Hazardous (Classified) Locations. A new list item (8) addresses a new Type P cable that has similar installation restrictions, and it must be installed in accordance with the requirements in 337.10. Type P cable is also required to be listed and terminated using fittings listed for the location. Type P cable is a fairly robust product, and has been used for years in the marine applications, and is commonly referred to as shipboard cable. A new informational note references ANSI/UL 1309, which is titled "Marine Shipboard Cable."

FR: 7727
SR: 7937

Equipment Grounding Conductor and Type "P" Cable

Significance of the Change

The acceptable wiring methods have been reorganized to clarify the requirements. List item (2) was broken up to allow for IMC and RMC threaded or threadless fittings as both can be dusttight and acceptable for the area. EMT or dusttight wireways were moved to item (3). List item (4) was expanded to include the other wiring types shown, and the previous requirements for spacing were eliminated, as Division 2 installations are not subject to dust layering. The phrase "include an equipment grounding conductor in addition to a drain wire" has been added in list items (4), (5), and (6). Types TC-ER, PLTC-ER, and ITC-ER product standards do not specifically require an equipment grounding conductor and furthermore, when present, may allow the drain wire to serve as the equipment grounding conductor. Any exposed run cable of this type should include an equipment grounding conductor for grounding because in some cases, the drain wire is not connected at both ends. List item (7) has been expanded to include PVC-coated RMC and PVC-coated IMC for locations where exposed metal conduit is insufficient for corrosion. Type P cable has been added as a new wiring method permitted for Class II, Division 2 locations.

Code Language

502.10(B)(1) General. ...(See *NEC* text)...

(4) Type MC, MV, TC, or TC-ER cable, including installation in cable tray systems. Type TC-ER cable shall include an equipment grounding conductor in addition to a drain wire that might be present...(See *NEC* text)...

(5) Types PLTC and PLTC-ER cable in accordance with Part II or III of Article 725...(See *NEC* text)...Type PLTC-ER cable shall include an equipment grounding conductor in addition to a drain wire that might be present.

(6) Types ITC and ITC-ER cable as permitted in 727.4 and terminated with listed fittings. Type ITC-ER cable shall include an equipment grounding conductor in addition to a drain wire.

(10) In industrial establishments... (See *NEC* text)...listed Type P cable with or without metal braid armor, with an overall jacket, terminated with listed fittings, and installed in accordance with 337.10.

(See NEC for actual text)

Change Summary

- The phrase "include an equipment grounding conductor in addition to a drain wire" has been added in items (4), (5), and (6).
- List item (7) now includes PVC-coated rigid and IMC for use in areas where corrosion is a concern.
- New list item (10) addresses Type P cable.

FR: 7668
SR: 7943

Connection Through Attachment Plug and Receptacle

Code Language

(5) Connections. To facilitate replacements, process control instruments shall be permitted to be connected through flexible cord, attachment plug, and receptacle, provided that all of the following conditions apply:

(1) Attachment plug and receptacle are listed for use in Class II, Division 2 locations, and listed for use with flexible cords.

Exception No. 1: A Class II, Division 2 listing is not required if the circuit involves only nonincendive field wiring.

Exception No. 2: In industrial establishments where the conditions of maintenance and supervision ensure that only qualified individuals service the installation, the Class II, Division 2 listing is not required when the requirements of list…(See NEC text)…

(See NEC for actual text)

Courtesy of Eaton

Change Summary

- A new list item (5) titled "Connections" has been added to 502.150(B).
- These new requirements mirror those already included in Section 501.105(B)(6).
- The same allowances apply for gaseous hazardous locations and hazardous locations due to combustible dusts.

Significance of the Change

The previous edition of the *NEC* did not include requirements for process control instrumentation in Class II, Division 2 locations using flexible cord, attachment plug, and receptacles. The provisions did exist in Section 501.105(B)(6) allowing similar connections for process connected instrumentation in Class I, Division 2 locations. The hazards in a Class II location are essentially the same as in a Class I location (though it is dust instead of flammable gases or vapors). The new requirements mirror those in 501.105(B)(6) and have been added here to allow for similar types of connection means of process control instrumentation connections installed in a Class II location. The new section allows attachment plugs, and receptacles listed for use in Class II, Division 2 locations, flexible core limited to 3-foot lengths and listed for extra-hard usage, or hard usage type if protection is provided. List item (3) indicates that only necessary receptacles are provided, meaning keep the quantity to the absolute minimum. List item (5) addresses the requirements for interlocking the contacts of the receptacles for connecting and disconnecting operations.

FR: 7858
SR: None

Equipment Grounding Conductor Plus Drain Wire

Significance of the Change

The phrase "include an equipment grounding conductor in addition to a drain wire" has been added in Section 503.10(A) list items (2), (3), and (4). Type PLTC-ER and Type ITC-ER product standards do not specifically require an equipment grounding conductor and furthermore, when present, may allow the drain wire to serve as the equipment grounding conductor. Any exposed run cable of this type should include an equipment grounding conductor for grounding. Substantiation indicated that the drain wire is typically not connected at both ends, thus rendering it ineffective as an equipment grounding conductor. Drain wires should not be used for this purpose. This revision clarifies that for Types PLTC-ER, ITC-ER, and TC-ER, an equipment grounding conductor must be included in the cable just as the TC-ER is required to have. Some drain wires perform only as shielding for wiring systems and are not intended as equipment grounding conductors. They are often left disconnected on one end of the cable or the other to avoid creating a loop. The requirement for including a separate EGC ensures that equipment can be grounded as required and the installation provides an effective ground-fault current path through the EGC.

Code Language

503.10(A)(1) General....(See *NEC* text)...

(2) Types PLTC and PLTC-ER cable in accordance with Part II or III... (See *NEC* text)... Type PLTC-ER cable shall include an equipment grounding conductor in addition to a drain wire that might be present.

(3) Types ITC and ITC-ER cable as permitted in 727.4 and terminated with listed fittings. Type ITC-ER cable shall include an equipment grounding conductor in addition to a drain wire.

(4) Type MV, TC, or TC-ER cable, including installation in cable tray systems. Type TC-ER cable shall include an equipment grounding conductor in addition to a drain wire that might be present. The cable shall be terminated with listed fittings...(See *NEC* text)...

(See NEC for actual text)

Change Summary

- The phrase "include an equipment grounding conductor in addition to a drain wire" has been added in items (2), (3), and (4).
- Equipment grounding conductors are required to be connected at both ends; some drain wires are not.
- The revision ensures that the required EGC is provided so connections at both ends would be made regardless of drain wire connections.

FR: 7681
SR: None

505.8(J)

Article 505 Zone 0, 1, and 2 Locations

Part NA

Protection by Electrical Resistance Trace Heating

Code Language

505.8 Protection Techniques. Acceptable protection techniques for electrical and electronic equipment in hazardous (classified) locations… (See *NEC* text)…

(J) Protection by Electrical Resistance Trace Heating "60079-30-1". This protection technique shall be permitted for electrical resistance trace heating equipment in Zone 1 or Zone 2 for which it is listed.

Informational Note: See Table 505.9(C)(2)(4) for the description of permitted locations for Electrical Resistance Trace Heating "60079-30-1".

(See NEC for actual text)

Change Summary

- A new protection technique has been incorporated into Section 505.8(J).
- This protection technique is identified as "Electrical Resistance Trace Heating."
- Permitted locations for use are provided in Table 505.9(C)(2)(4).
- The informational note references the applicable product standard ANSI/UL 60079-30-1.

Significance of the Change

Section 505.8 provides a list of protection techniques acceptable for electrical and electronic equipment in Zone 0, 1, and 2 hazardous (classified) locations. A new protection technique in subdivision (J) has been incorporated into this section. The title of subdivision (J) is "Protection by Electrical Resistance Trace Heating "60079-30-1." The *NEC Style Manual* typically restricts referencing other standards from requirements in the *NEC*. However, the standard reference is inherent to the title of this protection technique. The Informational Note refers users to Table 505.9(C)(2)(4) for permitted locations for electric resistance trace heating and references the ANSI/UL standard 60079-30-1, a new product standard introduced for the examination, testing, and marking of electrical resistance trace heating. Note that this protection technique is limited for use in the zones system and is not recognized within the division system requirements for hazardous (classified) locations. The term *Electric Resistance Trace Heating* is defined in new Part III of Article 100 as a "Type of Protection for the purpose of producing heat on the principle of electrical resistance and typically composed of one or more metallic conductors and/or an electrically conductive material, suitably electrically insulated and protected."

FR: 7880
SR: 8076

Optical Radiation

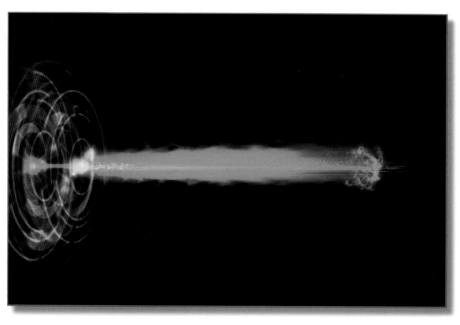

Code Language

506.8 Protection Techniques...(See *NEC* text)...

(K) Inherently Safe Optical Radiation "op is". This protection technique shall be permitted for equipment in Zone 20, 21, or 22 locations for which the equipment is identified.

(L) Protected Optical Radiation "op pr". This protection technique shall be permitted for equipment in Zone 21 or 22 locations for which the equipment is identified.

(M) Optical System with Interlock "op sh". This protection technique shall be permitted for equipment in Zone 20, 21, or 22 locations for which the equipment is identified.

(See NEC for actual text)

Significance of the Change

Section 506.8 provides a list of protection techniques acceptable for electrical and electronic equipment in Zone system hazardous (classified) locations. Three new protection techniques in subdivisions (K) through (L) have been incorporated to address optical radiation as an ignition source.

The Inherently Safe Optical Radiation protection technique shall be permitted for equipment in Zone 20, 21, and 22 locations for which the equipment is identified.

The Protected Optical Radiation protection technique shall be permitted for equipment in Zone 21 or 22 locations for which the equipment is identified.

The Optical System With Interlock protection technique shall be permitted for equipment in Zone 20, 21, or 22 locations for which the equipment is identified.

For each of the above protection techniques, the identified Zone depends on the intended explosive atmosphere and the number of faults applied as part of the protection technique evaluation. These types of protection for optical radiation are based on ANSI/UL 60079-28-2017. Optical radiation as a potential "non-electrical" risk of ignition in a hazardous (classified) location is largely generated by electrical means. Although most optical radiation is not a source of ignition, this standard allows determination of those that are a source of ignition.

Change Summary

- Three new protection techniques have been incorporated into Section 506.8.
- Each protection technique is directly related to optical radiation, which can, in some instances, be a source of ignition for explosive atmospheres.
- A definition of the term *Optical Radiation* has been added to Part III of Article 100.

FR: 7880
SR: 8076

Equipment Involving Optical Radiation

Code Language

(G) Equipment Involving Optical Radiation. For equipment involving sources of optical radiation (such as laser or LED sources) in the wavelength range from 380 nm to 10 µm, the risk of ignition from optical radiation shall be considered for all electrical parts and circuits that may be exposed to the radiation, both...(See *NEC* text)...

Informational Note: For additional information on types of protection that can be applied to minimize the risk of ignition in explosive atmospheres from optical radiation, see ANSI/UL 60079-28-2017, Explosive Atmospheres — Part 28: Protection of Equipment and Transmission Systems Using Optical Radiation.

(See NEC for actual text)

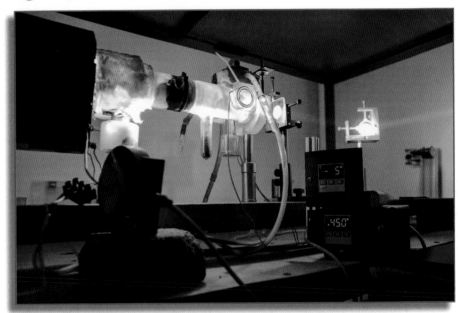

Change Summary

- A new subdivision (G) titled "Equipment Involving Optical Radiation" has been incorporated into Section 506.9.
- It describes sources of optical radiation such as lasers or LED sources.
- Wavelengths ranging from 380 nanometers (nm) to 10 micrometers (µm), present a risk of ignition from optical radiation and shall be considered for all electrical parts and circuits that may be exposed to it.

Significance of the Change

Optical radiation as a potential "non-electrical" risk of ignition in a hazardous (classified) location is largely generated by electrical means. A new subdivision (G) titled "Equipment Involving Optical Radiation" has been added to Section 506.9. This new subdivision indicates that there is a risk of ignition of explosive atmospheres, such as combustible dusts or gases, where exposed to waveforms within the range of 380 nanometers to 10 micrometers. The problems are not with the equipment producing the waveforms, which are typically located outside the hazardous (classified) location; it is when the omitted optical radiation enters such atmospheres. A new informational note provides a valuable reference to a standard having information on types of protection that can be applied to minimize the risk of ignition in explosive atmospheres from optical radiation, see ANSI/UL 60079-28-2017, which is titled "Explosive Atmospheres — Part 28: Protection of Equipment and Transmission Systems Using Optical Radiation." Although most optical radiation is not a source of ignition, this standard facilitates the determination of those that are a source of ignition. The exception in this new subdivision relaxes the requirement for luminaires (fixed, portable, or transportable) and hand lights intended to be supplied by mains (with or without galvanic isolation) or powered by batteries, with any continuous divergent light source, including LEDs.

FR: 7882
SR: 8081

Equipment Grounding Conductor Plus Drain Wire

Significance of the Change

The phrase "include an equipment grounding conductor in addition to a drain wire" has been added in list items (5), (6), and (7) in Section 506.15(C) covering Zone 22 applications. Type PLTC-ER and Type ITC-ER product standards do not specifically require an equipment grounding conductor and furthermore, when present, may allow the drain wire to serve as the equipment grounding conductor. Drain wires cannot serve as equipment grounding conductors. Equipment grounding conductors are required to be connected at both ends; some drain wires are not. Any exposed run cable of this type should include an equipment grounding conductor for grounding of equipment and to provide an effective ground-fault current path in case of a ground fault in the system. Substantiation indicated that the drain wire is typically not connected at both ends, thus rendering it ineffective as an equipment grounding conductor. Drain wires should not ever be used for this purpose. This revision clarifies that for Types PLTC-ER, ITC-ER and TC-ER, an equipment grounding conductor must be included in the cable just as the TC-ER is required to have.

Code Language

506.15(C) Zone 22…(See *NEC* text)…

(5) Type PLTC or PLTC-ER cable in accordance with Part II or III of Article 725, including installation in cable tray systems. The cable shall be terminated with listed fittings. Type PLTC-ER cable shall include an equipment grounding conductor in addition to a drain wire that might be present.

(6) Type ITC or ITC-ER cable as permitted in 727.4 and terminated with listed fittings. Type ITC-ER cable shall include an equipment grounding conductor in addition to a drain wire.

(7) Type MV, TC, or TC-ER cable, including installation in cable tray systems. Type TC-ER cable shall include an equipment grounding conductor in addition to a drain wire that might be present. The cable shall be terminated with listed fittings.

(See NEC for actual text)

Change Summary

- The phrase "include an equipment grounding conductor in addition to a drain wire" has been added in items (5), (6), and (7).
- Drain wires cannot serve as equipment grounding conductors.
- Equipment grounding conductors are required to be connected at both ends; some drain wires are not.

FR: 7707
SR: None

GFCI Required in Accordance with 210.8(B)

Code Language

511.12 Ground-Fault Circuit-Interrupter Protection for Personnel. Ground-fault circuit-interrupter protection for personnel shall be provided as required in 210.8(B).

513.12 Ground-Fault Circuit-Interrupter Protection for Personnel. Ground-fault circuit-interrupter protection for personnel shall be provided as required in 210.8(B).

(See NEC for actual text)

Change Summary

- Sections 511.12 and 513.12 have been revised and simplified to reference Section 210.8(B).
- The general requirements for GFCI protection in other than dwelling units are already covered in 201.8(B).
- There is no longer a need to list the types of equipment connected to circuits and receptacles that are required to provide GFCI protection.

Significance of the Change

The revisions to Sections 511.12 and 513.12 provide alignment with 210.8(B), which requires ground-fault circuit-interrupter (GFCI) protection for personnel. Section 210.8(B) provides GFCI requirements for other than dwelling units. As revised in the 2020 *NEC* this section requires GFCI protection for all 125-volt through 250-volt receptacles supplied by single-phase branch circuits rated 150 volts or less to ground, 50 amperes or less, and all receptacles supplied by 3-phase branch circuits rated 150 volts or less to ground, 100 amperes or less, installed in the locations specified in 210.8(B)(1) through (B)(12). The GFCI requirements found in Article 511 were introduced in the 1987 edition of the *NEC*. Section 210.8(B) was introduced in the 1993 edition of the *NEC*. The GFCI requirements in Articles 511 and 513 predated the requirements of 210.8(B) until the 2017 *NEC*, when they became the same. By simply referencing from these sections back to 210.8(B), these GFCI rules correlate with each other. The other revision is to remove the list of equipment for which GFCI requirements were intended. The revision removes the list and just requires GFCI protection regardless of what equipment is connected.

FRs: 7739, 7742

SR: None

Emergency Electrical Disconnects

Significance of the Change

A new last sentence has been added to Section 514.11. The requirements for emergency controls have been revised to require disconnection of the grounded conductor as it was in the 2014 *NEC*. The revision also clarifies that equipment grounding conductors must remain connected. In the 2017 *NEC*, this section was revised to remove the requirement to include the grounded conductor disconnect requirement for emergency controls. It already exists for maintenance operations, as indicated in Section 514.13. However, there are possibilities that the emergency control specified in 514.11 could, in some cases, also simultaneously serve as both the maintenance disconnect and the emergency control. The revision makes it clear that the emergency control disconnect has to ensure that all conductors, including the grounding conductor, must be disconnected when the emergency control is activated. The revision to this section also clarifies that the equipment grounding conductors of the circuit or system must remain connected. Restoring this requirement back in the *Code* will again provide the enforcers the clear language needed to comply with this requirement, regardless of the type of emergency controls installed.

Code Language

(A) Emergency Electrical Disconnects. Fuel dispensing systems shall be provided with one or more clearly identified emergency shutoff devices or electrical disconnects. Such devices or disconnects shall be installed in approved locations but not less than 6 m (20 ft) or more than 30 m (100 ft) from the fuel dispensing devices that they serve. Emergency shutoff devices or electrical disconnects shall disconnect power to all dispensing devices; to all remote pumps serving the dispensing devices; to all associated power, control, and signal circuits; and to all other electrical equipment...(See *NEC* text)...

[30A:6.7] The emergency shutoff device shall disconnect simultaneously from the source of supply, all conductors of the circuits, including the grounded conductor, if any. Equipment grounding conductors shall remain connected.

(See NEC for actual text)

Change Summary

• A new last sentence has been added to Section 514.11.

• The requirements for emergency controls have been revised to require disconnection of the grounded conductor as in 2014 *NEC*.

• The revision also clarifies that equipment grounding conductors must remain connected.

FR: 7743
SR: None

Categories, Type of Patient Care in Parenthesis

Code Language

517.18 Category 2 (General Care) Spaces. Each patient bed location shall be provided with at least two branch circuits, one from the critical branch and one from the normal system…(See *NEC* text)

517.19 Category 1 (Critical Care) Spaces. Each patient bed location shall be provided with at least two branch circuits…(See *NEC* text)

(See NEC for actual text)

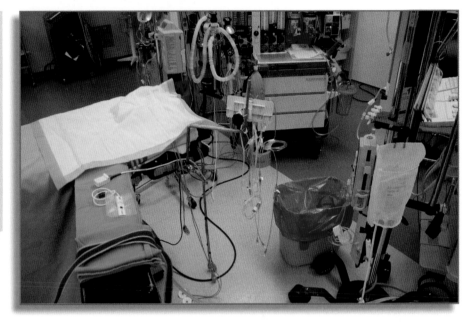

Change Summary

- The changes in terminology relative to levels of patient care and basic care, continue to transition in the 2020 *NEC*.

- The word "Category" now precedes the specific area or type of care, which follows in parenthesis.

- The revision aligns the terminology with that used in *NFPA 99*.

Significance of the Change

In response to the Correlating Committee Public Comment 1813 in the 2017 cycle, and in accordance with 4.3.3 of the *NEC Style Manual* and 2.3.2.11 of the Manual of Style for NFPA Technical Committee Documents, permission was sought and obtained from HEA-FUN to use parenthetic references between specific older and current *NFPA 99* terminology in the *NEC* as a transition. For 2020 *NEC*®, CMP 15 modifies the use of transitional terminology as follows: "Category 1 Space (Critical Care Space)," "Category 2 Space (General Care Space)," "Category 3 Space (Basic Care Space)," and "Category 3 Space (Support Space)." Essentially, this changes the wording sequence for each use of the types of care and spaces addressed in Article 517. This is the second stage of this transition, which moves the category as the primary text and the type of space or care now follows in parenthesis. The transition is occurring in similar fashion to that of the transition from fixtures, and lighting fixtures to luminaires as accomplished in previous *NEC* development cycles. The definitions in 517.2 will continue to provide descriptive information about what constitutes Category 1, 2, 3, and 4 spaces.

FR: 8795

SR: NA

Dental Office and Medical Office

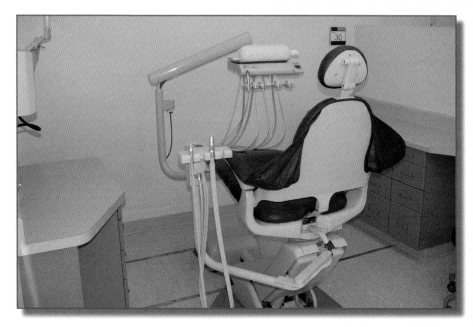

Code Language

517. 2 Definitions

Dental Office. A building or part thereof in which the following occur:

(1) Examinations and minor treatments/procedures are performed under the continuous supervision of a dental professional;

(2) Use of limited to minimal sedation and treatment or procedures that do not render the patient incapable of self-preservation under emergency conditions; and

(3) No overnight stays for patients or 24-hour operations. [**99**:3.3.38]

(See NEC for actual text)

Significance of the Change

A new definition of the term *Dental Office* has been added to Section 517.2. The definition of the term *Medical Office* in the 2017 *NEC* used to be combined with the term *Dental Office*, but now the definition of medical office stands alone. The definition of "Dental Office" is derived from and extracted from *NFPA 99: Health Care Facilities Code*. The specific criteria that must be met for a dental office are outlined within the definition as follows:

(1) Examinations and minor treatments/procedures are performed under the continuous supervision of a dental professional;

(2) Use of limited to minimal sedation and treatment or procedures that do not render the patient incapable of self-preservation under emergency conditions; and

(3) No overnight stays for patients or 24-hour operations.

The term is used in Article 517, and the new definition provides the needed differentiation between the term *Medical Office* and *Dental Office*. Dental offices include care and procedures limited to outpatient services only, no overnight stays for patients or 24-hour operations are provided.

Change Summary

- A new definition of the term *Dental Office* has been added to Section 517.2.

- The definition is derived from and extracted from *NFPA 99*, and it includes care limited to outpatient services, no overnight stays for patients or 24-hour operations.

- The term is used in Article 517, and the new definition provides the needed differentiation between the term *Medical Office* and *Dental Office*.

FRs: 8655, 8656

SR: None

Not Covered Part II Requirements

Code Language

(B) Not Covered. Part II shall not apply to the following:

(3) Areas used exclusively for any of the following purposes:

a. Intramuscular injections (immunizations)

b. Psychiatry and psychotherapy

c. Alternative medicine

d. Optometry

(See NEC for actual text)

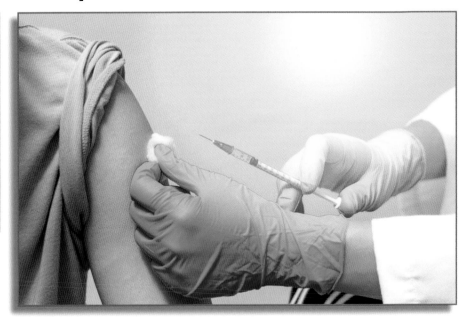

Change Summary

- A new second-level subdivision item (3) has been added to Section 517.10(B).
- This clarifies types of patient care and procedures that do not have to comply with the wiring requirements in Part II of Article 517.
- Designers, installers, and inspectors benefit from this practical relief that conveys what was intended in practice.

Significance of the Change

A new second-level subdivision item (3) has been added to Section 517.10(B), which addresses items not covered. There was a need identified by Public Input 1694 to provide additional clarification as to when the more restrictive wiring methods in Part II of Article 517 are triggered. As an example, some pharmacies are providing flu shots and other vaccinations, and some inspectors require those areas be wired in accordance with Part II of 517. This is overly restrictive, and it is not intended that these types of vaccinations are to be performed in rooms or locations wired in accordance with Article 517 Part II. Where there are no invasive procedures performed, and no electro-medical equipment connected to the body, and so forth, the shock risks are greatly reduced, which reduces the need for redundant equipment grounding paths with branch circuits serving those patient care spaces. This revision clarifies types of patient care and procedures that do not have to comply with the wiring requirements in Part II of Article 517. Engineers, designers, installers, and inspectors benefit from this practical relief that conveys what was intended in practice.

FR: 8662
SR: None

Use of Isolated Grounding Receptacles

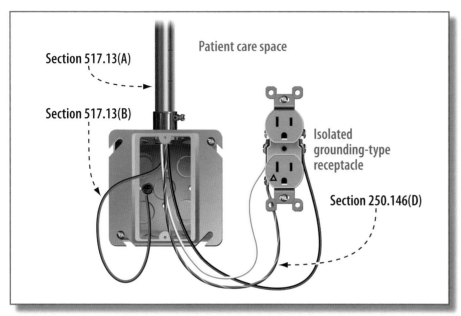

Section 517.13(A)

Section 517.13(B)

Patient care space

Isolated grounding-type receptacle

Section 250.146(D)

Significance of the Change

This section has been revised to clarify the isolated equipment grounding conductor requirements for areas outside of a patient vicinity. The driving text in this section is clear that the use of an isolated ground receptacle must not defeat the grounding systems required in Section 517.13. Section 517.13(A) requires a metallic raceway or cable that qualifies as an equipment grounding conductor for EGC path number one. Section 517.13(B) requires an insulated copper equipment grounding conductor to be included in the metal raceway or cable as EGC path number two. The IG equipment grounding conductor is in addition to the two paths required in 517.13 and must be identified using the color green with one or more yellow stripes. The changes to this section provide a better explanation of the use of isolated receptacles outside the patent care vicinity. It is the clear intent of this section that both grounding methods required in 517.13 be present in wiring methods used for isolated grounding receptacles. In addition, a separate equipment grounding conductor using a green insulation with a yellow stripe shall be connected to the equipment grounding terminal of the isolated grounding receptacle terminal.

Code Language

517.16 Use of Isolated Ground Receptacles. An isolated ground receptacle, if used, shall not defeat the purposes of the safety features of the grounding systems detailed in 517.13. [**99**:6.3.2.2.5(A)]

(A) Inside of a patient vicinity. (See *NEC* text)

(B) Outside of a Patient Care Vicinity. Isolated ground receptacle(s) installed in patient care spaces outside of a patient care vicinity(s) shall comply with 517.16(B)(1) and (B)(2).

(1) The equipment grounding terminals of isolated ground receptacles installed in branch circuits for patient care spaces shall be connected to an insulated equipment grounding conductor in accordance with 250.146(D) installed in a wiring method described in 517.13(A).

(See NEC for actual text)

Change Summary

- This section has been revised to clarify the isolated equipment grounding conductor requirements for areas outside of a patient vicinity.
- The IG equipment grounding conductor is in addition to the two paths required in 517.13 and must be identified using the color green with one or more yellow stripes.

FR: 8670

SR: None

Ground-Fault Protection of Equipment (GFPE)

Code Language

(A) Applicability. The requirements of 517.17 shall apply to buildings or portions of buildings containing health care facilities with Category 1 (critical care) spaces or utilizing electrical life-support equipment, and buildings that provide the required essential utilities or services for the operation of Category 1 (critical care) spaces or electrical life-support equipment.

(D) Testing. When equipment ground-fault protection of equipment is first installed...(See *NEC* text)... This testing shall be conducted by a qualified person(s) using a test process in accordance with the instruction provided with the equipment. A written record of this testing shall be made and shall be available to the authority having jurisdiction.

(See NEC for actual text)

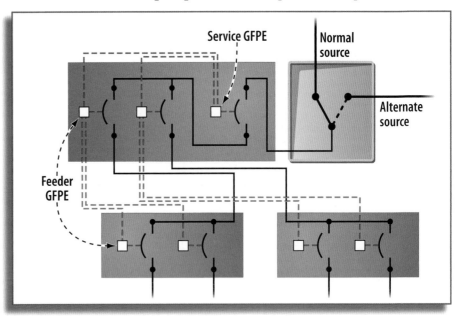

Change Summary

- The words "buildings or portions of buildings containing health care facilities with Category 1 (critical care) spaces" have been added to Subdivision (A).

- The requirements for additional levels of GFPE should not depend on occupancy, but risk factors.

- Subdivision (D) now requires qualified persons to perform the GFPE testing and provide a written record to the AHJ.

Significance of the Change

The words "buildings or portions of buildings containing health care facilities with Category 1 (critical care) spaces" have been added to Subdivision (A). The word "hospitals" has been removed, to provide clarification that the two levels of GFPE are required for any building that contains category 1 (critical care) spaces or utilizing electrical life-support equipment, and buildings that provide the required essential utilities or services for the operation of Category 1 (critical care) spaces or electrical life-support equipment. The requirements for additional levels of GFPE should not depend on occupancy, but risk factors. Subdivision (D) has been revised and expanded to require qualified persons to perform the GFPE testing. The testing has to be in accordance with the GFPE manufacturer's requirements and instructions. This revision provides clarity by performing a test process of primary current injection as required by equipment manufacturers. This correlates with the testing requirements in 230.95(C). The revision also includes written records of the testing to be kept, and they must be made available to the authority having jurisdiction.

FRs: 8681, 8701, 8685
SR: 7879

General Care Spaces – Exception No. 4

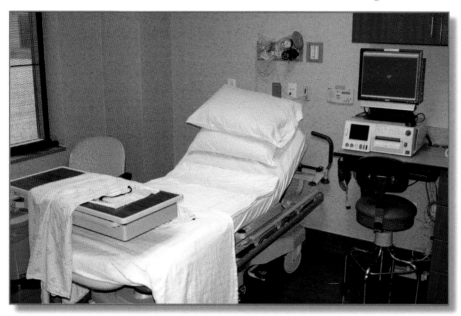

Significance of the Change

Many of the revisions in Article 517 in the 2020 *NEC* development cycle are necessary to correlate with revisions in *NFPA 99: Health Care Facilities Code*. As revised, Section 518.18 is now titled "Category 2 (General Care) Spaces" to align with the Article 517 revisions that will align the *NEC* with *NFPA 99*. A new Exception No. 4 allows circuits served by Type 2 essential electrical systems to be fed by the equipment branch of the EES. *NFPA 99* Section 6.5.2.2.1.2, Type 2 EES consists of the Life Safety and Equipment Branch. *NFPA 99* Section 6.3.2.2.10.2 allows Category 2 Spaces to be served by a Type 1 or Type 2 essential electrical system (EES). Section 6.5.2.2.1.2 indicates that a Type 2 essential electrical system (EES) consists of the Life Safety and Equipment Branches. Therefore, new Exception No. 4 is included to meet the intent without removing the term *critical branch*, which is important for clarity in the *NEC*. Section 517.44(A)(1) permits these types of configurations.

Code Language

517.18 Category 2 (General Care) Spaces.

(A) Patient Bed Location. Each patient bed location shall be supplied by at least two branch circuits, one from the critical branch and one from the normal system. All branch circuits from the normal system shall originate in the same panelboard. The electrical receptacles… (See *NEC* text)…

Exception No. 4: Circuits served by Type 2 essential electrical systems shall be permitted to be fed by the equipment branch of the essential electrical system.

(See NEC for actual text)

Change Summary

- This section is now titled "Category 2 (General Care) Spaces" to align with the Article 517 revisions that align with *NFPA 99*.

- A new Exception No. 4 allows circuits served by Type 2 essential electrical systems to be fed by the equipment branch of the EES.

- *NFPA 99* Section 6.5.2.2.1.2, Type 2 EES consists of the Life Safety and Equipment Branch.

FR: 8688

SR: None

Risk Assessment for Tamper Resistant Receptacles

Code Language

(C) Designated Category 2 (General Care) Pediatric Locations. Receptacles that are located within the patient rooms, bathrooms, playrooms, and activity rooms of pediatric units or spaces with similar risk as determined by the health care facility's governing body by conducting a risk assessment, other than infant nurseries, shall be listed tamper-resistant or shall employ a listed tamper-resistant cover. [99: 6.3.2.2.1(D)]

(See NEC for actual text)

A risk assessment conducted by the governing body of the health care facility determines the requirement for listed tamper-resistant receptacles in Category 2 Pediatric Locations.

Courtesy of Eaton

Change Summary

- A new subdivision (C) titled "Designated Category 2 (General Care) Pediatric Locations," has been added to Section 517.18.
- This revision aligns Article 517 with the same requirements in *NFPA 99*.
- A risk assessment conducted by the governing body of the health care facility determines the requirement for listed tamper-resistant receptacles.

Significance of the Change

A new subdivision (C) titled "Designated Category 2 (General Care) Pediatric Locations" has been added to Section 517.18. This new text addresses how requirements for tamper-resistant receptacles are determined within patient rooms, bathrooms, playrooms, and activity rooms or spaces in health care facilities. This revision aligns Article 517 with the same requirements in *NFPA 99* as indicated by the extract information in brackets following this new subdivision. This rule has two parts, which is rather unique in the *NEC*. First, a risk assessment should be performed by the governing body of the health care facility to determine the requirements for listed tamper-resistant receptacles for other than in infant nurseries. Many such locations are provided in a non-inclusive list within this section. This new tamper-resistant receptacle requirement within Article 517 provides a more continued correlation between other rules in the *NEC* that require tamper-resistant receptacles. The same hazards for unsuspecting children exist in some areas within health care facilities.

FR: 8795 Global
SR: None

GFCI Not Used on Life Support Equipment

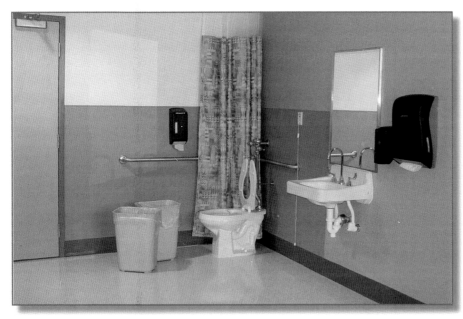

Significance of the Change

This section has been revised to include references to both Category 1 (critical care) and Category 2 (general care) spaces. The revised text also includes text relocated from 210.8(B)(5) Exception No. 2 to clarify the required use of GFCI for receptacles in these locations. Section 517.21 was clarified to differentiate the GFCI protection requirements for patient bed locations equipped with sinks or basins and the GFCI requirements for patient bathrooms and toilet rooms beyond the patient bed location, but still within the overall patient room. The new driving text in this section clarifies that receptacles are not required in these rooms or locations, but if they are provided, GFCI protection shall be provided in accordance with 210.8(B)(1). The new informational note indicates that information on the supply connection of life-support equipment to circuits providing ground-fault circuit-interrupter (GFCI) protection of personnel at outlets, is provided in ANSI/UL 943 Ground-Fault Circuit-Interrupters, Annex E, and also reminds users of installing GFCIs in accordance with 110.3(B), the manufacturers' installation instructions of listed ground-fault circuit interrupters.

Code Language

517.21 Ground-Fault Circuit-Interrupter Protection for Personnel in Category 2 (General Care) and Category 1 (Critical Care) Spaces. Receptacles shall not be required in bathrooms or toilet rooms. [99:6.3.2.2.2(D)] Receptacles located in patient bathrooms and toilet rooms in Category 2 (general care) spaces shall have ground-fault circuit-interrupter protection in accordance with 210.8(B)(1).

Ground-fault circuit-interrupter protection for personnel shall not be required for receptacles installed in those Category 2 (general care) and Category 1 (critical care) spaces where a basin, sink, or other similar plumbing fixture is installed in the patient bed location.

(See NEC for actual text)

Change Summary

- The new driving text indicates that receptacles are not required in these locations.
- This section has been revised to include both Category 1 (critical care) and Category 2 (general care) spaces.
- The new informational note refers to UL 943, Annex E, and mentions GFCI manufacturers' installation instructions.

FR: 8796
SR: 7859

Type 1 Essential Electrical Systems

Code Language

517.29 Type 1 Essential Electrical Systems.

(A) Applicability. The requirements of Part III, 517.29 through 517.35, shall apply to Type 1 essential electrical systems. Type 1 systems shall be required for Category 1 (critical care) spaces. Type 1 systems shall be permitted to serve Category 2 (general care), Category 3 (basic care), and Category 4 (support) spaces.

(B) Type 1 Essential Electrical Systems. Category 1 (critical care) spaces shall be served by a Type 1 essential electrical system. [99:6.4.1] Category 1 spaces shall not be served by a Type 2 EES. [99:6.4.2]

(See NEC for actual text)

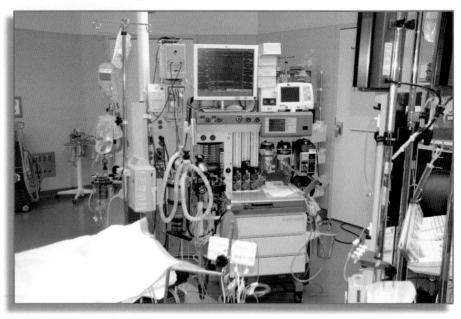

Change Summary

- Section 517.29 and its title were revised to specifically address Type 1 Essential Electrical Systems and to align with *NFPA 99*.
- Type 1 EES are required for Category 1 (critical care) spaces.
- Category 1 (critical care) spaces shall not be served by a Type 2 EES.

Significance of the Change

The title of Section 517.29 was revised to remove the reference to hospitals and include the term *Type 1* preceding the phrase "Essential Electrical System." The requirements in this section apply to all facilities that include Type 1 essential electrical systems for Category 1 (critical care) spaces, not just hospitals. These rules relate to the level of care and risks involved, not the specific occupancy, but the type of care within a given occupancy. This section was also revised to indicate that Type 1 essential electrical systems are permitted to serve Category 2 (general care), Category 3 (basic care) and Category 4 (support) spaces in a health care facility. The revisions to this section correlate with similar provisions in *NFPA 99: Health Care Facilities Code*. Subdivision (B) has been expanded to indicate that Category 1 (critical care) spaces are not permitted to be served by a Type 2 essential electrical systems. Specific references to the appropriate sections in *NFPA 99* are included in the bracketed text to meet Section 4.3.2.3 of the *NEC Style Manual*.

FR: 8714
SR: 7922

Types of Power Sources

Code Language

517.30 Sources of Power

(A) Two Independent Power Sources...(See *NEC* text)...

(B) Types of Power Sources...(See *NEC* text)...

(1) Generating Units...(See *NEC* text)...

(2) Fuel Cell Systems...(See *NEC* text)...

(3) Battery Systems. Battery systems shall be permitted to serve as the alternate source for all or part of an essential electrical system.

Informational Note: For information on installation of battery systems, see NFPA 111-2016, Standard on Stored Electrical Energy Emergency and Standby Power Systems.

(See NEC for actual text)

Significance of the Change

Section 517.30(A) requires a minimum of two independent sources of power for the essential electrical system (EES). One source generally supplies the entire electrical system, and any one of three types of alternate sources supply the essential electrical system if the normal power is interrupted. A new item (3) titled "Batteries" has been added to 517.30(B). Battery systems permitted to supply a portion of, or all of a Type 1 essential electrical system (EES). Battery technologies are improving all the time and are now considered acceptable as an alternate power source in an essential electrical system of a health care facility. Battery systems are an accepted Essential Electrical System Source in accordance with *NFPA 99* 6.7.1.3 and *NFPA 111*. The result is that generators, fuel cell systems, and batteries are acceptable as alternate power sources. The requirement for fuel cell systems being listed for emergency use has been deleted because listing requirements are already covered in *NFPA 853*. Article 517 does not utilize the term emergency to align with terminology used in *NFPA 99* and to reduce the misapplication of some Article 700 requirements. The new informational note references *NFPA 111: Standard on Stored Electrical Energy Emergency and Standby Power Systems*.

Change Summary

- A new item (3) titled "Batteries" has been added to 517.30(B).

- Battery systems permitted to supply a portion of, or all of a Type 1 essential electrical system (EES).

- The revision aligns with *NFPA 99* and *NFPA 111*, and a new informational note provides a reference to *NFPA 111*.

FR: 8719

SR: NA

Mechanical Protection of the Essential Electrical System

Code Language

(C) Wiring Requirements.

(1) Separation from Other Circuits…(See *NEC* text)…

(a) Raceways, cables, or enclosures of the life safety and critical branch shall be readily identified as a component of the essential electrical system (EES). Boxes and enclosures (including transfer switches, generators, and power panels) shall be field- or factory-marked and identified as a component of the EES. Raceways…(See *NEC* text)…at intervals not to exceed 7.6 m (25 ft).

(2) Isolated Power Systems…(See *NEC* text)…

(3) Mechanical Protection of the Essential Electrical System

(3) Listed flexible metal raceways and listed metal sheathed cable assemblies in any of the following:

(a) Where used…(See *NEC* text)…

(f) Luminaires installed in ceiling structures

(See NEC for actual text)

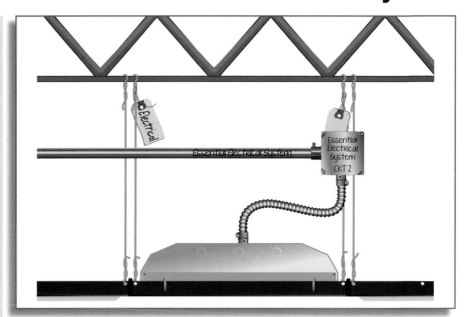

Change Summary

- Item (1)(a) provides an identification requirement for raceways, cables, and enclosures of an essential electrical system at intervals not exceeding 25 feet.
- Item (3)(f) has been revised and broadened to all types of ceiling structures.
- Luminaires are now permitted to be wired using flexible metal raceways or metal-sheathed cable assemblies.

Significance of the Change

Item (1)(a) is new and provides an identification requirement for raceways, cables, and enclosures of an essential electrical system at intervals not exceeding 25 feet. Identification of emergency circuits already exists in Section 700.10(A) for emergency systems, and now is applicable in Article 517 for the essential electrical system. Various methods are permitted to be used for the identification as long as the marked component is readily identifiable as a component of the essential electrical system. The identification is permitted to be factory- or field-applied.

Section 517.31(C)(3) provides specific wiring requirements for the life safety and critical branches of the essential electrical system. The main objective in this section is to require mechanical protection for the wiring of the essential electrical system (EES). Item (3)(f) has been revised and broadened in application to all types of ceiling structures. Luminaires in any ceiling structure are now permitted to be wired using flexible metal raceways and metal-sheathed cable assemblies. The revision relaxes the previous requirement for providing mechanical protection by wiring using non-flexible metal raceways.

FRs: 8772, 8748

SR: 7957

Relocation of 517.35(C) to 517.43(G)

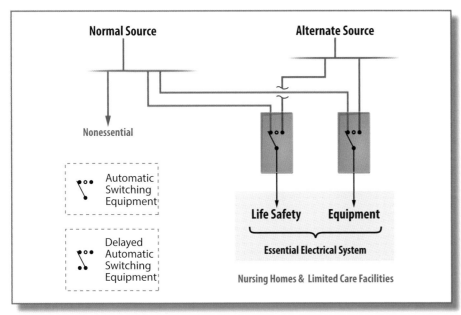

Nursing Homes & Limited Care Facilities

Code Language

517.43 Automatic Connection to Life Safety and Equipment Branch...(See *NEC* text)...

(A) through (F)...(See *NEC* text)...

(G) AC Equipment for Non-delayed Automatic Connection. Generator accessories, including, but not limited to, the transfer fuel pump, electrically operated louvers, and other generator accessories essential for generator operation shall be arranged for automatic connection to the alternate power source. [**99**:6.7.6.2.1.6(C)]

(See NEC for actual text)

Significance of the Change

Section 517.35(C) has been relocated to Section 517.43(G). The text in this section covered Type 2 essential electrical systems (EES), not Type 1 EES, which is covered in 517.35(C) and thus was not located in the proper section of Article 517. Sections 517.40 through 43 provide requirements specific to Type 2 essential electrical systems for nursing homes and limited care facilities. Type 2 essential electrical systems are less robust than Type 1. The revision will reduce possible misapplication of loads being connected to Type 2 EES. The relocation solves two problems (1) The material contained in this rule is extracted from *NFPA 99*. Section 6.5 of *NFPA 99* addresses only Type 2 EES, but as previously written in the 2017 *NEC*, Section 517.35 addressed Type 1 EES. (2) The text in former 517.35(C) was in conflict with section 517.33(F), which directs that generator accessories and other like equipment be connected to the Life Safety Branch of the Essential Electrical System, rather than the Equipment Branch of the EES. Relocating subdivision (C) to 517.43(G) resolves the previous conflict. This section is also extracted directly from *NFPA 99* and includes the reference to *NFPA 99* in bracketed text.

Change Summary

- Section 517.35(C) has been relocated to Section 517.43(G).

- The text in this section addresses Type 2 essential electrical systems (EES), not Type 1 EES, which is covered in 517.35(C).

- This section is extracted from *NFPA 99* and includes the reference to *NFPA 99* in bracketed text.

FR: 8777
SR: None

REVISION

Delayed Automatic/Manual Connection Equipment Branch

Code Language

(B) Delayed Automatic or Manual Connection to the Equipment Branch. The following equipment shall be permitted to be connected...(See *NEC* text)...

(3) Optional Connections to the Equipment Branch. Additional illumination, receptacles, and equipment shall be permitted to be connected only to the critical branch.

(4) Multiple Systems. Where one switch serves multiple systems as permitted in 517.43, transfer for all loads shall be non-delayed automatic.

[99:6.7.6.2.1.6(E)]

Informational Note: For elevator cab lighting, control, signal system requirements, see 517.43(G). [99:A.6.7.6.2.1.6(E)(2)]

(See NEC for actual text)

Change Summary

- This section has been revised by removing the term *critical equipment branch*.

- This section has been rearranged into a list format to meet the requirements of the *NEC Style Manual*.

- Where only one transfer switch serves multiple systems, the transfer of all loads must be non-delayed and automatic.

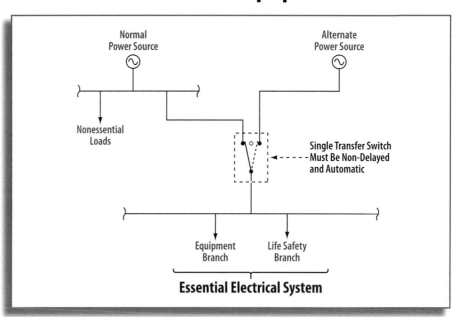

Significance of the Change

Section 517.44(B) provides a list of equipment that are permitted to be connected to the equipment branch by either a delayed manual or delayed automatic connection. The loads include, but are not limited to, equipment that provides heat to general patient rooms, temporary operation of elevator service, additional illumination, receptacles, and other equipment. This section has been revised by removing the term *critical equipment branch* and arranging it in a list format to meet the requirements of the *NEC Style Manual*, Section 2.1.5.1. The term *critical equipment branch* is not used anywhere within Article 517 and is an apparent editorial error in the 2017 *NEC*. As revised, this section now clearly indicates which optional loads are permitted to be connected by delayed or automatic means. List item (4) is new and indicates that where only one transfer switch serves multiple systems, the transfer of all loads must be non-delayed and automatic. This revision provides needed clarification about the use of a single transfer switch, as permitted in 517.43. As restructured, the last sentence in (4) dealing with elevator cab loads has been relocated into a new informational note following this section.

FR: 8780
SR: None

Illumination

Code Language

518.6 Illumination. Illumination shall be provided for all working spaces about fixed service equipment, switchboards, switchgear, panelboards, or motor control centers installed outdoors that serve assembly occupancies. Control by automatic means only shall not be permitted. Additional lighting outlets shall not be required where the workspace is illuminated by an adjacent light source.

(See NEC for actual text)

Significance of the Change

This revision adds a new section 518.6 *Illumination*. This will require that illumination be provided for all working spaces of service equipment, switchboards, switchgear, panelboards, or motor control centers that supply assembly occupancies and are installed outdoors. The existing requirement in 110.26(D) requires illumination to be provided for all working spaces about service equipment, switchboards, switchgear, panelboards, or motor control centers installed indoors.

It is very common for assembly occupancies to locate service equipment and distribution equipment outdoors. Due to the nature and the types of assembly occupancy venues referenced in 518.2(A), building designers very often locate all electrical equipment outdoors. In accordance with 518.1, the scope of Article 518, an assembly occupancy is the gathering together of 100 or more persons for purposes such as deliberation, worship, entertainment, eating, drinking, amusement, awaiting transportation, or similar purposes. This new requirement is safety driven and recognizes the need for quick access to the service and distribution equipment supplying an assembly occupancy. Ensuring that all outdoor electrical equipment requiring working space is illuminated, will assist installers and maintenance personnel that may need quick illuminated access to the equipment.

Change Summary

- New 518.6 requires illumination for all equipment working spaces installed outdoors.
- Assembly occupancies typically locate service and distribution equipment outdoors.
- 110.26(D) requires the illumination of working spaces installed indoors only.

FR: 8823
SR: None

Wiring Method Protection and GFCI Protection

Code Language

525.20(G) Protection. Flexible cords or cables accessible to the public… (See *NEC* text) minimize the tripping hazard and … (See *NEC* text) covered with nonconductive matting secured to the walkway surface or protected with another approved cable protection method, provided that the matting or other protection method does not constitute a greater tripping hazard than the uncovered cables. Burying cables shall be permitted… (See *NEC* text)

525.23 GFCI Protection.

(A) Where GFCI Protection Is Required. In addition to the requirements of 210.8(B)… (See *NEC* text)

(See NEC for actual text)

Change Summary

- Where nonconductive matting is used to protect cables, it must be secured to the walkway surface.
- The requirements of 210.8(B) apply unless specifically modified.
- 525.23(B) and (C) specifically modify the general GFCI requirements in 210.8(B).

FR: 8844
SRs: 7987, 7993

Significance of the Change

Section 525.20 provides requirements for wiring methods installed to supply carnivals, circuses, fairs, and similar events. Wiring methods accessible to the public must be arranged to minimize tripping hazards. Previous text required nonconductive matting provided the matting did not create a greater tripping hazard than the uncovered cables. This requirement is revised to require nonconductive matting to be secured to the walkway surface. It is permitted to bury the cables, and the requirements of 300.5 do not apply.

Article 525 is located in Chapter 5, which is titled "Special Occupancies." Section 90.3 explains how this *Code* is arranged. Requirements in Chapter 5 supplement or modify requirements in Chapters 1 through 7. This has led to significant confusion with respect to GFCI requirements that are located in other than Section 210.8. The requirements for GFCI protection in Section 210.8 are the general requirements, and they apply globally unless they are specifically supplemented or modified in another article. A global effort to provide clarity resulted in revisions in 525.23(A), which provides requirements for where GFCI protection is required in a carnival, circus, fair, or similar event. The new text clearly explains that the requirements of 525.23(A) are in addition to the requirements of 210.8(B) for other than dwelling units. 525.23(B) permits receptacles that are not accessible from grade level and that only facilitate quick disconnect to be installed without GFCI protection. Egress lighting is not permitted to be protected by a GFCI in 525.23(C). All other outdoor receptacles must comply with 210.8(B).

Manufactured Buildings and Relocatable Structures

Significance of the Change

The title of Article 545 is modified to include *relocatable structures*. These revisions are based upon previous requirements in 550.4(A), which addressed mobile homes not intended as dwelling units. Article 550 is titled mobile homes, manufactured homes, and mobile home parks. The definition of mobile home clarifies that it is factory assembled, transportable, built on a permanent chassis, and designed to be used as a dwelling unit without a permanent foundation. The key difference between a relocatable structure and a mobile home is that a mobile home is a dwelling unit and the relocatable structure is not.

The scope of this article in 545.1 is modified to include relocatable structures and the conductors that connect relocatable structures to a supply of electricity. For clarity, a new definition is added to 545.2 to define *relocatable structure*. This new definition clarifies that a relocatable structure is a factory-assembled structure or structures transportable in one or more sections that are built on a permanent chassis. These relocatable structures are designed to be used as other than dwelling units and without permanent foundations. A new informational note following the definition provides examples of relocatable structures. These include, but are not limited to, jobsite trailers, training facilities, shower facilities and restrooms, dressing rooms, and more.

Code Language

545.1 Scope. This article covers... (See *NEC* text) relocatable structures, and the conductors that connect relocatable structures to a supply of electricity.

545.2 Definitions.

Relocatable Structure. A factory-assembled structure or structures transportable in one or more sections that are built on a permanent chassis and designed to be used as other than a dwelling unit without a permanent foundation.

IN: Examples ... (See *NEC* text) sleeping purposes only, contractors and other on-site offices, construction job dormitories, studio dressing rooms, banks, clinics, stores, shower facilities and restrooms, training centers, or for the display or demonstration of merchandise or machines.

(See NEC for actual text)

Change Summary

- The title of Article 545 is revised to *Manufactured Buildings and Relocatable Structures*.

- New requirements are added to address the previous requirements of 550.4(A), which addressed mobile homes not intended as dwelling units.

- A new definition is added in 545.2 for *Relocatable Structures*.

FR: 8993
SR: 7518

Article 545, Part II Relocatable Structures

Change Summary

- A new Part II is added to Article 545 for requirements related to *relocatable structures*.

- Requirements for mobile homes not intended as dwelling units are deleted in 550.4(A).

- Six new sections are added with requirements for relocatable structures.

FR: 8993

SRs: 7519, 7529, 7541, 7548, 7550, 7559, 7561, 7570, 7533, 7524

Significance of the Change

A new Part II is added to Article 545 to provide requirements for relocatable structures. Relocatable structures must comply with the requirements of Part II and any applicable sections in Part I of Article 545. Feeders supplying relocatable structures must include four insulated color-coded conductors, one of which is the EGC. The EGC is permitted to be bare when part of a cable assembly. In general, each relocatable structure is limited to a single feeder. Where two or more relocatable structures are structurally connected, and there is a factory-installed panelboard in each structure, each panelboard is permitted to be supplied by a separate feeder. The identification requirements in 225.37 do not apply to relocatable structures, provided the requirements of 545.22(C) are met. 545.22(D) permits the bonding conductor required in 545.26 to serve as a grounding electrode conductor tap where a common grounding electrode conductor arrangement is installed for two or more relocatable structures that are connected to form a single unit. Each relocatable structure must have a single disconnecting means provided in a readily accessible location. Panelboards installed in relocatable structures must be readily accessible. Where two or more relocatable structures are structurally connected to form a single unit, it is permitted to install a single intersystem bonding termination in accordance with 250.94, provided the requirements of 545.27 are met. In addition to the requirements in 210.8(B), compartments accessible from outside the relocatable structure must have GFCI protection for personnel.

GFCI Protection of Receptacles

Significance of the Change

Both Article 547 and 550 are located in Chapter 5, which is titled "Special Occupancies." Section 90.3 explains how this *Code* is arranged. Requirements in Chapter 5 supplement or modify requirements in Chapters 1 through 7. This has led to significant confusion with respect to GFCI requirements that are located in other than Section 210.8. The requirements for GFCI protection in Section 210.8 are the general requirements, and they apply globally unless they are specifically supplemented or modified in another article. A global effort to provide clarity resulted in revisions in 547.5(G) and 550.13(B) with respect to the general GFCI requirements in 210.8. The general rule in each of these requirements is that GFCI protection must be provided as required in 210.8. Each of these requirements [547.5(G) and 550.13(B)] contain modifications in a list format that permits other than 125-volt, 15- and 20- amp receptacles to be installed without GFCI protection.

547.5(G) permits other than 125-volt,15- and 20-amp receptacles to be installed without GFCI protection in areas within the equipotential plane, outdoors, damp or wet locations, and dirt confinement areas for livestock. 550.13(B) permits other than 125-volt,15- and 20-amp receptacles to be installed without GFCI protection in compartments accessible from outside the unit, bathrooms (includes receptacles in luminaires), kitchens where receptacles serve the countertop surface, receptacles within 6 feet of sinks and dishwashers. Note the GFCI requirements of 422.5 for appliances apply. See Section 90.3 for *Code* arrangement. Receptacle requirements in 550.32(E) are revised in a similar manner.

Code Language

547.5(G) Receptacles

550.13(B) GFCIs. Ground-fault circuit-interrupter protection shall be provided as required in 210.8(A). GFCI protection shall not be required for other than 125-volt, 15- and 20-ampere receptacles installed … (See *NEC* text) following areas:

List items in 547.5(G)

(1) Areas having an equipotential plane

(2) Outdoors

(3) Damp or wet locations

(4) Dirt confinement areas for livestock

List items in 550.13(B)

(1) Compartment accessible from outside the unit

(2) Bathrooms, including receptacles in luminaires

(3) Kitchens… (See *NEC* text) receptacles… (See *NEC* text) countertop surfaces

(4) Sinks… (See *NEC* text) within 6 ft

(5) Dishwashers

(See NEC for actual text)

Change Summary

- GFCI requirements in Articles 547 and 550 are modified for clarity.

- The general requirements of 210.8(A) and (B) (where applicable) apply unless modified.

- Modifications to the general rules for GFCI protection are provided in list format.

FR: 8169
CC: 7654, 7634
SCR: 28, 29

551.40(D)

NEW

Reverse Polarity Device

Code Language

551.40(D) Reverse Polarity Device. A reverse polarity indicating device that provides a continuous visible or audible signal shall be installed in the recreational vehicle in accordance with the installation instructions and shall respond to the reversal of the ungrounded and the grounded conductors in the 120-volt ac system.

(See NEC for actual text)

Change Summary

- New 551.40(D) requires a reverse polarity device be installed in recreational vehicles.
- Reverse polarity is where the ungrounded (hot) conductor is swapped with the grounded (neutral) conductor.
- The reverse polarity device must respond to the reversal of the ungrounded and grounded conductors in the 120-volt ac system.

Significance of the Change

A new first-level subdivision 551.40(D) is added to require a reverse polarity device be installed in recreational vehicles. Reverse polarity is where the ungrounded (hot) conductor is swapped with the grounded (neutral) conductor. This can result in potentially serious shock scenarios. Historical data proves the reverse polarity is a known cause of shock incidents involving recreational vehicles. While it is unlikely that reverse polarity exists at receptacle outlets for recreational vehicles in an RV campground, it is possible. Recreational vehicles are often energized (plugged in) in locations other than an RV campground. When and where a recreational vehicle is plugged in, the potential for reverse polarity exists. The potential for reverse polarity increases when owners of recreational vehicles use non-listed adapters that can be inserted backward creating a reverse polarity situation.

This new requirement mandates that a reverse polarity indicating device that provides a continuous visible or audible signal be installed in accordance with the installation instructions. The reverse polarity device must respond to the reversal of the ungrounded and grounded conductors in the 120-volt ac system.

FR: 8404
SR: None

GFCI Protection and Tamper Resistant Receptacles

Code Language

551.71 Type Receptacles Provided.

(A) 20-Ampere. Every recreational vehicle site with electrical supply shall be equipped with recreational vehicle site supply equipment with at least one 20-ampere,125-volt weather-resistant receptacle.. This receptacle, when used in recreational vehicle site electrical equipment, shall not be required to be tamper-resistant in accordance with 406.12.

(F) GFCI Protection. (Revisions failed due to action of the floor of the NFPA Technical Session)

(See NEC for actual text)

Significance of the Change

Part VI of Article 551 contains requirements for recreational vehicle parks. Section 551.71 provides requirements for the type of receptacles that must be provided in RV site equipment. 551.71 requires all recreational vehicle sites with electrical supply to include at least one 20-amp, 125-volt receptacle. New text is added to require that this 20-amp, 125-volt receptacle be of the weather-resistant type. While this text is new, the existing requirements in 406.9 mandate that all receptacles installed in damp or wet locations be of the weather-resistant type. New text is added in 551.71(A) permitting the required 20-amp, 125-volt receptacle to not be tamper-resistant in accordance with 406.12.

Requirements for GFCI protection in RV site equipment in 551.71(F) were significantly modified for clarity during the revision process. However, due to action of the floor of the NFPA Technical Session, these revisions failed and reverted back to previous text in the 2017 *NEC*.

It is extremely likely that a Tentative Interim Amendment (TIA) will revise this requirement as follows:

551.71(F) GFCI Protection. Ground-fault circuit-interrupter protection shall be provided as required in 210.8(B). GFCI protection shall not be required for other than 125-volt, 15- and 20-ampere receptacles used in the recreational vehicle site equipment.

Change Summary

- Requirements for receptacle types in RV Parks are modified.
- The required 20-amp, 125-volt receptacle must be weather resistant and is not required to be tamper-resistant.
- GFCI protection revisions failed during the last stage of the process. Expect to see a TIA significantly revising 551.71(F).

FR: 8475

CC: 7659

SCR: 30

Connected Devices, Connection to RV Site Equipment

Code Language

551.72 Distribution System.

(E) Connected Devices. The use of autotransformers shall not be permitted. The use of listed surge protective devices shall be permitted.

(F) Connection to Recreational Vehicle Site Equipment. Each recreational vehicle shall be powered by only one 30-ampere or one 50-ampere external power supply cord.

Informational Note: The requirement in 551.72(F) does not preclude the use of the 15- or 20-ampere receptacle convenience outlet on the recreational vehicle supply equipment.

(See NEC for actual text)

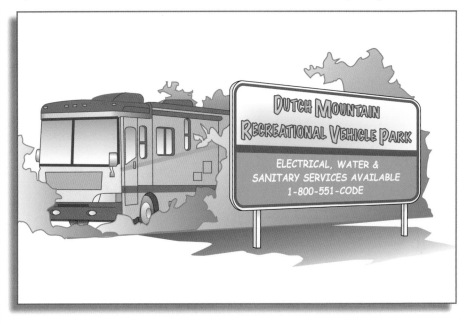

Change Summary

- New 551.71(E) prohibits the use of autotransformers and permits surge protective devices.

- New 551.71(F) requires that each recreational vehicle be powered by only one 30-amp or one 50-amp external power cord.

Significance of the Change

New first-level subdivision 551.71(E) provides requirements for connected devices. This revision specifically prohibits the use of autotransformers, such as a buck-boost type transformer. Substantiation provided to support this revision claims that where autotransformers are used severe additional stress is applied to the surrounding electrical infrastructure. RV park operators have reported that low-voltage conditions typically exist when surrounding RV sites use these "add on devices." Additionally, this new subdivision permits the use of listed surge protective devices. While this text may be new in Article 551 *RV Parks and Recreational Vehicles*, they have always been permitted to use listed surge protective devices.

New first-level subdivision 551.71(F) now requires each recreational vehicle to be powered by only one 30-amp or one 50-amp external power supply cord. This will prevent modified recreational vehicles from plugging into more than one source. Substantiation provided to support this revision explained that many large recreational vehicles are modified by their owners to require two 50-amp circuits. Supplying a recreational vehicle from more than one source is a dangerous practice. This new requirement now limits each recreational vehicle to one power source, meaning it can be supplied by only one 30-amp or one 50-amp external power supply cord.

FRs: 8414, 8472
SR: 7681

Floating Building Requirements Relocated

Code Language

~~Article 553 Floating Buildings~~

Article 555 Marinas, Boatyards, Floating Buildings, and Commercial and Noncommercial Docking Facilities

555.1 Scope... (See *NEC* text) floating buildings... (See *NEC* text)

Informational Note No. 2: Where boats, floating buildings, docks, and similar structures are connected to an electrical source or a supply of electricity, hazardous voltages and currents may create serious safety concerns.

Informational Note No. 3: Text that is followed by a reference in brackets has been extracted from NFPA 303-2016, *Fire Protection Standard for Marinas and Boatyards*, and NFPA 307-2016, *Standard for the Construction and Fire Protection of Marine Terminals, Piers, and Wharves*... (See *NEC* text)

(See NEC for actual text)

Significance of the Change

Article 553 *Floating Buildings* is deleted, and requirements for floating buildings are relocated into Article 555. In order to logically separate requirements and for clarity, Article 555 has been separated into three parts: Part I General, Part II Marinas, Boatyards and Docking Facilities, and Part III Floating Buildings. The title of Article 555 now includes *floating buildings*. The previous requirements (ten sections in Article 553) for floating buildings now exist in Article 555, Part I General and Part III Floating Buildings. The hazards addressed in Articles 555 and 553 are similar in nature. Previously, there were some overlap requirements between these articles. Combining requirements for floating buildings into Article 555 increases clarity, usability, and ensures consistent application of safety-driven requirements.

Two new informational notes are added to follow 555.1 *Scope*. Informational Note No. 2 explains that where boats, floating buildings, docks, and similar structures are connected to an electrical source or a supply of electricity, hazardous voltages and currents may create serious safety concerns. This new IN addresses all sources of electrical supply. A boat, floating building, dock, or similar structure may be supplied from a service and may also have standby generating capacity. New Informational Note No. 3 explains that some text in Article 555 has been extracted from *NFPA 303* and *NFPA 307*.

Change Summary

- Article 553 is deleted, and existing requirements are merged into Article 555.
- Article 555 is separated into parts for clarity.
- Article 555 is editorially restructured.

FRs: 8978, 8951
FCR: 269
SR: 7694

Definitions

Code Language

555.2 Definitions.

Berth.

Boatyard. A facility used for constructing, repairing, servicing, hauling from the water, storing (on land and in water), and launching of boats. [303:3.3.2]

Bulkhead, Crane, Docking Facility, Floating Building,

Marina. A facility, generally on the waterfront, that stores and services boats in berths, on moorings, and in dry storage or dry stack storage. [303:3.3.12]

Monorail, Mooring,

Shore Power. The electrical equipment required to power a floating vessel including, but not limited to, the receptacle and cords.

Slip, Storage-Dry Stack, Wharf

(See NEC for actual text)

Change Summary

- Twelve new definitions are extracted from *NFPA 303* and *NFPA 307*.
- The definition of *Electrical Datum Plane* is modified for clarity and relocated into Article 100.
- New 555.3 contains requirements for electrical datum plane.

FR: 8952
SR: None
SCR: 77

Significance of the Change

This revision provides clarity by adding new definitions into Article 555. In the first draft stage of this revision, cycle 15, new definitions were extracted from *NFPA 303: The Fire Protection Standard for Marinas and Boatyards* and *NFPA 307: The Standard for the Construction and Fire Protection of Marine Terminals, Piers, and Wharves.*

The existing definition of electrical datum plane was modified to remove requirements in accordance with the *NEC Style Manual.*

"**Electrical Datum Plane.** A specified distance above a water level above which electrical equipment can be installed, and electrical connections can be made." This definition was relocated to Article 100. A new Section 555.3 was created to contain requirements for electrical datum plane distances.

Three of the new definitions were also moved to Article 100 in the second draft stage because they apply globally; they are *Pier*, *Pier Fixed*, and *Pier Floating.*

The definition of floating building is relocated into 555.2 as Article 553 was merged into Article 555. The addition of these definitions into Article 555 provides significant clarity. For example, the term *boatyard* is now defined as "A facility used for constructing, repairing, servicing, hauling from the water, storing (on land and in the water) and launching of boats."

See multiple definitions that are extracted into 555.2.

Datum Plane, Service Equipment, Maximum Voltage

Significance of the Change

The previous definition in 555.2 of *Electrical Datum Plane* has been modified to comply with the *NEC Style Manual* because it contains requirements. The definition has been moved to Article 100 to apply globally. New Section 555.3 provides electrical datum plane distances for (A) *Floating Piers*, (B) *Areas Subject to Tidal Fluctuations*, and (C) *Areas Not Subject to Tidal Fluctuations*.

Section 555.4 provides prescriptive requirements for the location of service equipment. This section is revised to include service equipment for floating buildings, docks, and marinas. Service equipment must be located *on land* adjacent to the structure served, but not on or in the structure itself, or on any other floating structure.

The title of Section 555.5 is revised to *Maximum Voltage* and is revised in general, to limit pier power distribution systems to not more than 250 volts phase-to-phase. Where qualified persons service the equipment under engineering supervision, distribution systems are permitted to exceed 250-volts, but not more than 600-volts. It should be noted that this is not simply permission to go as high as 600-volts where qualified persons are involved, this can only be done under *engineering supervision* as well. Electrical hazards are significantly increased in a marina environment. This change is safety-driven with the general rule to not permit distribution systems at more than 250 volts phase-to-phase.

Code Language

555.3 Electrical Datum Plane Distances.

(A) **Floating Piers.**

(B) **Areas Subject to Tidal Fluctuations.**

(C) **Areas Not Subject to Tidal Fluctuations.**

555.4 Location of Service Equipment.

555.5 Maximum Voltage. Pier distribution systems shall not exceed 250 volts phase to phase. Pier distribution systems under engineering supervision shall be permitted to exceed 250 volts but not exceed 600 volts.

(See NEC for actual text)

Change Summary

- The definition of electrical datum plane is revised to remove requirements, which are added into new section 555.3.
- 555.4 is revised to address service equipment for floating buildings, docks, etc.
- In general, the maximum distribution voltage is limited to not exceed 250 volts phase-to-phase. Provisions are provided under restrictions to go up to 600 volts.

FRs: 8809, 8978, 8955
SRs: 7715, 7695

Transformers and Boat Hoists

Code Language

555.7 Transformers.

(A) General. Transformers and enclosures shall be identified for wet locations. The bottom of transformer enclosures shall not be located below the electrical datum plane.

(B) Replacements. Transformers and enclosures shall be identified for wet locations where replacements are made.

555.9 Boat Hoists. GFCI protection for personnel shall be provided for outlets not exceeding 240 volts that supply a boat hoist installed at dwelling unit docking facilities.

(See NEC for actual text)

Change Summary

- 555.7(A) now requires transformers and enclosures to be identified for wet locations. The bottom of transformers cannot be located below the electrical datum plane.
- Transformer replacements must be identified for wet locations.
- GFCI requirements for boat hoists are relocated from 210.8(C) to new 555.9.

Significance of the Change

Section 555.7 is editorially separated into second-level subdivisions. 555.7(A) *General* is modified to require that transformers and enclosures be identified for wet locations. The previous text required that they be *specifically approved*. This revision removes ambiguity and provides clarity by specifically requiring identification for wet locations. A new requirement for transformer replacement is added in 555.7(B) *Replacements*. Where transformers and enclosures are replaced they must be identified for wet locations.

GFCI requirements for boat hoists are relocated from 210.8(C) into a new Section 555.9. GFCI protection for personnel is required for outlets that do not exceed 240-volts that supply a boat hoist installed at dwelling unit docking facilities. This GFCI requirement is specifically limited to dwelling unit locations. A boat hoist installed in a commercial boatyard is not required to be GFCI protected without regard to the voltage supplied. The term *boatyard* is now defined in 555.2 as:

Boatyard. A facility used for constructing, repairing, servicing, hauling from the water, storing (on land and in water), and launching of boats. [303:3.3.2]

FRs: 8957, 8976

SR: None

Electrical Connections

Code Language

555.30 Electrical Connections.

(A) Floating Piers.

(B) Fixed Piers.

(C) Replacements. Replacement electrical connections shall be located at least 305 mm (12 in.) above the deck of a floating pier. Conductor splices, within junction boxes identified for wet locations, utilizing sealed wire connector systems listed and identified for submersion shall be required where located above the waterline but below the electrical datum plane for floating piers.

(See NEC for actual text)

Significance of the Change

Requirements for electrical connections, previously located in 555.9, are relocated into Part II *Marinas, Boatyards, and Docking Facilities*, Section 555.30. This revision separates the requirement into three first-level subdivisions. 555.30(A) *Floating Piers*, now requires electrical connections to be at least 12 inches above the deck of a floating pier and conductor splices identified for wet locations. 555.30(B) *Fixed Piers*, requires electrical connections to be at least 12 inches above the deck of a fixed pier but are not permitted below the electrical datum plane. The requirements in 555.30(C) address *replacements* and are new in this cycle. Any repair or modification of existing electrical connections must comply with this new requirement. The title of 555.30 is *Replacements* and applies to both fixed and floating piers. However, these requirements address only floating piers. Replacement electrical connections must be located at least 12 inches above the deck of a floating pier. Where conductor splices are located above the water line but below the electrical datum plane for floating piers, they must be installed in junction boxes identified for wet locations, and utilize sealed wire connector systems that are listed and identified for submersion.

Change Summary

- Requirements for electrical connections are relocated from 555.9 into new 555.30.
- Splices on floating piers located above the waterline but below the electrical datum plane must be in junction boxes identified for wet locations and must utilize sealed wire connectors that are listed and identified for submersion.

FR: 8959

SR: None

GFCI Protection, Outdoor Feeders, and BCs

Code Language

555.33 Receptacles

(B) Other Than Shore Power.

(1) GFCI Protection for Personnel. Receptacles in other locations shall be protected in accordance with 210.8.

(C) Replacement Receptacles. The requirements in 555.33 shall apply to the replacement of marina receptacles.

555.34(B)(2) Outdoor Branch Circuits and Feeders. Multiple feeders and branch circuits shall be permitted ... (See *NEC* text) Only Part I of Article 225 shall apply to marina installations.

(See NEC for actual text)

Change Summary

- All receptacles for other than shore power must be protected in accordance with 210.8.
- Replacement receptacles must comply with all requirements in 555.33.
- Multiple feeders and branch circuits are now specifically permitted for marinas, piers, boat docks, etc.

Significance of the Change

Requirements for receptacles are relocated from 555.19 to 555.33. Requirements for receptacles supplying other than shore power are located in 555.33(B). GFCI protection for personnel is addressed in 555.33(B)(1). The previous text provided prescriptive requirements for receptacles located outdoors, in boat houses, in buildings or structures used for storage, maintenance, or repair to be GFCI protected. The existing last sentence referenced 210.8(B) for receptacles and other locations. As written, this text seems to supersede the requirements of 210.8. Section 90.3 explains how this *Code* is arranged, and the general GFCI requirements in 210.8 apply unless specifically modified or supplemented in Chapters 1 through 7. This requirement is modified for clarity to state that for other than shore power, receptacles must comply with 210.8. A new first-level subdivision 555.33(C) is added to clearly require that the replacement of any receptacle within the scope of Article 555 must comply with the requirements of 555.33.

The installation of wiring methods previously addressed in 555.23 are relocated into new 555.34. The previous requirement mandated that outside branch circuits and feeders comply with Article 225. This prescriptively limited each boat dock or other structure to a single feeder. Each boat dock would be considered a separate structure. Some boat docks may have a significant number of boat slips and marina power outlets. Permitting multiple feeders or branch circuits will allow for significantly lower values of ground fault protection on each feeder, increasing safety on each boat dock or pier.

FRs: 8975, 8965

SR: None

GFPE and GFCI Protection

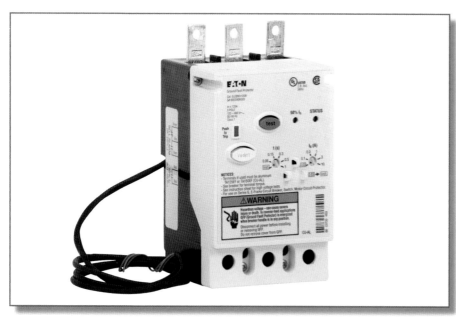

Courtesy of Eaton

Code Language

555.35 Ground-Fault Protection of Equipment (GFPE) and Ground-Fault Circuit-Interrupter (GFCI) Protection.

(A) Ground-Fault Protection.

(1) Receptacles Providing Shore Power.

(2) GFCI Protection for Personnel.

(3) Feeder and Branch-Circuit Conductors with GFPE.

Exception to (3): Transformer secondary conductors ... (See NEC text)

(See NEC for actual text)

Significance of the Change

The existing requirement in 555.3 for ground-fault protection is relocated into new Section 555.35 *Ground-Fault Protection of Equipment (GFPE) and Ground-Fault Circuit-Interrupter (GFCI) Protection* and is significantly revised. Requirements for ground-fault protection in 555.35(A) applies to marinas, boatyards, commercial, and non-commercial docking facilities. 555.35(A)(1) requires that shore power receptacles have individual GFPE set to open, not exceeding 30 mA. 555.35(A)(2) provides requirements for GFCI protection for personnel and requires all 125 volt, single-phase 15- and 20-amp receptacles for other than shore power to be protected in accordance with 555.33(B)(1) and (B)(2). This requires that these receptacles (other than shore power) be protected in accordance with 210.8, and permits them to be enclosed in marina power outlets with receptacles that provide shore power provided the receptacles are marked to clearly indicate that they are not to be used to supply power to boats. 555.35(A)(3) requires that all feeder and branch circuit conductors installed on docking facilities be provided with GFPE set to open at currents not exceeding 100 mA. This requirement permits coordination with downstream GFPE at the feeder overcurrent protective device. There is an exception for transformer secondary conductors that do not exceed 10 feet in length and are installed in a raceway.

Change Summary

- All shore power receptacles must have GFPE protection not to exceed 30 mA. 555.35(A)(3) requires all branch circuits and feeders to have GFPE protection not to exceed 100 mA.

- An exception to 555.35(A)(3) permits transformer secondary conductors not more than 10 feet long and in a raceway to be installed without GFPE.

FR: 8954
SR: 7712

GFPE and GFCI Protection

Code Language

555.35 Ground-Fault Protection of Equipment (GFPE) and Ground-Fault Circuit-Interrupter (GFCI) Protection.

(B) Leakage Current Measurement Device. Where more than three receptacles supply shore power to boats, a leakage current measurement device shall be available and be used to determine leakage current from each boat that will utilize shore power.

Informational Note No. 1
Informational Note No. 2

(See NEC for actual text)

Courtesy of Marina Electrical Equipment

Change Summary

- Where more than three receptacles supply shore power to boats, a leakage current measurement device must be available and must be used to determine leakage current from each boat.

- The leakage current measurement device will provide the facility operator with the capability to identify a boat that is creating problems.

Significance of the Change

The existing requirement in 555.3 for ground fault protection is relocated into new Section 555.35 *Ground-Fault Protection of Equipment (GFPE) and Ground-Fault Circuit-Interrupter (GFCI) Protection* and is significantly revised. 555.35(B) requires that where more than three receptacles supply shore power to boats, a leakage current measurement device must be available and be used to determine leakage current from each boat utilizing shore power. It is well understood that in many cases the source of current flow in the water in marinas, boatyards, and other docking facilities is defective wiring in a boat supplied from shore power.

Two informational notes provide the *Code* reader with additional information on leakage current devices and the ability to identify boats with defective wiring. Informational Note No. 1 explains that leakage current measurement provides a capability to determine that an individual boat has defective wiring or other problems. This will allow the facility operator to identify problem boats. In some cases, a single boat can cause an upstream GFPE device to open. Informational Note No. 2 explains that an annual test of each boat with the leakage current measurement device is a prudent step towards determining if a boat has defective wiring. Where a problem boat is identified, repairs should be made to the boat before it is permitted to utilize shore power to prevent hazardous voltage and current in the water.

FR: 8954
SR: 7712

Ground-Fault Protection, Floating Buildings

Code Language

555.53 Ground-Fault Protection. The main overcurrent protective device that feeds the floating building shall have ground-fault protection not exceeding 100 mA. Ground-fault protection of each individual branch circuit or feeder shall be permitted as a suitable alternative.

(See NEC for actual text)

Significance of the Change

Requirements for floating buildings previously existed in Article 553. Those requirements are relocated into a new Part III *Floating Buildings* in Article 555. A new Section 555.53 *Ground-Fault Protection* is added to require the floating building main overcurrent protective device (OCPD) be ground-fault protected. This new requirement mandates that the main OCPD supplying a floating building have ground-fault protection not to exceed 100 mA. Additional text permits ground-fault protection of each individual branch circuit and feeder as a suitable alternative. A floating building is defined in 555.2 as follows:

Floating Building. A building unit, as defined in Article 100, that floats on water, is moored in a permanent location, and has a premises wiring system served through connection by permanent wiring to an electrical supply system not located on the premises.

It is not unusual for one or more floating buildings to exist in a marina, boatyard, or other docking facility. This ground-fault protection requirement for floating buildings is part of a global effort to address the potential for hazardous voltage and current in the water around marinas, boatyards, and other docking facilities. Larger floating buildings may have problems with a single main OCPD provided with ground-fault protection at 100 mA. These floating buildings will be permitted to provide ground-fault protection on each feeder and branch circuit as a suitable alternative.

Change Summary

- Main OCPDs supplying floating buildings must have GFPE protection not to exceed 100 mA.
- Ground-fault protection of each individual branch circuit and feeder is a suitable alternative.

FR: 8978

SR: None

Splices, New Exception for Construction Sites

Code Language

590.4(G) Splices

Exception No. 2: On construction sites, branch-circuits that are permanently installed in framed walls and ceilings and are used to supply temporary power or lighting, and that are GFCI protected, the following shall be permitted: (1) A box cover shall not be required for splices installed completely inside of junction boxes with plaster rings. (2) Listed pigtail-type lampholders shall be permitted to be installed in ceiling-mounted junction boxes with plaster rings. (3) Finger safe devices shall be permitted for supplying and connection of devices.

(See NEC for actual text)

Change Summary

- A new Exception No. 2 is added to 590.4(G) for temporary installations on construction sites.
- This new exception will permit permanently installed branch circuits that are GFCI protected and inside of a junction box and tile ring to be installed without a cover.
- Listed pigtails are permitted in ceiling mounted junction boxes with plaster rings.

Significance of the Change

Section 590.4(G) includes requirements for splices of temporary wiring. The general rule is that a box, conduit body, or other enclosure with a cover be used for all splices. Exception No. 1 permits: (1) open splices where nonmetallic multiconductor cord or cable assemblies are used, and (2) where metal-sheathed cable assemblies terminate in listed fittings that mechanically secure the cable sheath to maintain effective electrical continuity are used.

This revision addresses significant problems that occur during the construction of apartments, condo units, or similar venues. As these jobs progress, there is a need for lighting in each room, apartment, condo unit, or similar venue. In many cases, it is not feasible or practical to provide temporary lighting with Type NM cable. Framers and drywall installers cut cables loose, and they end up on the floor. This begins to leave rooms within the apartments and condos in the dark and creates serious safety concerns.

A new exception No. 2 is added to permit branch circuits on construction sites that are permanently installed in framed walls and ceilings. Where used to supply temporary power for power or lighting, these branch circuits are not required to have a cover on each box provided they are GFCI protected. This exception specifically permits: (1) splices installed completely inside of a junction box with plaster rings without a box cover, (2) listed pigtail type lamp holders in ceiling-mounted junction boxes with plaster rings, and (3) finger-safe devices for supplying and connection of devices inside junction boxes with plaster rings.

FR: 8770
SR: 7894

Assured Equipment Grounding Conductor Program

Code Language

590.6 Ground Fault Protection for Personnel.

(B) Other Receptacle Outlets.

(2) AEGCP… (See *NEC* text) The assured equipment grounding conductor program shall be documented and made available to the authority having jurisdiction.

Informational Note: The Occupational Safety and Health Administration 29 CFR 1910 and 1926 contain requirements for assured equipment grounding conductor programs. Additional information is provided in NFPA 70E-2018, *Standard for Electrical Safety in the Workplace.*

(See NEC for actual text)

Significance of the Change

Section 590.6 provides requirements for ground fault protection of personnel and requires that all temporary wiring installations comply with 590.6(A) and (B). Receptacle outlets are addressed in 590.6(A). All 125-volt, single-phase 15-, 20-, and 30-amp receptacle outlets that are not part of the permanent wiring that is used by personnel must be GFCI protected as required by 590.6(A)(1). In addition to this requirement, listed cord sets or devices incorporating listed GFCI protection for personnel that is identified for portable use are permitted. 590.6(A)(2) requires GFCI protection be provided where existing receptacle outlets or permanent wiring is in use by personnel. 590.6(A)(3) requires GFCI protection for receptacles that are part of portable generators rated 15 kW or less.

590.6(B) applies to other receptacle outlets. This means other than 125-volt, single-phase 15-, 20-, and 30-amp receptacle outlets. Where receptacle outlets for welders, saws, swing scaffolds, and other equipment are supplied, for example at 208-volts, 30-amps, 590.6(B) applies. This requires either GFCI protection in accordance with 590.6(B)(1) or an assured equipment grounding conductor program (AEGCP) in 590.6(B)(2). The requirements for AEGCP are revised and now require the program to be documented and made available to the AHJ. It is important to note that the electrical contractor is responsible only for the short length of cord and female cord connector leaving the panel board or other enclosure. Where other trades require extension cords to supply equipment at other than 125-volt, single-phase 15-, 20-, and 30-amps, they are responsible for their own AEGCP.

Change Summary

- 590.6(B)(2) is modified to require that, where used, an AEGCP must be documented and made available to the AHJ.
- The requirements of 590.6(B)(2) do not apply to every temporary installation.
- A new informational note refers to AEGCP requirements in OSHA standards and *NFPA 70E.*

FR: None
SR: 7904

Overcurrent Protective Devices

Code Language

590.8 Overcurrent Protective Devices.

(A) Where Reused. Where overcurrent protective devices that have been previously used are installed in a temporary installation, these overcurrent protective devices shall be examined to ensure these devices have been properly installed, properly maintained, and there is no evidence of impending failure.

(B) Service Overcurrent Protective Devices. Overcurrent protective devices for solidly grounded wye electrical services of more than 150 volts to ground but not exceeding 1000 volts phase-to-phase shall be current limiting.

Informational Note: ... (See *NEC* text)

(See NEC for actual text)

Change Summary

- 590.8(A) now requires reused OCPDs installed in a temporary installation to be examined.

- Reused OCPDs must be examined for proper installation, proper maintenance, and to ensure there is no evidence of impending failure.

- 590.8(B) now requires service OCPDs in wye connected services more than 150-volts to ground and not exceeding 1000-volts phase-to-phase be current limiting.

Significance of the Change

A new Section 590.8 *Overcurrent Protective Devices* (OCPDs) is added to address the condition of OCPDs where reused and to add specific requirements for service overcurrent protective devices. Electrical distribution equipment used for temporary power and light is used over and over again to reduce costs. This new requirement in 590.8(A) *Where Reused* mandates that previously used OCPDs applied as part of a temporary installation, be examined to ensure they are properly installed, properly maintained, and there is no evidence of impending failure. There are multiple factors that could impact circuit breakers or fuses, including, but not limited to, exposure to the weather, improper storage, the potential damage during removal, storage, redelivery, and more. An informational note is included to explain "evidence of impending failure" and to reference applicable standards.

New 590.8(B) *Service Overcurrent Protective Devices* requires that OCPDs for solidly grounded wye services of more than 150-volts to ground, but not exceeding 1000-volts phase-to-phase, be currently limiting. This will require all OCPDs protecting service supplied equipment at 480/277-volts to be current limiting. Temporary power is typically supplied directly from utility-owned transformers that are very close in proximity, to the temporary service equipment resulting in high levels of available fault current. This requirement is intended to reduce potential injury and damage to equipment by mandating current limitation.

FR: None
SR: 7919

NECA/IBEW Representation in the *NEC*

IBEW	NECA
NEC Correlating Committee	
Palmer L. Hickman	Michael J. Johnston
James T. Dollard, Jr	Timothy James Schultheis
CMP-1	
Palmer L. Hickman	Harry Sassaman
Mark Christian	Larry Geyer
CMP-2	
John McCamish	Michael Weaver
Daniel J. Naughton	Fred Neubauer
CMP-3	
Paul Casparro	Kyle Krueger
Michael J. Farrell III	David J Hendershot
CMP-4	
Wendell R. Whistler	Ronald J. Toomer
Harold C. Ohde	Steven Emert
CMP-5	
Gary A. Beckstrand	Nathan Philips
Derrick L. Atkins	Bobby J. Gray
CMP-6	
Todd Crisman	Kelly Lamp
Samuel R. La Dart	Shane Douglas Custer
CMP-7	
Richard A. Paredes	Wesley L. Wheeler
Gerald D. Dix	Philip Ostrow
CMP-8	
Rhett A. Roe	Larry D. Cogburn
Dan Rodriguez	Raymond H Smith
CMP-9	
Rodney D. Belisle	Timothy James Schultheis
Michael O'Connell	Haley Masbruch

IBEW	NECA
CMP-10	
James T. Dollard, Jr	Charles Robert Carter
Richard E. Lofton, II	Nathan Philips
CMP-11	
Jebediah J. Novak	Tim Hinson
Darryl Hill	Mashell D Carissimi
CMP-12	
Jeffrey L. Holmes	Scott Cline
Richard R. Shawbell, Jr.	Clinton Summers
CMP-13	
Linda J. Little	Richard Tice
James T. Dollard, Jr.	Anthony F. Punzalan
CMP-14	
John L. Simmons	Michael W. Smith
Thomas E. Dunne	Scott Masters
CMP-15	
Gary A. Beckstrand	Bruce D. Shelly
	Don Rabel
CMP-16	
Terry C. Coleman	Robert Davies
Christopher Rawson	
CMP-17	
Brian Myers	Timothy R. O'Brien
Ryan Andrew	Thomas H. Wood
CMP-18	
Paul Costello	Bobby J. Gray
Daniel Van Sickle, III	Paul Yesbeck

Chapter 6

Articles 600–695
Special Equipment

Host Sign, Retrofit Kit (2 types), Subassembly

Code Language

600.2 Definitions

Host Sign. A sign or outline lighting system already installed in the field that is designated for field conversion of the illumination system with a retrofit kit.

Retrofit Kit, General Use.

Retrofit Kit, Sign Specific.

Subassembly. Component parts or a segment of a sign, retrofit kit, or outline lighting system that, when assembled, forms a complete unit or product.

(See NEC for actual text)

Change Summary

- Four new definitions are added to 600.2 to address retrofitting signs.
- A host sign is already installed and is designated for field conversion of the illumination system.
- Two new definitions of "Retrofit Kit" are necessary to address retrofitting signs.

FRs: 8153, 8148, 8156, 8154

SR: None

Significance of the Change

Four new definitions are added to Article 600 that apply to retrofitting signs. This is necessary because signs are not mass produced. Unlike luminaires, which are standardized and mass-produced, signs are custom made and have distinctly different structural and illumination characteristics, including multi-location corporate signage programs, which are dissimilar in size. Article 100 defines the term *Retrofit Kit* as a general term for a complete subassembly of parts and devices for field conversion of utilization equipment. This defined term applies well to mass-produced equipment, such as luminaires. In addition to the structural anomalies, field conversions from neon, fluorescent or HID to LEDs are distinctly different. A *Host Sign* is defined as being already installed in the field that is designated for field conversion of the illumination system with a retrofit kit. There are two definitions for retrofit kits that apply only to signs. A *General Use Retrofit Kit* has only the major components, not all of the parts necessary will be included. A *Sign Specific Retrofit Kit* will include all of the parts and hardware necessary to complete a retrofit in the field. These kits are intended to be installed on a specific (host) sign. The term *Subassembly* is defined as component parts or a segment of a sign, retrofit kit, or outline lighting system that, when assembled, forms a complete unit or product. This definition is similar to the one in UL 48.

See new Section 600.35 *Retrofit Kits*.

Branch Circuits

Code Language

600.5 Branch Circuits

(A) Required Branch Circuit… (See *NEC* text) A sign or outline lighting outlet shall not be required at entrances for deliveries, service corridors, or service hallways that are intended to be used only by service personnel or employees.

(B) Marking. A disconnecting means for a sign, outline lighting system, or controller shall be marked to identify the sign, outline lighting system, or controller it controls.

Exception: An external disconnecting means that is mounted on the sign body, sign enclosure, sign pole, or controller shall not be required to identify the sign or outline lighting system it controls.

(See NEC for actual text)

Significance of the Change

Section 600.5(A) requires that each commercial building and commercial occupancy accessible to pedestrians be provided with at least one outlet at an accessible location at each entrance to each tenant space for a sign or outline lighting. A new last sentence is added to clarify that a sign or outline lighting outlet is not required at entrances for deliveries, service corridors, or service hallways that are intended to be used only by service personnel or employees.

New first-level subdivision 600.5(B) *Marking* now requires that the disconnecting means for signs, outline lighting systems or controllers be marked to identify the signs, outline lighting systems or controller that it supplies. An exception is added for external disconnects that are mounted on the sign body, enclosure, pole, or controller. This revision recognizes that external disconnecting means in remote locations may not be readily associated with the sign, etc.

600.5(D) contains requirements for wiring methods used to supply signs. 600.5(D)(1) is modified to recognize that the wiring method used to supply signs and outline lighting systems is permitted to terminate in a panelboard. Large signs may contain a panelboard. 600.5(D)(2) is modified to clarify that transformer enclosures may be used as pull or junction boxes, provided the sign disconnecting means de-energizes all current-carrying conductors in those enclosures.

Change Summary

- A sign or lighting outlet is not required at entrances for deliveries, service corridors, or service hallways.
- All disconnects supplying signs or outline lighting systems that are remotely located must be marked with the identity of the sign or lighting system it controls.

FRs: 8171, 8174, 8180, 8186

SRs: 8232, 8234

Disconnect in Remote Location

Code Language

600.6 Disconnects.

(A) Location.

(A)(4) Remote Location. The disconnecting means, if located remote from the sign, sign body, or pole, shall be mounted at an accessible location available to first responders and service personnel. The location of the disconnect shall be marked with a label at the sign location and marked as the disconnect for the sign or outline lighting system. The label shall comply with 110.21(B).

(See NEC for actual text)

Change Summary

- New 600.6(A)(4) requires remote disconnects to be installed in an accessible location.

- The location of the remote disconnect must be marked with the sign location.

- This new requirement will identify the location of the disconnect for service personnel and first responders.

Significance of the Change

A new requirement addressing remotely located disconnects is added in 600.6(A)(4). Where a disconnecting means supplying a sign, sign body, or pole is located remotely, it must be installed in an accessible location available to both first responders and service personnel. The location of the remote disconnect must be marked with a label at the sign location and marked as the disconnect for the sign or other equipment.

This requirement mandates accessibility for first responders and service personnel. The revision in 600.5(B) requires all disconnects to be marked with the identity of the sign, outline lighting system, or the controller it controls. These requirements are intended to allow quick access to first responders, as well as service personnel.

Additional requirements for disconnecting means for first responders is added in this 2020 *NEC* revision cycle for services in 230.85, batteries in 480.7(A), generators in 445.18, and energy storage systems in 706.15.

FR: 8289
SR: None

NEW

600.35

Article 600 Electric Signs and Outline Lighting
Part II Field-Installed Skeleton Tubing, Outline Lighting...

Retrofit Kits

Significance of the Change

New Section 600.35 *Retrofit Kits* is added in Part II of Article 600. General requirements are located in 600.35(A), mandating that a general use or sign specific retrofit kit must include installation instructions and requirements for field conversion of host signs. Retrofit kits are required to be listed and labeled. See 600.2, which includes new definitions for host sign, general retrofit kit, and sign specific retrofit kit. 600.35(B) requires retrofit kits be installed in accordance with the installation instructions using wiring methods in accordance with Chapter 3 of the *NEC*. During a conversion, all parts that are not replaced by a retrofit kit must be inspected for damage. Any damaged parts found during the conversion of the sign must be replaced or repaired to maintain the sign or outline lighting systems dry, damp, or wet location rating. All work performed during a conversion must be in a neat and workmanlike manner. Section 110.12 is referenced in 600.35(A)(3). A retrofitted sign must be marked in accordance with 600.4(B). This requires that the sign be marked to inform persons that the illumination system has been replaced. The marking must include the retrofit kit provider and installer's name or identifier. Signs that are converted to tubular LED lamps powered by the existing sign sockets must include a label to alert personnel that the sign has been modified. The label must include a warning not to install fluorescent lamps. That label must be visible during re-lamping.

Code Language

600.35 Retrofit Kits.

(A) General. A general-use or sign-specific retrofit kit for a sign or outline lighting system shall include installation instructions and requirements for field conversion of a host sign. The retrofit kit shall be listed and labeled.

(B) Installation. The retrofit kit shall be installed in accordance with the installation instructions.

(1) Wiring Methods. ... (See *NEC* text)

(2) Damaged Parts. ... (See *NEC* text)

(3) Workmanship. ... (See *NEC* text)

(4) Marking. ...(See *NEC* text)

(See NEC for actual text)

Change Summary

- New Section 600.35 contains requirements for retrofit kits.
- Retrofit kits must be listed and installed in accordance with the installation instructions.
- During a sign conversion, any parts found to be damaged must be replaced or repaired.

FR: 8227
SR: None

Signage (Selectively Coordinated OCPDs)

Code Language

620.65 Signage. Equipment enclosures containing selectively coordinated overcurrent devices shall be legibly marked in the field to indicate that the overcurrent devices are selectively coordinated. The marking shall meet the requirements of 110.21(B), shall be readily visible, and shall state the following: CAUTION: OVERCURRENT DEVICES IN THIS ENCLOSURE ARE SELECTIVELY COORDINATED. EQUIVALENT REPLACEMENTS AND TRIP SETTINGS ARE REQUIRED.

(See NEC for actual text)

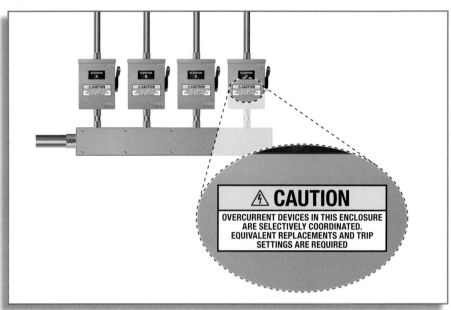

⚠ **CAUTION**

OVERCURRENT DEVICES IN THIS ENCLOSURE ARE SELECTIVELY COORDINATED. EQUIVALENT REPLACEMENTS AND TRIP SETTINGS ARE REQUIRED

Change Summary

- Editorial revisions are made in 620.62.
- New 620.65 requires signage on all enclosures containing selectively coordinated OCPDs.
- CAUTION: OVERCURRENT DEVICES IN THIS ENCLOSURE ARE SELECTIVELY COORDINATED. EQUIVALENT REPLACEMENTS AND TRIP SETTINGS ARE REQUIRED.

Significance of the Change

Section 620.62 requires that where more than one driving machine disconnecting means is supplied by the *same source*, the overcurrent protective devices (OCPDs) in each disconnecting means must be selectively coordinated with any other supply-side OCPDs. The previous text referenced supply by the *same feeder* (single feeder), is now clarified with the words *same source*. Two exceptions (similar to those in Articles 700 and 701) are added to reference primary and secondary transformer OCPDs and devices of the same rating.

New Section 620.65 *Signage* now requires all equipment enclosures that contain selectively coordinated OCPDs to be legibly marked in the field to indicate that they are selectively coordinated. The marking must be readily visible and must state:

CAUTION: OVERCURRENT DEVICES IN THIS ENCLOSURE
ARE SELECTIVELY COORDINATED.
EQUIVALENT REPLACEMENTS AND
TRIP SETTINGS ARE REQUIRED.

This marking will ensure that any replacement OCPD continues to be selectively coordinated with any other supply-side OCPD.

FR: 8309
SR: None

Electric Vehicle Power Transfer System

Code Language

625.1 Scope. This article covers the electrical conductors and equipment connecting an electric vehicle to premises wiring for the purposes of charging, power export, or bidirectional current flow.

(See NEC for actual text)

Significance of the Change

The previous title of Article 625 *Electric Vehicle Charging* is revised to correlate with other significant revisions to *Electric Vehicle Power Transfer System*. Similar revisions are made in 625.1 *Scope* to address new technology and new requirements within this article. The previous article scope addressed only conductors and equipment external to an electric vehicle that connected the vehicle to a supply of electricity and the installation of equipment and devices related to electric vehicle charging. The revised scope now covers electrical conductors and equipment connecting an electric vehicle to premises wiring for the purposes of *charging, power export, or bidirectional current flow*.

This is a significant revision in scope and clarifies three separate modes of operation: (1) An electric vehicle connected to a supply of electricity for *electric vehicle charging*, (2) An electric vehicle connected to an external load for power export from the electric vehicle to electrical equipment or systems, and (3) An electric vehicle connected to a supply of electricity for *charging and also for power export* from the electric vehicle through the same equipment (bi-directional current flow).

The scope of the *NEC* is modified to recognize this expansion of Article 625. New list item (6) in 90.2(A) recognizes *Installations used to export electric power from vehicles to premises wiring or for bidirectional current flow*. Electric vehicles can now be used as a standby power source, such as a generator or energy storage system. The *NEC* now recognizes this use.

Change Summary

- Article 625 is retitled *Electric Vehicle Power Transfer System*.
- EVs can be connected for the purposes of charging, power export, or bidirectional current flow.
- EVs can now be used as a standby power source in a similar manner to the use of a standby generator or energy storage system.

FRs: 8383, 8385

SR: 7776

625.2

Article 625 Electric Vehicle Power Transfer System
Part I General

NEW
DELETION
REVISION

625.2 Definitions

Code Language

Electric Vehicle Power Export Equipment (EVPE). The equipment, including the outlet on the vehicle, that is used to provide electrical power at voltages greater than or equal to 30 Vac or 60 Vdc to loads external to the vehicle, using the vehicle as the source of supply.

Informational Note: Electric vehicle power export equipment and electric vehicle supply equipment are sometimes contained in one piece of equipment, sometimes referred to as a bidirectional EVSE.

(See NEC for actual text)

Change Summary

- The definition of *Electric Vehicle* is modified and relocated to Article 100.
- A new definition of *Electric Vehicle Power Export Equipment (EVPE)* is added to clarify that it includes the *outlet on the vehicle* used to provide electrical power, using the vehicle as a source of supply.
- Multiple definitions are editorially deleted.

Significance of the Change

Significant revisions are made in 625.2 to correlate with new requirements and the change in scope of this article. The definition of *Electric Vehicle* is modified and relocated to Article 100. The definitions of *Plug-In Hybrid Electric Vehicle* and *Rechargeable Energy Storage System* were only used in the definition of Electric Vehicle and are deleted. The definition of *Electric Vehicle Storage Battery* is not used in this article and is deleted. Construction requirements within Article 625 have been deleted (two sections left) along with the definitions of *Electric Vehicle Coupler* and *Electric Vehicle Inlet*. A new definition of *Electric Vehicle Power Export Equipment (EVPE)* is added to clarify that it includes the outlet on the vehicle used to provide electrical power at voltages greater than or equal to 30-volts ac or 60-volts dc to loads external to the vehicle, using the vehicle as a source of supply. This definition recognizes the power export capability of electric vehicles. The definition of *Electric Vehicle Supply Equipment (EVSE)* is modified to clarify that it includes the personal protection system required (625.22) to protect against electric shock.

FRs: 8389, 8410, 8597, 8397, 8391
SRs: 7783, 7789, 7790

Cords and Cables

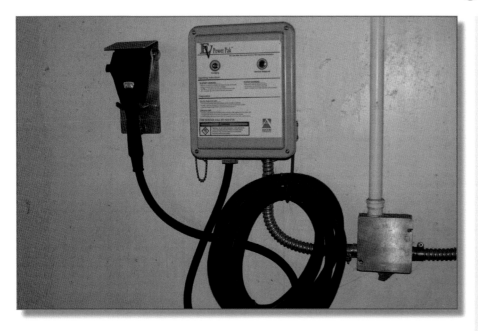

Significance of the Change

Section 625.17 contains construction requirements for cords and cables. The permitted length of the power supply cord in 625.17(A) is modified as follows: (1) for portable equipment the power supply cord is not permitted to be longer than 12 inches, and (2) for stationary equipment the power supply cord is not permitted to be longer than 6 feet, and the equipment must be installed at a height that prevents the power supply cord from contacting the floor when it is connected to the proper receptacle. The limitation to 12 inches for portable equipment is due to potential abuse in a vehicle parking area that could damage the power supply cord. For stationary equipment, the EVSE must be mounted at a height to keep the power supply cord off of the floor, and a maximum length of 6 feet is permitted. This requirement exists to prevent long lengths of power supply cord. Limiting the length of the cord and requiring the installation keeps it off the floor, and is necessary to prevent damage to the cord.

A new first-level subdivision 625.17(D) *Interconnecting Cabling Systems* is added to permit engineered solutions implemented in the field based on the product listings. The number of fast charger stations is growing exponentially. Long-range mass-market produced electric vehicles will require more and more charger stations. Larger vehicles and larger battery sizes are necessary to increase the power delivery rates to keep the charging times reasonable. This new requirement now permits engineered solutions that are part of listed EVSE.

Code Language

625.17(A)(3)(a) … (See *NEC* text)

(i) For portable equipment in accordance with 625.44(A), the power supply cord shall be not more than 300 mm (12 in.) long.

(ii) For stationary equipment in accordance with 625.44(B), the power supply cord shall be not more than 1.8 m (6 ft) long and the equipment shall be installed at a height that prevents the power supply cord from contacting the floor when it is connected to the proper receptacle.

(D) Interconnecting Cabling Systems. Other cabling systems that are integral parts of listed EVSE and are intended to interconnect pieces of equipment within an EVSE system using approved installation methods shall be permitted.

(See NEC for actual text)

Change Summary

- Permitted lengths of power supply cords are modified.
- Portable equipment is limited to 1 foot and stationary equipment up to 6 feet in length.
- Other cabling systems that are integral parts of listed EVSE are permitted.

FRs: 8496, 8509

SR: None

Power Transfer Equipment Rating

Code Language

625.42 Rating. ... (See *NEC* text) Adjustable settings shall be permitted on fixed-in-place equipment only. ... (See *NEC* text) Restricted access shall prevent the user from gaining access to the adjusting means. Restricted access shall be accomplished by at least one of the following:

(1) A cover or door that requires the use of a tool to open

(2) Locked doors accessible only to qualified personnel

(3) Password protected commissioning software accessible only to qualified personnel

(See NEC for actual text)

Change Summary

- New 625.42 permits power transfer equipment to have adjustable output settings.
- Service and feeder size calculations are based on the actual setting.
- Three methods are provided to achieve restricted access, including password protected commissioning software accessible only to qualified persons.

Significance of the Change

Electric Vehicle Supply Equipment (EVSE) have output and input current ratings correlated. This equipment is manufactured with an adjustment means that can limit the output of the EVSE to the vehicle supplied. This equipment can also be adjusted to match the branch circuit sizing. Section 625.42 now permits adjustable settings on fixed in place equipment only. This will allow a single EVSE to be used in many different types of installations supplying different vehicles and supplied by branch circuits of different voltages and ratings. Calculations of services and feeders are permitted to match the adjusting means chosen. At the time of installation, the adjustable output settings are determined and set. This requirement mandates restricted access to prevent the end-user from gaining access to the adjusting means. There are three methods permitted to accomplish the required restricted access: (1) a cover or door that requires the use of the tool to open, (2) locked doors accessible only to qualified persons, and (3) password protected commissioning software accessible only to qualified persons.

FR: 8556
SR: None
SCR: 21
CC: 7802

GFCI Protection and Receptacle Enclosures

Code Language

625.54 GFCI Protection for Personnel. In addition to the requirements in 210.8, all receptacles installed for the connection of electric vehicle charging shall have ground-fault circuit-interrupter protection for personnel.

625.56 Receptacle Enclosures. ... (See *NEC* text) An outlet box hood installed for this purpose shall be listed and shall be identified as extra duty. Other listed products, enclosures, or assemblies providing weatherproof protection that do not utilize an outlet box hood shall not be required to be marked extra duty.

(See NEC for actual text)

Significance of the Change

A new Section 625.54 is added to require GFCI protection of all receptacles installed for the connection of electric vehicle charging equipment. The general GFCI protection requirements of 210.8 are referenced as they will apply in all cases unless modified. This now requires that all receptacles supplying electric vehicle charging equipment be GFCI protected without regard to the voltage or system. Charging electric vehicles at 125-volts nominal increases the time to recharge. In order to extend the range of electric vehicles, 240-volt portable charging capability is essential. The primary reason behind this revision is to address the safety of person's that may be plugging and unplugging 250-volt cord caps into receptacles in wet or damp environments. This will also drive the need for an in-use cover for 250-volt receptacle outlets serving electrical vehicle charging equipment.

Section 625.56 requires that receptacles installed in wet locations for electric vehicle charging have an enclosure that is weatherproof with the attachment plug inserted or removed. New text is added to require that outlet box hoods installed for this purpose be listed and identified as extra duty. An additional sentence clarifies that other listed products, enclosures, or assemblies providing weatherproof protection that do not utilize an outlet box hood are not required to be marked extra duty.

Change Summary

- All receptacles installed for electric vehicle charging must be GFCI protected.
- This GFCI requirement applies to all voltages and systems.
- Where these receptacles are installed in wet locations, they must have listed outlet box hoods identified as extra duty.

FRs: 8581, 8584

SR: 7809

625.60

NEW

AC Receptacle Outlets Used for EVPE

Code Language

625.60 AC Receptacle Outlets Used for EVPE. AC receptacles installed in electric vehicles and intended to allow for connection of off-board utilization equipment shall comply with 625.60(A) through (D).

(A) Type. ... (See *NEC* text) receptacle outlet... (See *NEC* text) listed.

(B) Rating. The receptacle outlet shall be rated 250 volts maximum, single phase 50 amperes maximum.

(C) Overcurrent Protection. ... (See *NEC* text)

(D) GFCI Protection for Personnel. Ground-fault circuit-interrupter protection for personnel shall be provided for all receptacles. The ground-fault circuit-interrupter indication and reset shall be installed in a readily accessible location.

(See NEC for actual text)

Change Summary

- AC receptacles in electric vehicles intended to supply off-board utilization equipment must comply with 625.60.
- These receptacles must be listed, and overcurrent protection must be provided.
- GFCI protection is required. Indication and reset capabilities for the GFCI device must be readily accessible.

Significance of the Change

New Section 625.60 now includes requirements for receptacle outlets used for electric vehicle power export. This requirement addresses the outlet on the vehicle. As defined in Article 100, *Electric Vehicle Power Export Equipment (EVPE)* is where the electric vehicle becomes the source of supply.

The parent text of this new section requires ac receptacles installed in electric vehicles for connection of off-board utilization equipment comply with all of these requirements. 625.60(A) requires the receptacle installed in the vehicle to be listed. 625.60(B) limits the receptacle rating at 250-volts maximum, single-phase, and 50-amps maximum. 625.60(C) requires overcurrent protection integral to the power export system. The overcurrent protection provided must be nominally rated to protect the receptacle and must also be rated for the available fault current. 625.60(D) requires the ac receptacles installed in the vehicle for off-board utilization to be GFCI protected. The GFCI indication and reset buttons must be installed in a readily accessible location.

FR: 8534
SRs: 7796, 7798, 7799, 7800, 7801

Cables Installed Under Raised Floors

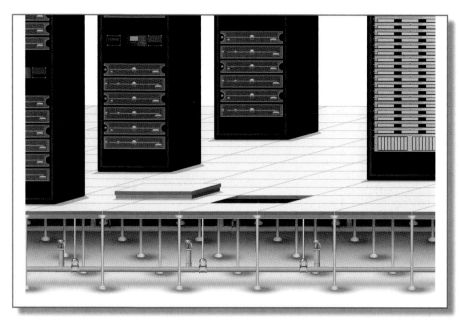

Significance of the Change

Article 645 provides alternative wiring methods to Chapter 3, Parts I and III of Article 725, and I and V of Article 770, where all of the conditions of 645.4 are met. Section 645.5 provides requirements for supply circuits and interconnecting cables. 645.5(E) provides requirements for power cables, communications cables, connecting cables, interconnect cables, cord and plug connections, and receptacles associated with information technology equipment installed under raised floors.

These requirements are significantly revised to correlate with requirements in *NFPA 75: The Standard for Fire Protection of Information Technology Equipment*.

645.5(E)(2) *Installation Requirements for Electrical Supply Cords, Data Cables, Interconnecting Cables, and Grounding Conductors Under a Raised Floor* is modified to limit the alternative cables included. Only where the air space under a raised floor is protected by an automatic fire suppression system are these cable types permitted. List item (5) is added to permit wiring in accordance with 725.135(C) and 725.154(A), where the air space under a raised floor is not protected by an automatic fire suppression system.

The requirements in 645.5(E)(3) (Optical Fiber Cables) are modified in the same manner. List item (1) requires protection by an automatic fire suppression system under a raised floor to permit the cable types identified. List item (2) requires cables in accordance with 770.113(C) where an automatic fire suppression system is not installed under a raised floor.

Code Language

645.5 Supply Circuits and Interconnecting Cables.

(E) Under Raised Floors.

(2) Installation Requirements for Electrical Supply Cords, Data Cables, Interconnecting Cables, and Grounding Conductors Under a Raised Floor. (See *NEC* text)

(4) Where the air space under a raised floor is protected by an automatic fire suppression system... (See *NEC* text)

(5) Where the air space under a raised floor is not protected by an automatic fire suppression system... (See *NEC* text)

(3) Installation Requirements for Optical Fiber Cables Under a Raised Floor. ...(See *NEC* text)

(1) Where the air space under a raised floor is protected by an automatic fire suppression system... (See *NEC* text)

(2) Where the air space under a raised floor is not protected by an automatic fire suppression system... (See *NEC* text)

(See NEC for actual text)

Change Summary

- Alternative cabling methods in 645.5(E) are modified for spaces under raised floors.
- Automatic fire suppression systems are required under raised floors to permit alternative cable types.

FR: 8348
SR: None

Definition of Corrosive Environment

Code Language

Corrosive Environment. Areas where pool sanitation chemicals are stored, handled, or dispensed, and confined areas under decks adjacent to such areas, as well as areas with circulation pumps, automatic chlorinators, filters, open areas under decks adjacent to or abutting the pool structure, and similar locations.

Informational Note: Sanitation chemicals ... (See *NEC* text) risk of corrosion (gradually damage or destroy materials) due to the presence of oxidizers (e.g., calcium hypochlorite, sodium hypochlorite, bromine, chlorinated isocyanurates) and chlorinating agents that release chlorine when dissolved in water. More information... (See *NEC* text)

(1) EPA website... (See *NEC* text)

(See NEC for actual text)

Change Summary

- A new definition of *Corrosive Environment* is added to 680.2.
- Section 680.14 is modified to contain the permitted wiring methods in corrosive environments.
- An informational note provides multiple resources for more on swimming pool chemicals.

Significance of the Change

A new definition of *Corrosive Environment* is added in Section 680.2. This definition is based on the text in existing 680.14(A), which described a corrosive environment and listed wiring methods permitted in 680.14(B). A corrosive environment is an area where pool sanitation chemicals are stored, handled, or dispensed. Additionally, confined areas under decks adjacent to such areas, as well as areas with circulation pumps, automatic chlorinators, filters, open areas under decks adjacent to or up against the pool structure and similar locations, are considered corrosive environments. An informational note is included to explain that sanitation chemicals and the pool water pose a risk of corrosion which will damage or destroy materials due to the presence of oxidizers. Additional information is referenced including:

(1) The Environmental Protection Agency website. (See web link.)

(2) *NFPA 400-2019: Hazardous Materials Code* and,

(3) Advisory: Swimming Pool Chemicals: Chlorine, OSWER 90-008.1, June 1990, available from the EPA National Service Center for Environmental Publications (NSCEP)

Additionally, Section 680.14 is modified to contain the permitted wiring methods in corrosive environments.

For additional information, visit qr.njatcdb.org Item #5292

FR: 8891
SR: 8036

Definition of Fountain, Immersion Pool, ...

Courtesy of Donny Cook

Significance of the Change

The definition of *Fountain* in Section 680.2 is modified for clarity. The last sentence is modified for compliance with the *NEC Style Manual*, and for clarity to explain that this definition does not include *drinking water coolers*, which are sometimes called drinking fountains. Additional text is added to explain that a fountain contains a water feature using pumped water jets to create decorative, effects, operate splash pads, and create ornamental display and reflection pools that are not intended for human immersion.

A new definition of *Immersion Pool* is added in 680.2. These pools are intended only for ceremonial or ritual immersion of persons. They are designed and intended to have their contents drained or discharged. Two new sections with requirements for immersion pools are added in this cycle. 680.35 now contains requirements for storable and portable immersion pools, and 680.45 contains requirements for permanently installed immersion pools.

A new definition of *Splash Pad* is added in 680.2. It is important to note that the term *splash pad* is used in the definition of *Fountain*, *which means requirements for fountains apply to splash pads*. A splash pad is a fountain with very shallow depth and is intended for recreational use by pedestrians. This new definition explains that a splash pad is a fountain with the pool depth of 1 inch or less intended for recreational use by pedestrians. Additional text explains that this defined term does not include showers intended for rinsing prior to use of the pool, spa or other water feature.

Code Language

Fountain. An ornamental structure or recreational water feature from which one or more jets or streams of water are discharged into the air, including splash pads, ornamental pools, display pools, and reflection pools. The definition does not include drinking water fountains or water coolers.

Immersion Pool. A pool for ceremonial or ritual immersion of users, which is designed and intended to have its contents drained or discharged.

Splash Pad. A fountain with a pool depth 25 mm (1 in.) or less, intended for recreational use by pedestrians. This definition does not include showers intended for hygienic rinsing prior to use of a pool, spa, or other water feature.

(See NEC for actual text)

Change Summary

- The definition of *Fountain* is modified for clarity.
- A new definition of *Immersion Pool* is added. These pools are for ceremonial or ritual immersion of persons.
- A new definition of *Splash Pad* is added. This is a fountain with a depth of one inch or less intended for recreational use by pedestrians.

FRs: 8731, 8733, 8735
SRs: 8044, 8049, 8052

Approval of Equipment, Inspections After Installation

Code Language

680.3 Approval of Equipment. All electrical equipment and products covered by this article shall be installed in compliance with this article and shall be listed

680.4 Inspections After Installation. The authority having jurisdiction shall be permitted to require periodic inspection and testing.

(See NEC for actual text)

Courtesy of Donny Cook

Change Summary

- All electrical equipment and products under the scope of Article 680 are required to be listed.
- The authority having jurisdiction is permitted to require periodic inspection and testing of aging pools.
- Many municipalities have regulations that require annual inspections of commercial and public pools, but it is extremely uncommon to see any inspections of aging privately owned pools.

Significance of the Change

Previous requirements for approval of equipment in 680.4 are significantly modified and relocated to 680.3. The previous requirement mandated that all electrical equipment in water, walls, or decks of pools, fountains, and similar installations must comply with Article 680 and be listed. This requirement is revised to require all electrical equipment and products covered in Article 680, be installed in compliance with the requirements within, and must also be listed. Substantiation for this revision explained that the intent was for all equipment to be listed, and this change provides that clarity.

A new Section 680.4, *Inspections After Installation*, is added to address aging pool installations. This new requirement permits the authority having jurisdiction to require periodic inspection and testing of all installations under the scope of Article 680. As written, this new section will have no impact, whatsoever, on new installations. It is well understood that aging pool installations can create shock and other hazards due to equipment failure, termination failure, lack of maintenance or additions/repairs that are not in compliance with Article 680. Many municipalities have regulations that require annual inspections of commercial and public pools. However, it is extremely uncommon to see any inspections of aging privately owned pools.

FRs: 8737, 8746
SR: 8057

Underground Wiring

Courtesy of Donny Cook

Significance of the Change

Requirements for underground wiring in Section 680.11 are revised to include additional wiring methods, to add a prescriptive distance from the pool, and for clarity. This requirement is separated into three first-level subdivisions for logical separation of the requirements and for clarity. 680.11(A) *Underground Wiring* now permits underground wiring within 5 feet horizontally from the inside wall of the pool. The permitted wiring methods are provided in a list format. Previously permitted wiring methods, including RMC, IMC, PVC, and RTRC, are in list items (1) through (4). Type MC cable is now permitted in list item (5) provided that it is jacketed and listed for burial use. Two new wiring methods are listed. New list item (6) liquidtight flexible nonmetallic conduit is listed for direct burial use, and (7) liquidtight flexible metal conduit is listed for direct burial use. First-level subdivision 680.11(B) *Wiring Under Pools* continues to prohibit underground wiring under the pool unless it is necessary to supply pool equipment permitted in this Article. 680.11(C) *Minimum Cover Requirements* requires burial depths in accordance with Table 300.5.

Code Language

680.11 Underground Wiring. Underground wiring shall comply with 680.11(A) through (C).

(A) Underground Wiring. Underground wiring within 1.5 m (5 ft) horizontally from the inside wall of the pool shall be permitted. The following wiring methods shall be considered suitable for the conditions in these locations:

(1) Rigid metal conduit, (2) Intermediate metal conduit, (3) Rigid polyvinyl chloride conduit, (4) Reinforced thermosetting resin conduit, (5) Jacketed Type MC cable that is listed for burial use, (6) Liquidtight flexible nonmetallic conduit listed for direct burial use, (7) Liquidtight flexible metal conduit listed for direct burial use

(B) Wiring Under Pools.

(C) Minimum Cover Requirements.

(See NEC for actual text)

Change Summary

- Section 680.11 is editorially revised into subdivisions for clarity.
- In general, underground wiring is permitted within 5 feet of the inside wall of the pool.
- Permitted wiring methods are provided in seven list items.

FR: 8801
SR: 8071

GFCI Protection/Replacement of Pool Pump Motors

Code Language

680.21 Motors.

(C) GFCI Protection. Outlets supplying all pool motors on branch circuits rated 150 volts or less to ground and 60 amperes or less, single- or 3-phase, shall be provided with Class A ground-fault circuit-interrupter protection.

Exception: Listed low-voltage motors not requiring grounding, with ratings not exceeding the low-voltage contact limit that are supplied by listed transformers or power supplies that comply with 680.23(A)(2), shall be permitted to be installed without GFCI protection.

(D) Pool Pump Motor Replacement. Where a pool pump motor in 680.21(C) is replaced for maintenance or repair, the replacement pump motor shall be provided with ground-fault circuit-interrupter protection.

(See NEC for actual text)

Change Summary

- Requirements for GFCI protection of pool motors are revised for clarity.
- An exception is provided for listed low-voltage motors not exceeding the low-voltage contact limit.
- New Section 680.21(D) requires GFCI protection for replacement pool pump motors.

Courtesy of Donny Cook

Significance of the Change

Requirements for GFCI protection of pool motors in 680.21(C) are modified for clarity. New text is added to clarify that the GFCI requirement is for the outlet and not the branch circuit supplying the pool motor. The previous reference to outlets rated 120-volts through 240-volts is deleted and the GFCI requirement now applies to pool motor outlets rated 150-volts or less to ground, and 60-amps or less single or three-phase. The new text requires Class A GFCI protection. This text is included to ensure that an installer does not attempt to use a device that provides SPGFCI protection (special purpose GFCI). These devices do not operate at the same current levels as a Class A device. Low-voltage motors, which were previously excluded from this GFCI requirement, continue to be excluded through an exception that provides significant clarity. This exception permits listed low-voltage motors that do not require grounding, with ratings that do not exceed the low-voltage contact limit and are supplied by listed transformers or power supplies that comply with 680.23(A)(2) to be installed without GFCI protection.

A new Section 680.21(D), now requires that where a pool pump motor requiring GFCI protection in accordance with 680.21(C) is replaced, the replacement pump motor must be provided with GFCI protection.

FRs: 8778, 8775
SR: 8095

NEW
REVISION

680.22(A)(4) & 680.22(A)(5)
Article 680 Swimming Pools, Fountains, and Similar Installations
Part II Permanently Installed Pools

GFCI Protection, Pool Equipment Room Receptacles

Courtesy of Donny Cook

Code Language

680.22(A) Receptacles.

(4) GFCI Protection. All 15- and 20-ampere, single-phase, 125-volt receptacles located within 6.0 m (20 ft) of the inside walls of a pool shall be provided with the following: protected by a Class A ground-fault circuit interrupter. Also see 680.22(A)(5).

(5) Pool Equipment Room. At least one GFCI-protected 125-volt, 15- or 20- ampere receptacle on a general-purpose circuit shall be located within a pool equipment room, and all other receptacles supplied by branch circuits rated 150 volts or less to ground within a pool equipment room shall be GFCI protected.

(See NEC for actual text)

Significance of the Change

Section 680.22 contains requirements for lighting, receptacles, and equipment. The GFCI requirements in 680.22(A)(4) are modified to require protection by a Class A GFCI. This revision is made to ensure that an installer does not choose an SPGFCI type device (special purpose GFCI). These devices do not open at the same current level as a Class A GFCI device. Additional text is added to send a user to new 680.22(A)(5), which contains GFCI requirements for receptacles in pool equipment rooms.

A new second-level subdivision 680.22(A)(5) is added to address receptacles in *Pool Equipment Rooms*. This new subdivision will require at least one GFCI-protected 125-volt, 15- or 20-ampere receptacle on a general-purpose circuit to be located within a pool equipment room. Additionally, this requirement mandates that all other receptacles supplied by branch circuits rated 150-volts or less to ground within a pool equipment room be GFCI protected. It is important to note that there is no ampere rating limitation in this requirement. This new requirement for a GFCI-protected receptacle within the pool equipment room is safety driven and recognizes that power tools may be necessary when maintenance is performed on the pool equipment within the room. Without access to a GFCI-protected receptacle within the pool equipment room, persons performing maintenance may use an extension cord run to a receptacle outlet that may not be GFCI protected.

Change Summary

- GFCI protection required in 680.22(A) must be a Class A GFCI.
- At least one GFCI-protected 125-volt, 15- or 20- ampere receptacle must be installed in pool equipment rooms.
- All other receptacles supplied by branch circuits rated 150-volts or less to ground within a pool equipment room must be GFCI protected.

FR: 8789
SR: None
SCR: 62
CC: 8128

680.22(C) & 680.22(E)

NEW
REVISION

Switching Devices, Other Equipment

Code Language

680.22 Lighting, Receptacles and Equipment

(C) Switching Devices. Switching devices shall be located at least 1.5 m (5 ft) horizontally from the inside walls of a pool unless separated from the pool by a solid fence, wall, or other permanent barrier that provides at least a 1.5 m (5 ft) reach distance... (See *NEC* text)

(E) Other Equipment. Other equipment with ratings exceeding the low-voltage contact limit shall be located at least 1.5 m (5 ft) horizontally from the inside walls of a pool unless separated from the pool by a solid fence, wall, or other permanent barrier.

(See NEC for actual text)

Change Summary

- 680.22(C) is modified to address a 5-foot reach distance around a fence, wall, or barrier to a switching device.
- New 680.22(E) requires that other equipment exceeding the low-voltage contact limit be located 5 feet or more from the inside wall of the pool.
- This includes any type of electrical equipment, such as standby generators or alternate power sources.

Courtesy of Tesla Energy

Significance of the Change

Requirements for lighting, receptacles, and equipment in the area around the pool are addressed in 680.22. Switching devices are required to be at least 5 feet horizontally from the inside walls of a pool unless separated from the pool by a solid fence, wall, or other permanent barrier. As written, this infers that a switching device is inaccessible from the pool area. New text is added to clarify that the 5-foot measurement can wrap around a wall or partition. The revised text clarifies that the separation distance is a solid fence, wall, or other permanent barrier that provides at least a *five-foot reach distance*.

A new first-level subdivision 680.22(E) is added to address *Other Equipment* in the area around the pool. This requirement is extremely general in nature, and mandates that other equipment with ratings exceeding the low-voltage contact limit be located at least 5 feet horizontally from the inside walls of a pool unless separated from the pool by a solid fence, wall, or other permanent barrier. This new text addresses any type of electrical equipment, including, but not limited to, standby generators, and alternate power sources, such as wind energy or PV.

FR: 8791
SR: 8106

Equipotential Bonding, Bonded Parts

Courtesy of Donny Cook

Significance of the Change

Section 680.26 addresses equipotential bonding around pools. The intent of this section, as seen in 680.26(A) *Performance*, is to reduce voltage gradients in the pool area. This issue of voltage gradients in the pool area has seen significant attention over the last several *Code* cycles. All of the requirements in Article 680 exist to protect persons from shock hazards in and around pools and similar areas. There were multiple significant revisions in 680.26 this cycle.

Requirements for *bonded parts* are located in 680.26(B). There are seven second-level subdivisions to address bonding requirements for equipment and material in the pool area. 680.26(B)(1) is modified to clarify that conductive pool shells are not poured in place concrete they are *cast in place concrete.* A new last sentence is added to require that reconstructed pool shells meet all of the requirements of 680.26. The reconstruction of a pool shell will impact perimeter surfaces, and older pools must be upgraded to the latest bonding requirements in Article 680.

Perimeter surface bonding requirements in 680.26(B)(2) are editorially modified to rename (b) *Alternate means* to (b) *Copper Ring*. A new List item (c) *Copper Grid* reintroduces the use of copper grid, as seen in previous additions of the *NEC*. There are now three methods to comply with 680.26(B)(2), *structural reinforcing steel, copper ring, or copper grid*.

680.26(B)(5) *Metal Fittings* is modified to address metallic pool cover anchors. These metal anchors do not require bonding.

Code Language

680.26 Equipotential Bonding.

(B) Bonded Parts.

(1) Conductive Pool Shells. …(See *NEC* text) Cast in place concrete… (See *NEC* text). Reconstructed pool shells shall also meet the requirements of this section.

(2) Perimeter Surfaces. …(See *NEC* text)

(a) *Structural Reinforcing Steel.*

(b) *Copper Ring.*

(c) *Copper Grid.*

(5) Metal Fittings. …(See *NEC* text) Metallic pool cover anchors intended for insertion in a concrete or masonry deck surface, 25 mm (1 in.) or less in any dimension and 51 mm (2 in.) or less in length, and metallic pool cover anchors intended for insertion in a wood or composite deck surface, 51 mm (2 in.) or less in any flange dimension and 51 mm (2 in.) or less in length, shall not require bonding.

(See NEC for actual text)

Change Summary

- Reconstructed pool shells must meet all of the requirements of 680.26.
- Permitted methods for perimeter bonding are expanded to include *Copper Grid*.
- Metallic pool cover anchors are not required to be bonded.

FRs: 8825, 8839
SR: 8126

Storable and Portable Immersion Pools

Code Language

680.35 Storable and Portable Immersion Pools. ...(See NEC text)

(A) Cord Connection for Self-Contained Storable and Portable Immersion Pools.

(B) Storable and Portable Pumps.

(C) Storable and Portable Heaters.

(D) Audio Equipment.

(E) Location Proximate to Luminaires, Lighting Outlets, and Ceiling-Suspended (Paddle) Fans.

(F) Location Proximate to Switches.

(G) Receptacles.

(See NEC for actual text)

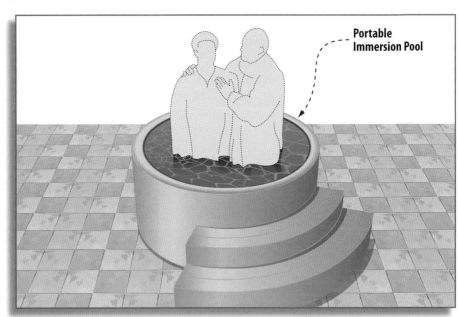

Portable Immersion Pool

Change Summary

- A new Section 680.35 provides requirements for storable and portable immersion pools.

- These pools are intended for ceremonial or ritual immersion of persons.

- This new requirement mirrors existing requirements for other pools mandating distances and GFCI protection.

FRs: 8904, 8897

SR: 8131

Significance of the Change

The title of Part III in Article 680 is modified to include *storable immersion pools*. A new Section 680.35 is added to provide requirements for *Storable and Portable Immersion Pools*. There are seven first-level subdivisions to logically separate requirements for storable and portable immersion pools. 680.35(A) contains requirements for cord connections and permits self-contained storable and portable immersion pools with identified integral switches, controls, pumps, etc. rated at 120-volts and 20-amps or less. These units are permitted to be cord and plug connected with a cord not shorter than 6 feet but not longer than 15 feet and must be GFCI protected. 680.35(B) requires cord connected pumps used with immersion pools to be listed, identified for swimming pool and spa use, and comply with 680.31. 680.35(C) provides requirements for storable and portable heaters. The requirements are similar to those in 680.35(A) with respect to rating and GFCI protection. Provisions are included for heaters 250-volts and 30-amps or less, which must also be GFCI protected. 680.35(D) prohibits audio equipment in or on a pool and provides requirements for audio equipment and GFCI protection if it is installed within 6 feet from the inside walls of the pool. 680.35(E) prohibits luminaires on or in a storable immersion pool and requires a 10-foot distance from all outlets. 680.35(F) requires that switches be installed at least 5 feet from the pool. 680.35(G) requires that all receptacles 250-volts, 50-amps or less within 20 feet of the inside wall of the pool that are used to supply the pool in any manner to comply with 680.32 and 680.34 for GFCI and location requirements.

NEW

680.45
Article 680 Swimming Pools, Fountains, and Similar Installations
Part IV Spas, Hot Tubs, and Permanently Installed Immersion Pools

Permanently Installed Immersion Pools

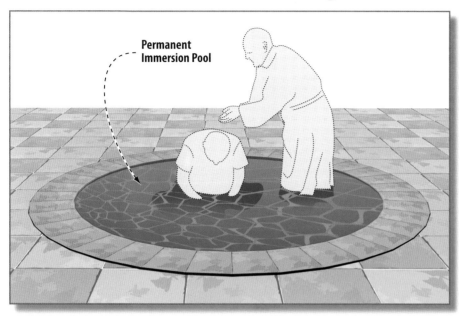

Permanent Immersion Pool

Code Language

680.45 Permanently Installed Immersion Pools. Electrical installations at permanently installed immersion pools, whether installed indoors or outdoors, shall comply with the provisions of Part I, Part II, and Part IV of this article except as modified by this section and shall be connected by the wiring methods of Chapter 3. With regard to provisions in Part IV of this article, an immersion pool shall be considered to be a spa or hot tub.

(A) Cord and Plug Connections.

(B) Storable and Portable Pumps.

(C) Heaters.

(C)(1) Permanently Installed Heaters.

(C)(2) Storable and Portable Heaters.

(D) Audio Equipment.

(See NEC for actual text)

Significance of the Change

The title of Part IV in Article 680 is modified to include *permanently installed immersion pools*. A new Section 680.45 is added to provide requirements for *Permanently Installed Immersion Pools*. There are four first-level subdivisions to logically separate requirements for permanently installed immersion pools. The parent text of this section requires permanently installed immersion pools installed indoors or outdoors, to comply with Part I, Part II, and Part IV of Article 680, except as modified by this section. The requirements in Part IV are applied because an immersion pool is considered to be a spa or hot tub. 680.45(A) contains requirements for cord and plug connections rated at 120-volts and 20-amps or less. These units are permitted to be cord and plug, connected with a cord not shorter than 6 feet and not longer than 15 feet, and must be GFCI protected. 680.45(B) requires cord connected pumps used with, but not permanently connected, to be identified for swimming pool and spa use, and be constructed with double insulation or its equivalent. GFCI protection is required and must be an integral part of the attachment plug or located in the power supply cord within 12 inches of the attachment plug. 680.45(C) provides requirements for permanently installed, storable, and portable heaters. All heaters supplied at 150-volts or less to ground must be GFCI protected. Cord and plug connections are permitted and are similar to 680.45(A). 680.45(D) prohibits audio equipment in or on a permanently installed immersion pool and provides requirements for audio equipment and GFCI protection if it is installed within 6 feet from the inside walls of the pool.

Change Summary

- New 680.45 provides requirements for permanently installed immersion pools.
- These pools are intended for ceremonial or ritual immersion of persons.
- This new requirement mirrors existing requirements for other types of pools mandating distances and GFCI protection.

FR: 8907
SRs: 8136, 8135

680.53 & 680.54

Article 680 Swimming Pools, Fountains, and Similar Installations

Part V Fountains

Grounding and Bonding

Code Language

680.54 Grounding and Bonding.

(A) Grounding. The following equipment shall be connected to the equipment grounding conductor: ... (See *NEC* text)

(B) Bonding. ... (See *NEC* text)

(1) All metal piping systems... (See *NEC* text)

(2) All metal fittings... (See *NEC* text)

(3) Metal parts of electrical equipment associated with the fountain water-circulating system, including pump motors

(4) & *(5)* Metal raceways *(All metal surfaces)* that are within 5 ft of the inside wall or perimeter of the fountain and that are not separated from the fountain by a permanent barrier

(6) Electrical devices and controls that are not associated with the fountain and are located less than 1.5 m (5 ft) of the inside wall or perimeter of the fountain

(See NEC for actual text)

Change Summary

- 680.53 is deleted, and bonding requirements are relocated into 680.54.
- Metal fittings, raceways, other electrical equipment, fittings, and piping systems must all be bonded.
- All parts must be bonded together and connected to an EGC.

Significance of the Change

Section 680.53 *Bonding* is deleted, and requirements for bonding metal piping systems associated with fountains are significantly expanded and relocated into 680.54. The previous bonding requirements were general and simply identified as "all metal piping systems associated with the fountain." Section 680.54 is separated into first-level subdivisions for clarity. The existing grounding requirements of 680.54 are relocated into first-level subdivision 680.54(A) *Grounding*. A new second-level subdivision 680.54(B) *Bonding* is added to address bonding and requires all metal parts in six new list items to be bonded together and connected to an equipment grounding conductor on a branch circuit supplying the fountain. The following metal equipment is required to be bonded in 680.54(B): (1) all metal piping systems associated with the fountain, (2) all metal parts within or attached to the fountain, (3) all metal parts of electrical equipment associated with the fountain (this includes all of the circulating system and any pumps and motors), (4)/(5) all metal raceways and all metal surfaces within 5 feet of the inside wall or perimeter of the fountain that are not separated by a permanent barrier, (6) all electrical devices and controls not associated with the fountain that are located less than 5 feet from the inside wall or perimeter of the fountain.

FR: 8910
SR: 8138

GFCI, Permanently Installed Nonsubmersible Pumps

Code Language

680.59 GFCI Protection for Permanently Installed Nonsubmersible Pumps. Outlets supplying all permanently installed nonsubmersible pump motors rated 250 volts or less and 60 amperes or less, single- or 3-phase, shall be provided with ground-fault circuit-interrupter protection.

(See NEC for actual text)

Significance of the Change

A new Section 680.59 is added into Part V *Fountains*. This section is titled *GFCI Protection for Permanently Installed Nonsubmersible Pumps*. The first section in Part V *Fountains*, 680.50 *General* requires that Part I and Part V of Article 680 apply to all permanently installed fountains. Part I of Article 680 does not contain any GFCI requirements. GFCI requirements for permanently installed pools are located in 680.21(C). Submersible pumps used in a permanently installed fountain are required to be protected by a GFCI in 680.51(A). However, prior to this new section, permanently installed non-submersible pumps were not required to be GFCI protected.

All permanently installed non-submersible pumps used in a permanently installed fountain must be GFCI protected. Outlets supplying all pump motors rated 250-volts or less and 60-amps or less, single- or 3-phase are included.

Change Summary

- New 680.59 requires GFCI protection for permanently installed non-submersible pumps supplying a fountain.
- The GFCI requirements of 680.51(A) applied only to submersible pumps.
- This applies to all pumps rated 250-volts or less and 60-amps or less, single- or 3-phase.

FR: 8911

SR: None

Electrically Powered Pool Lifts

Code Language

680.80 General. ... (See *NEC* text) Part VIII shall not be subject to the requirements of other parts of this article except where the requirements are specifically referenced.

680.82 Protection. Pool lifts connected to premises wiring and operated above the low-voltage contact limit shall be provided with GFCI protection and comply with 680.5.

680.84 Switching Devices and Receptacles. Switches and switching devices that are operated above the low-voltage contact limit shall comply with 680.22(C). Receptacles for electrically powered pool lifts that are operated above the low-voltage contact limit shall comply with 680.22(A)(3) and (A)(4).

(See NEC for actual text)

Change Summary

- The application of Parts I through VII with Part VIII is clarified.
- GFCI requirements in 680.82 must comply with 680.5.
- 680.84 is modified to include receptacles, and to mandate compliance with 680.22(A)(3) and (A)(4).

Significance of the Change

Part VIII of Article 680 contains requirements for *electrically powered pool lifts*. The first section in Part VIII, 680.80 *General* did not provide any guidance on how Parts I through VII impacted the requirements of Part VIII in the 2017 *NEC*. New text is added in 680.80, explaining that Part VIII is not subject to the requirements of other parts of Article 680 unless those requirements are specifically referenced in Part VIII.

Section 680.82 *Protection* requires pool lifts connected to premises wiring that operates above the low voltage contact limit be provided with GFCI protection. This requirement is also revised to require that Section 680.5 applies to pool lifts connected to premises wiring that operates above the low voltage contact limit. 680.5 requires that GFCIs be self-contained units, circuit-breaker or receptacle types, or other listed types and that the GFCI requirements in Article 680, unless otherwise noted, are in addition to the requirements in 210.8.

The title of Section 680.84 is revised to include receptacles. This section requires that switches and switching devices that are operated above the low-voltage contact limit shall comply with 680.22(C), which requires 5-foot separation from the inside walls of the pool for switching devices. A new last sentence is added to require that receptacles operated above the low voltage contact limit comply with 680.22(A)(3) and (A)(4). These requirements mandate that all 15/20 amp, single-phase, 125-volt receptacles within 20 feet of the inside wall of a pool be GFCI protected.

FR: 8751
SRs: 8139, 8140

Industrial Application

Code Language

682.4 Industrial Application. This article shall not apply in industrial applications where there is alarm indication of equipment faults and the following conditions are in place:

(1) Conditions of maintenance and supervision ensure that only qualified persons service and operate the installed systems.

(2) Continued circuit operation is necessary for safe operation of equipment or processes.

(See NEC for actual text)

Significance of the Change

Article 682 provides requirements for *Natural and Artificially Made Bodies of Water*. Natural bodies of water include natural lakes, natural ponds, creeks, and rivers. Artificially made bodies of water include man-made lakes and ponds. For example, Lake Mead just east of Las Vegas is a man-made lake. Artificially made bodies of water would also include ponds for fisheries, water collection/processing at water treatment and wastewater facilities, mining operations, industrial facilities, and many more.

A new Section 682.4 *Industrial Application* is added to provide conditions to allow industrial applications to be exempt from the requirements of Article 682. This requirement allows industrial applications to be exempt from the requirements of Article 682 where there is alarm indication of equipment faults and the following two conditions exist: (1) conditions of maintenance and supervision to ensure that only qualified persons service and operate the installed systems, and (2) continued circuit operation is necessary for safe operation of equipment or processes.

This exemption of requirements for industrial applications is necessary due to the unique characteristics of water treatment and wastewater facilities. There are multiple other industrial applications that may not be able to function without this exemption.

Change Summary

- New 682.4 exempts some industrial applications from the requirements of 682.
- Conditions of maintenance and supervision must ensure that only qualified persons service and operate the system.
- Continued circuit operation must be necessary for the safe operation of equipment or processes.

FR: None
SR: 8143

Electrical Datum Plane Distances

Code Language

682.5 Electrical Datum Plane Distances. The electrical datum plane shall consist of one of the following:

(1) In land areas subject to tidal fluctuation... (See *NEC* text)

(2) In land areas not subject to tidal fluctuation

(3) In land areas subject to flooding... (See *NEC* text)

The electrical datum plane for floating structures and landing stages that are (a) installed to permit rise and fall response to water level, without lateral movement, and (b) that are so equipped that they can rise to the datum plane established for (1) or (2) above, shall be a horizontal plane 750 mm (30 in.) above the water level at the floating structure or landing stage and a minimum of 300 mm (12 in.) above the level of the deck.

(See NEC for actual text)

Change Summary

- The definition of *Electrical Datum Plane* is deleted from 680.2.
- New Section 682.5 is titled *Electrical Datum Plane Distances* and is modified editorially to contain mandatory language.
- Three new definitions for Pier are added into Article 100.

FR: 8915
SR: None
SCR: 77

Significance of the Change

A new definition of *Electrical Datum Plane* is added into Article 100 this revision cycle. The existing definition of *Electrical Datum Plane* in 682.2 is deleted and relocated into a new Section 682.5. The definition added to Article 100 is generic as follows:

> **Electrical Datum Plane.** A specified distance above a water level, above which electrical equipment can be installed and electrical connections can be made. (CMP-7)

New Section 682.5 is titled *Electrical Datum Plane Distances* and is modified editorially to contain mandatory language. This revision is part of a global effort to correlate terms used throughout the *NEC*, specifically in Article 555 for *Marinas, Boatyards, Floating Buildings, and Commercial and Noncommercial Docking Facilities* and Article 682. Additionally, there are three new definitions for Pier added into Article 100. These definitions will now apply to electrical installations within the scope of Article 682. Those definitions are:

> **Pier.** A structure extending over the water and supported on a fixed foundation (fixed pier), or on flotation (floating pier), that provides access to the water. [303:3.3.17] (CMP-7)

> **Pier, Fixed.** Pier constructed on a permanent, fixed foundation, such as on piles, that permanently establishes the elevation of the structure deck with respect to land. [303:3.3.17.2] (CMP-7)

> **Pier, Floating.** Pier designed with inherent flotation capability that allows the structure to float on the water surface and rise and fall with water level changes. [303:3.3.17.3] (CMP-7)

Ground-Fault Protection

Courtesy of Donny Cook

Significance of the Change

Ground fault circuit interrupter protection (GFCI) requirements in Article 682 are expanded and modified for clarity. New ground fault protection requirements are added for feeders and branch circuits on piers.

Existing Section 682.15 is modified with a new title, new parent text, and is separated into first-level subdivisions for clarity. 682.15 *Ground-Fault Protection* now clarifies that the GFCI requirements of 210.8 apply in all areas under the scope of Article 682. Additionally, the protective devices required must be located not less than 12 inches above the established electrical datum plane. 682.15(A) *Outlets* now requires that all outlets supplied by branch circuits not exceeding 150-volts to ground and 60 amps, single phase, be GFCI protected. 682.15(B) *Feeder and Branch Circuits on Piers* requires that feeders and branch circuit conductors installed on piers be provided with GFP protection not exceeding 30 mA. It is important to note that there are three new definitions located in Article 100 for *Piers*. Additional text permits coordination with downstream ground fault protection at the feeder overcurrent protective device. This will permit the feeder overcurrent protective device to be protected at a value above 30 mA. There are two exceptions added for 682.15(B). These exceptions exempt transformer secondary conductors not exceeding 15-volts ac that do not exceed 10-feet and low-voltage circuits not requiring grounding and not exceeding the low-voltage contact limit as defined in 680.2. The last sentence of 682.33(B) is deleted. The GFCI requirements located there were out of place.

Code Language

682.15 Ground-Fault Protection. The GFCI ... (See *NEC* text) in addition to the requirements in 210.8... (See *NEC* text) The protection device shall be located not less than 300 mm (12 in.) above the established electrical datum plane.

(A) Outlets. Outlets supplied by branch circuits not exceeding 150 volts to ground and 60 amperes, single-phase, shall be provided with GFCI protection for personnel.

(B) Feeder and Branch Circuits on Piers. ... (See *NEC* text) shall be provided with ground-fault protection not exceeding 30 mA. Coordination with downstream GFP shall be permitted at the feeder overcurrent protective device.

Exception No. 1

Exception No. 2

(See NEC for actual text)

Change Summary

- 682.15 is modified to now address GFP and GFCI requirements.
- Feeders and branch circuits supplying piers are now required to be GFP protected.
- In addition to the requirements of 682.15(A), Section 210.8 applies in all areas under the scope of Article 682.

FRs: 8915, 8917

SR: 8029

SCR: 65

Bonding Equipotential Planes

Code Language

682.33 (C) Bonding.

(1) Bonded Parts. ... (See *NEC* text)

(2) Outdoor Service Equipment and Disconnects. Outdoor service equipment or disconnecting means that control equipment in or on water, that have a metallic enclosure and controls accessible to personnel, and that are likely to become energized shall be bonded to the equipotential plane.

(3) Walking Surfaces. Surfaces directly below the equipment specified in 682.33(C)(2) but not less than 900 mm (36 in.) in all directions from the equipment from which a person would be able to stand and come in contact with the equipment shall be bonded to the equipotential plane. Bonding to this surface shall be wire mesh or other conductive elements on, embedded in, or placed under the walk surface within 75 mm (3 in.).

(See NEC for actual text)

Change Summary

- 682.33(C) is modified to clarify equipotential plane bonding requirements.
- 682.33(C)(2) identifies equipment to be bonded.
- 682.33(C)(3) requires wire mesh or other conductive elements embedded on/in or placed under the walking surface within 3 inches.

FR: 8920
SR: None

Significance of the Change

Section 682.33 provides requirements for equipotential planes and bonding of equipotential planes. The intent of this requirement is to mitigate step and touch voltages at electrical equipment. 682.33(A) requires that equipotential planes be installed at outdoor service equipment or disconnects that control equipment in or on the water that has a metallic enclosure and controls that are accessible to persons. The equipotential plane must extend 36 inches in all directions from where a person would be able to stand and come in contact with the equipment.

First-level subdivision 682.33(C) *Bonding* is separated into second-level subdivisions for clarity and modified to prescriptively identify the equipment and walking surfaces to be bonded. 682.33(C)(1) retains the existing requirement to bond identified parts to the electrical grounding system with a copper conductor not smaller than 8 AWG. These bonding connections must be made by exothermic welding, or listed pressure connectors or clamps, made of stainless steel brass copper or copper alloy. New 682.33(C)(2) *Outdoor Service Equipment and Disconnects* requires that outdoor service equipment or disconnects that control equipment in or on the water with a metallic enclosure accessible to personnel must be bonded to the equipotential plane. New 682.33(C)(3) *Walking Surfaces* requires surfaces below the equipment referenced in 682.33(C)(2) be bonded to the equipotential plane. This bonding must include wire mesh or other conductive elements embedded on/in or placed under the walking surface within 3 inches. The 3-foot distance referenced in 682.33(A) is repeated.

690.2 & 690.6

Article 690 Solar Photovoltaic (PV) Systems

Part I General

AC Modules and Systems

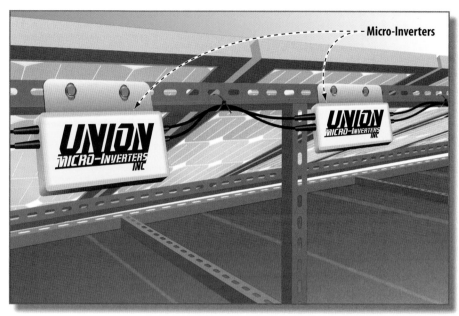

Micro-Inverters

Code Language

690.2 AC Module System. An assembly of ac modules, wiring methods, materials, and subassemblies that are evaluated, identified, and defined as a system.

690.6 AC Modules and Systems.

(A) PV Source Circuits. The requirements of Article 690 pertaining to PV source circuits shall not apply to ac modules or ac module systems. The PV source circuit, conductors, and inverters shall be considered as internal components of an ac module or ac module system.

(See NEC for actual text)

Significance of the Change

A new definition of *AC Module System* is added in 690.2 to correlate with the new requirements for *AC Module Systems*. These systems are an assembly of ac modules, wiring methods, materials, and subassemblies that are evaluated, identified, and defined as a system. This new definition is necessary for proper application of the revised requirement in 690.6 related to ac module systems. These *AC Module Systems* incorporate multiple array components into functional systems that are optimized for specific configurations. *AC Module Systems* are typically field assembled but are limited to the manufacturers' specific configurations and equipment. As noted in the committee statement to support the addition of this new definition, these new designs may increase the reliability of PV systems.

The title of Section 690.6 is modified to include *AC Systems*. This section is revised to clarify that the requirements of Article 690 that pertain to PV source circuits do not apply to *AC Module Systems*. Additional text in this section clarifies that the PV source circuit conductors, and inverters, are considered as internal components of an AC module or an *AC Module System*.

Change Summary

- An *AC Module System* is an assembly of ac modules, wiring methods, materials, and subassemblies that are evaluated, identified, and defined as a system.
- Requirements for PV source circuits do not apply to *AC Module Systems*.
- PV source circuit conductors and inverters are considered as internal components of an AC module or an *AC Module System*.

FRs: 8520, 8152
SRs: 7876, 7930

Definition of Array

Code Language

690.2 Array. A mechanically and electrically integrated grouping of modules with support structure, including any attached system components such as inverter(s) or dc-to-dc converter(s) and attached associated wiring.

(See NEC for actual text)

Change Summary

- The definition of *array* is modified to include equipment that is essential for the safe conversion of sunlight to electricity.
- This definition is clarified to enhance implementation of requirements that reference the array, including those for rapid shutdown.
- An *array* is a mechanically and electrically integrated grouping of modules with a support structure.

Significance of the Change

The definition of the term *array* is modified for clarity. Requirements for rapid shutdown of PV systems on buildings are based upon the *array boundary*. These rapid shutdown requirements include controlled limits, and the *array boundary* is clarified to include all mechanical and electrical components up to one foot from the *array* in all directions. The intent of this revision is to limit an array to equipment that is essential for the safe conversion of sunlight to electricity. PV systems may include multiple arrays. This revision clarifies that an *array* is a mechanically and *electrically* integrated grouping of modules with a support structure. The reference to an *assembly of modules* is deleted. An *array* is now a *grouping of modules* with a support structure. The additional text clarifies that any attached system components, such as inverters or dc-to-dc converters and attached associated wiring are part of the *array*. The reference to a structure foundation is deleted because the foundation has nothing to do with the function of electrical components in the array. The reference to a *tracker* is deleted because it is included in the reference to "support structure."

There were multiple other changes in 690.2 that relocated some definitions to Article 100 and deleted those that were not necessary.

FR: 8519
SR: None

Electronic Power Converters

Significance of the Change

A new definition of *Electronic Power Converter* is added in 690.2. This term includes many different types of devices and refers to them generally as a device that uses power electronics to convert one form of electrical power into another form of electrical power. The associated informational note (IN) provides examples of these devices, which includes, but is not limited to inverters, dc-to-dc converters, and electronic charge controllers. The IN also explains that these *Electronic Power Converters* have limited current capabilities based on the device ratings at continuous rated power.

A new first-level subdivision 690.4(F) *Electronic Power Converters Mounted in Not Readily Accessible Locations* permits these devices to be mounted on roofs or other exterior areas that are not readily accessible and requires a disconnect in accordance with 690.15.

Section 690.8 contains requirements for circuit sizing and current. 690.8(A) contains requirements for the calculation of maximum circuit current and permits one of the methods listed in 690.8(A)(1) or (A)(2). A new 690.8(A)(2) *Circuits Connected to the Input of Electronic Power Converters* is added to clarify that the maximum current is permitted to be the rated input of the electronic power converter where the circuit is protected with an overcurrent device not exceeding the conductor ampacity.

Editorially, the term *Electronic Power Converters* is used throughout Article 690.

Code Language

690.2 Electronic Power Converter. A device that uses power electronics to convert one form of electrical power into another form of electrical power.

Informational Note: Examples of electronic power converters include, but are not limited to, inverters, dc-to-dc converters, and electronic charge controllers. These devices have limited current capabilities based on the device ratings at continuous rated power.

690.4(F) Electronic Power Converters Mounted in Not Readily Available Locations. ... (See *NEC* text)

690.8(A)(2) Circuits Connected to the Input of Electronic Power Converters. ... (See *NEC* text)

(See NEC for actual text)

Change Summary

- A new definition is added to 690.2 to address all electronic power converters.
- **Electronic Power Converter.** A device that uses power electronics to convert one form of electrical power into another form of electrical power.
- Multiple new requirements are added to address accessibility and maximum current of these devices.

FRs: 8526, 8574, 8194
SRs: 7893, 8133

Source and Output Circuits

Code Language

PV Source Circuit. The dc circuit conductors between modules and from modules to dc combiners, electronic power converters, or a dc PV system disconnecting means.

PV Output Circuit.

PV System DC Circuit.

DC-to-DC Converter Source Circuit.

DC-to-DC Converter Output Circuit.

(See NEC for actual text)

Change Summary

- Multiple definitions of source and output circuits in 690.2 are modified for clarity.
- Proper application of Article 690 requires an understanding of all of these definitions.
- A *PV Source Circuit* is the dc circuit conductors between modules, and from modules to dc combiners, electronic power converters, or a dc PV system disconnecting means.

FRs: 8555, 8557, 8522, 8559

SRs: 7910, 8129, 8130, 7885, 7887

Significance of the Change

Multiple revisions are made to provide clarity with respect to source and output circuits. These definitions are critical to the application of requirements throughout Article 690. The definition of *Photovoltaic Power Source* is deleted because this term is self-explanatory and does not sufficiently describe a PV system. The term *PV Source Circuit* is modified to clarify that it is the dc circuit conductors between modules and from modules to the dc combiners, electronic power converters or a dc PV system disconnecting means. The definition of *PV Output Circuit* is modified to include only the dc circuit conductors from two or more connected PV source circuits to their point of termination. The previous text identified conductors between the PV source circuit and the inverter or dc utilization equipment. The definition of *PV System DC Circuit* is clarified to cover any dc conductor in PV source circuits, PV output circuits, dc-to-dc converter source circuits and dc-to-dc converter output circuits. The definition of *DC-to-DC Converter Output Circuit* is modified for clarity removing the termination point from dc utilization equipment to the dc PV system disconnecting means as follows: The dc circuit conductors connected to the output of a dc combiner for dc-to-dc converter source circuits.

The definition of *DC-to-DC Converter Source Circuit* remains unchanged.

NEW
REVISION

Overcurrent Protection of Circuits and Equipment

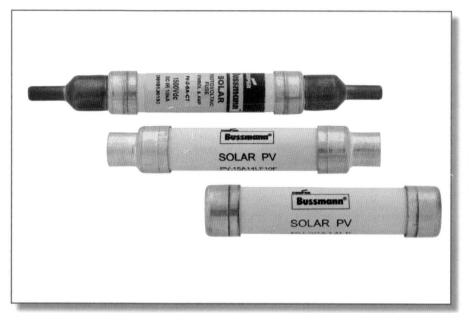

Courtesy of Eaton

Code Language

690.9 Overcurrent Protection.
(A) Circuits and Equipment.
(A)(1) Circuits Where Overcurrent Protection Not Required.
(A)(2) Circuits Where Overcurrent Protection is Required on One End.
(A)(3) Other Circuits
(B) Device Ratings.

(See NEC for actual text)

Significance of the Change

Section 690.9 provides requirements for overcurrent protection. 690.9(A) requires all PV system dc circuit and inverter output conductors and equipment to be protected against overcurrent. Three new second-level subdivisions are added for clarity. The previous exception is rolled into positive text in 690.6(A)(1), for circuits where overcurrent protection is not required. New 690.9(A)(2) provides requirements for conductors that must have overcurrent protection on one end. This requirement addresses a conductor rated for the maximum current from a current limited supply that is also connected to a source having an available maximum circuit current greater than the ampacity of the conductor. In this case, the conductor must be protected from overcurrent at the point of connection to the higher current source. 690.9(A)(3) *Other Circuits* addresses all circuits that do not comply with 690.9(A)(1) or (A)(2). These overcurrent requirements mandate one of the following methods: (1) conductors not longer than 10 feet in length and not in buildings be protected on one end, (2) conductors not longer than 10 feet in length and in buildings be protected on one end and be installed in raceway or metal-clad cable, (3) conductors protected from overcurrent on both ends. 690.9(A)(3)(4) permits conductors not installed on or in buildings to be protected from overcurrent on one end where the circuit complies with four list items. New text in 690.9(B) *Device Ratings* permits electronic devices that are listed to prevent backfeed current in PV system dc circuits to prevent overcurrent of conductors on the PV array side of the device.

Change Summary

- Requirements for overcurrent protection in 690.9 are significantly revised.
- The existing exception is located in positive text to 690.9(A)(1).
- Two new second-level subdivisions are added to address situations where overcurrent protection is required on one end and all other circuits.

FR: 8226
SRs: 7951, 7952, 7959
SCR: 1
CC: 7966

Rapid Shutdown of PV on Buildings

Code Language

690.12 Rapid Shutdown of PV on Buildings. PV system circuits installed on or in buildings shall include a rapid shutdown function to reduce shock hazard for firefighters... (See *NEC* text)

(A) Controlled Conductors. Requirements for controlled conductors shall apply to the following:

(1) PV system dc circuits

(2) Inverter output circuits originating from inverters located within the array boundary

(B) Controlled Limits.

(B)(2) Inside the Array Boundary.

(C) Initiation Device.

(See NEC for actual text)

Change Summary

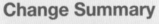

- Rapid shutdown reduces the risk of electrical shock that dc/ac circuits in a PV system could pose for firefighters.

- To prevent PV arrays with attached inverters from having energized ac conductors within the PV array(s). Those circuits are also specifically controlled after shutdown initiation.

- DC and AC circuits of PV arrays must be controlled without regard to their source of supply.

FRs: 8242, 8253, 8249, 8251

SRs: 7994, 7998, 8025, 8005

Significance of the Change

The requirements of 690.12 for rapid shutdown of PV systems on buildings are significantly revised to reduce shock hazards for firefighters. 690.12(A), *Controlled Conductors*, is revised for clarity to specifically identify the controlled conductors. The previous text of this requirement included PV circuits supplied by the PV system. This revision identifies controlled conductors in two list items including: (1) PV system dc circuits, and (2) inverter output circuits originating from inverters located within the array boundary. This revision clarifies that this requirement does not apply only to dc circuits of PV arrays. This includes any ac inverter output circuits that originate within the array boundary. It is extremely important to note that this revision clarifies that dc and ac circuits of PV arrays must be controlled without regard to their source of supply. This requires each installation be evaluated and listed equipment installed to achieve rapid shutdown. An informational note is included to explain why inverter output circuits from inverters located within the array boundary must be controlled. Requirements in 690.12(B)(1) are modified to require a *PV Hazard Control System* be listed for the purpose. The associated informational note explains that a *PV Hazard Control System* can be an individual piece of equipment or multiple pieces of equipment coordinated to fulfill necessary functions to reduce the risk of electric shock within a damaged PV array. 690.12(C) *Initiation Device* is revised to include detached garages and associated storage buildings associated with dwelling units. Additionally, new text is added to require rapid shutdown for a single PV system by the operation of any single initiating device.

Photovoltaic System Disconnecting Means

Significance of the Change

Section 690.13 requires a disconnecting means to disconnect the PV system from all wiring systems, including power systems, energy storage systems, utilization equipment, and associated premises wiring. A new last sentence is added to 690.13(A) *Location*, requiring disconnects of systems operating at above 30 volts to be locked or require a tool to open. This revision applies where an enclosure door or hinged cover that exposes live parts when open is readily accessible to unqualified persons (general public). PV systems are installed in many different venues, including dwelling units, and these systems are sometimes accessible to unqualified persons, including the general public. The intent of this revision is to eliminate potential exposure to unqualified persons. 690.13(C) *Suitable for Use* previously required a PV system disconnect that is connected to the supply side of the service disconnecting means be listed as suitable for use as service equipment. This requirement is deleted because it is covered in 705.12(A).

Requirements for the type of disconnect permitted are significantly revised in 690.13(E). The PV system disconnecting means or its remote operating device, or the enclosure providing access to the disconnecting means, must be capable of being locked in accordance with 110.25. The permitted types of disconnecting means are provided in five list items. They include a manually operable switch or circuit breaker, a connector in accordance with 690.33(D)(1) or (D)(3), a pullout switch with the required interrupting rating, a remote-controlled switch or circuit breaker, and devices listed or approved for the intended application.

Code Language

690.13 Photovoltaic System Disconnecting Means.

(A) Location. ... (See *NEC* text) Where disconnecting means of systems above 30 V are readily accessible to unqualified persons, any enclosure door or hinged cover that exposes live parts when open shall be locked or require a tool to open.

(E) Type of Disconnect. The PV system disconnecting means shall simultaneously disconnect... (See *NEC* text) The PV system disconnecting means or its remote operating device or the enclosure providing access to the disconnecting means shall be capable of being locked in accordance with 110.25... (See *NEC* text)

(See NEC for actual text)

Change Summary

- Readily accessible disconnects for systems above 30 volts, readily accessible to unqualified persons, must be locked or require a tool to open.
- 690.13(C) *Suitable for Use* is deleted because it is covered by 705.12(A).
- 690.13(E) now requires disconnects to be capable of being locked in accordance with 110.25. Five list items are provided with permitted types of disconnects.

FRs: 8264, 8266, 8290, 8295
SR: 8033

Disconnecting Means for Isolating PV Equipment

Code Language

690.15 Disconnecting Means for Isolating PV Equipment.

(A) Location.

(B) Isolating Device. ... (See *NEC* text) Where an isolating device is not rated for interrupting the circuit current, it shall be marked "Do Not Disconnect Under Load" or "Not for Current Interrupting."... (See *NEC* text)

(C) Equipment Disconnecting Means.

(D) Type of Disconnecting Means.

(See NEC for actual text)

Change Summary

- 690.15 is clarified to apply to disconnects for *isolating* PV equipment.

- This requirement is for isolation, and 690.13 requires a means to disconnect the PV system from all other systems and wiring.

- Isolating devices that are not rated for interrupting the circuit current must be marked "Do Not Disconnect Under Load" or "Not for Current Interrupting."

Significance of the Change

The title of 690.15 is revised along with the parent text, clarifying that this section addresses disconnects to isolate PV equipment. Additional modifications remove requirements related to circuits over 30 amps and relocate those into 690.15(C). Requirements in 690.15(B) *Interrupting Rating* are deleted and re-located into 690.15(C). An isolating device is not required to have an interrupting rating as per 690.15(B). These devices cannot be opened under load. A new marking requirement is added for isolating devices that are not rated for interrupting the circuit current. They must be marked "Do Not Disconnect Under Load" or "Not for Current Interrupting." The requirements related to circuits over 30 amps deleted from the parent text is significantly modified and relocated into 690.15(D) *Type of Disconnecting Means*. Where disconnects are required to isolate equipment, there are two separate requirements. (1) An equipment disconnecting means in accordance with 690.15(C) is required to isolate dc circuits with a maximum circuit current over 30 amperes. This requires the disconnect types outlined in 690.13. The second in list item (2) permits an isolating device in accordance with 690.15(B) for circuits other than those covered by 690.15(D)(1).

FRs: 8305, 8307, 8311, 8316, 8321, 8327

SRs: 8037, 8039, 8045, 8042

Wiring Systems, Identification and Grouping

Code Language

690.31 Wiring Methods.

(A) Wiring Systems.... (See *NEC* text) The ampacity of 105°C (221°F) and 125°C (257°F) conductors shall be permitted to be determined by Table 690.31(A)(b)... (See *NEC* text)

(B) Identification and Grouping. PV system dc circuits and Class 1 remote control, signaling, and power-limited circuits of a PV system shall be permitted to occupy the same equipment wiring enclosure, cable, or raceway... (See *NEC* text)

(See NEC for actual text)

Significance of the Change

New text is added in 690.31(A) to permit the ampacity of conductors rated at 105°C and 125°C to be determined by a new Table 690.31(A)(b). This table specifically recognizes conductor types PVC, CPE, and XLPE at 105°C and types XLPE and EPDM rated at 125°C. A new last sentence is added in 690.31(A) to require application of the ambient temperature correction factors in Table 690.31(A)(a) for ambient temperatures greater than 30°C. Table 690.31(A)(a) now contains only temperature correction factors for 105°C and 125°C. Other conductors must be applied as required by Article 310. 690.31(B) is revised to specifically permit PV system dc circuits and Class 1 remote control, signaling, and power-limited circuits of a PV system to occupy the same equipment, enclosures, cables, or raceways. An exception is added for PV system dc circuits in multiconductor jacketed cable, MC cable, or listed wiring harnesses identified for the application. These wiring methods shall be permitted to contain inverter output circuits and other non-PV systems. Where this exception is applied, all conductors and equipment must have an insulation rating equal to the maximum circuit voltage of any conductor. Additional text is added to clarify that PV system dc circuits must be separated from other circuits. They may only occupy the same enclosure, cable, or raceway as other non-PV systems or inverter outputs where separated by a partition. The identification requirements of 690.31(B)(1) are modified to mirror the marking requirements of 210.5(C)(2). New text is added to permit only solidly grounded PV system circuit conductors to be marked in accordance with 200.6.

Change Summary

- New Table 690.31(A)(b) is permitted for cable types PVC, CPE, and XLPE at 105°C and types XLPE and EPDM rated at 125°C.

- PV system dc circuits and Class 1 remote control, signaling and power-limited circuits of a PV system, are permitted to occupy the same equipment, enclosures, cables, or raceways.

- An exception is added in 690.31(B) for mixing PV system dc circuits and other circuits in identified wiring methods.

FRs: 8645, 8647, 8648, SRs: 8050, 8053, 8055

Cables

Code Language

690.31 Wiring Methods.

(C) Cables. Type PV wire or cable and Type distributed generation (DG) cable shall be listed.

(C) (1) Single-Conductor Cable. Single-conductor cable in exposed outdoor locations in PV system dc circuits within the PV array shall be permitted to be one of the following:

(1) PV wire or cable

(2) Single-conductor cable marked sunlight resistant and Type USE-2 and Type RHW-2

… (See *NEC* text) supported and secured at intervals not to exceed 600 mm (24 in.) … (See *NEC* text)

(C)(2) Cable Tray.

(C)(3) Multiconductor Jacketed Cables.

(See NEC for actual text)

Change Summary

- Type DG, distributed generation cable is permitted for PV installations.

- Type PV wire or cable and Type distributed generation (DG) cable must be listed.

- 690.31(C)(3) is modified to address multiconductor jacketed cables and now contains prescriptive installation requirements.

FRs: 8650, 8940

SRs: 8149, 8056, 8060, 8062

Significance of the Change

690.31(C) is retitled Cables, and 690.31(C)(1) is retitled *Single Conductor Cable*. New parent text is added to require that all PV wire or cable and Type DG cable (distributed generation) cable be listed. 690.31(C)(1) is modified to permit types of single conductor cable that is in exposed outdoor locations for PV systems and within the PV array. PV wire and cable and single conductor cable marked as sunlight resistant and Type USE-2 or RHW-2 are permitted. A new sentence is added for the support/securement of single conductor cable. Exposed cables must be supported/secured not to exceed 24 inches by cable ties, straps, hangers, or similar fittings, listed and identified for securement and support in outdoor locations. An exception for support securement references 691.4 for large scale PV installations. 690.31(C)(2) *Cable Tray* is modified to permit single conductor PV wire or cable of all sizes or distributed generation (DG) cable of all sizes, with or without a cable tray rating. Requirements for multiconductor jacketed cables in 690.31(C)(3) are modified to require cables to be installed with manufacturers' instructions and product listings. Additionally, these cables must be installed in raceways where on or in buildings other than rooftops. Where not in raceways: multiconductor jacketed cables exposed outdoors must be sunlight resistant, protected from physical damage, most closely follow the surface of the support structure, be secured at intervals not to exceed 6 feet and within 24 inches of connectors or enclosures, and must be marked direct burial where buried. Requirements in previous (E), (F), and (H) are relocated into 690.31(C).

690.31(D) & (F)
Article 690 Solar Photovoltaic (PV) Systems
Part IV Wiring Methods and Materials

DC Circuits on or in Buildings, Mounting Systems

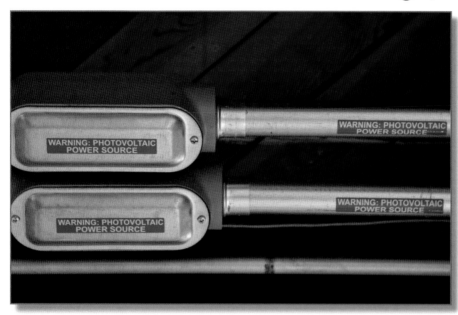

Code Language

690.31 Wiring Methods.

(D) DC Circuits on or in Buildings. Where inside buildings, PV system dc circuits that exceed 30 volts or 8 amperes shall be contained in metal raceways, in Type MC metal-clad cable that complies with 250.118(10), or in metal enclosures.

Exception: PV hazard control systems... (See *NEC* text)

(F) Wiring Methods and Mounting Systems. Roof-mounted PV array mounting systems shall be permitted to be held in place with an approved means other than those required by 110.13 and shall utilize wiring methods that allow any expected movement of the array.

(See NEC for actual text)

Significance of the Change

The previous requirements of 690.31(G) are relocated into 690.31(D), retitled as *DC Circuits on or in Buildings*, and are significantly modified. The previous requirements mandated that PV system DC circuits run inside a building must be contained in metal raceways, MC cable, or metal enclosures. The revised text requires PV system dc circuits inside buildings that exceed 30 volts or 8 amps be contained in metal raceways, MC cable, or metal enclosures. The substantiation provided for this revision noted that there is little benefit to containing low voltage and low energy circuits in metal raceways. An exception is added for PV hazard control systems. These systems are permitted in nonmetallic enclosures, nonmetallic raceways, and cables other than Type MC, at the point of penetration of the surface of the building to the PV hazard control actuator. The previous requirement for circuits embedded in building surfaces in 690.31(G)(2) is deleted, as that wiring method is no longer in use. The marking requirements in 690.31(D)(2) are modified to recognize installations where the purpose of a raceway enclosure or conduit body is evident. The marking requirements only apply where it is not evident that the circuit is PV. The required marking removes the word *warning*. These markings are not for firefighters or first responders; they are for installers/maintainers. The marking requirements are modified to permit both, PHOTOVOLTAIC POWER SOURCE or SOLAR PV DC CIRCUIT. New 690.31(F) requires PV array mounting systems to be held in place with an approved means, and to use wiring methods that allow for expected movement of the array to recognize ballasted installations.

Change Summary

- PV system dc circuits inside buildings that exceed 30 volts or 8 amps must be contained in metal raceways, MC cable or metal enclosures.

- An exception is added for PV hazard control systems.

- The marking requirements are modified to permit both, PHOTOVOLTAIC POWER SOURCE or SOLAR PV DC CIRCUIT.

FRs: 8692, 8695
SRs: 8073, 8080

System Grounding, Ground-Fault Protection

Code Language

690.41 System Grounding.

(B) Ground-Fault Protection. PV system dc circuits that exceed 30 volts or 8 amperes shall be provided with dc ground-fault protection meeting the requirements of 690.41(B)(1) and (B)(2) to reduce fire hazards... (See *NEC* text)

(B)(1) Ground-Fault Detection. ... (See *NEC* text) For dc-to-dc converters not listed as providing GFP, where required, listed GFP equipment identified for the combination of the dc-to-dc converter and GFP device shall be installed to protect the circuit.

(B)(3) Indication of Faults. Ground-fault protection equipment shall provide indication of ground faults at a readily accessible location... (See *NEC* text)

(See NEC for actual text)

Change Summary

- PV system dc circuits that exceed 30 volts or 8 amps must be provided with dc ground fault protection.

- GFP equipment is required to provide an indication of ground faults at a readily accessible location.

- Not all PV equipment includes GFP. Some dc-to-dc converters without integral GFP on their input side can prevent other GFP from functioning properly.

FRs: 8481, 8398, 8401, 8402
SRs: 8087, 8092, 8099

Significance of the Change

PV system grounding requirements are located in 690.41. 690.41(B) contains requirements for *Ground-Fault Protection* (GFP) of PV systems. The previous requirement mandated that all DC PV arrays be provided with dc ground fault protection to reduce fire hazards. The revised text requires PV system dc circuits that exceed 30 volts or 8 amps be provided with dc ground fault protection. Substantiation for this revision noted that these low-voltage and power levels do not pose an arcing or other fire risk. The reference to the threshold of 30 volts or 8 amps correlates with requirements in 690.31(D) for PV systems circuits on or in buildings. The existing exception is deleted and modified for clarity into positive text. A new informational note (IN) explains that not all inverters, charge controllers, or dc-to-dc converters include GFP. 690.41(B)(1) *Ground-Fault Detection* is modified to require dc-to-dc converters that are not listed as providing ground fault protection include listed GFP identified for the combination of the dc-to-dc converters and the GFP device utilized. A new IN explains that some dc-to-dc converters without integral GFP on their input side can prevent other GFP from functioning properly. A new second-level subdivision 690.41(B)(3), *Indication of Faults*, requires that GFP equipment provide an indication of ground faults at a readily accessible location. In many cases, inverters are not located in a readily accessible location, such as under an array or on the roof. This revision requires that indication must be provided at a readily accessible location if a ground fault occurs. A new IN provides examples of indication.

DC PV Circuits, Marking

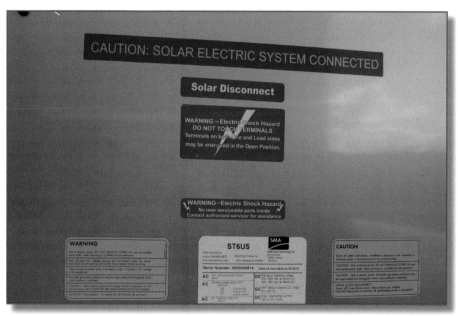

Code Language

690.53 DC PV Circuits. A permanent readily visible label indicating the highest maximum dc voltage in a PV system, calculated in accordance with 690.7, shall be provided by the installer at one of the following locations:

(1) DC PV system disconnecting means

(2) PV system electronic power conversion equipment

(3) Distribution equipment associated with the PV system

(See NEC for actual text)

Significance of the Change

The marking requirements for dc PV circuits in 690.53 are modified for clarity, recognizing both the need for these markings and the fact that listing requirements mandate marking by the manufacturers of the PV equipment. Product standards have incorporated many of the marking requirements that originated in Article 690. These marking requirements are safety driven and are needed by qualified persons that will service and maintain the equipment. This revision limits the number of labels that must be applied, as well as the amount of information contained in the label. The parent text of 690.53 is modified to require a permanent *readily visible* label that indicates the highest dc voltage in a PV system, calculated in accordance with the requirements of 690.7. There are three options for the placement of this label, including the dc PV system disconnect, the PV system electronic power conversion equipment or the distribution equipment associated with the PV system.

Change Summary

- The marking requirements of 690.53 are modified to limit the amount of information necessary, and the number of locations that must be labeled.

- The information on these labels must be available to qualified persons before servicing PV equipment.

- There are three options for the placement of this label, including the dc PV system disconnect, the PV system electronic power conversion equipment, or the distribution equipment associated with the PV system.

FR: 8711

SR: None

Buildings with Rapid Shutdown

Code Language

690.56 Identification of Power Sources.

(A) Facilities with Stand-Alone Systems. Plaques or directories shall be installed in accordance with 710.10.

(C) Buildings with Rapid Shutdown. Buildings with PV systems shall have a permanent label located at each service equipment location to which the PV systems are connected or at an approved readily visible location and shall indicate the location of rapid shutdown initiation devices. The label shall include a simple diagram of a building with a roof and shall include the following words:... (See *NEC* text)

(See NEC for actual text)

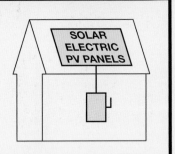

SOLAR PV SYSTEM EQUIPPED WITH RAPID SHUTDOWN

TURN RAPID SHUTDOWN SWITCH TO THE "OFF" POSITION TO SHUT DOWN PV SYSTEM AND REDUCE SHOCK HAZARD IN THE ARRAY.

SOLAR ELECTRIC PV PANELS

Change Summary

- Rapid shutdown initiation devices for standalone systems must have plaques or directories installed in accordance with 710.10.
- The required labels must include a simple diagram of a building with a roof and the required text.
- The example label is now included in an informational note figure.

Significance of the Change

Marking requirements for facilities with stand-alone systems in 690.56(A) are modified for clarity and require plaques or directories to be installed in accordance with Section 710.10.

The marking requirements for buildings with rapid shutdown in 690.56(C) are modified to relocate the general marking requirement into the parent text. Buildings with PV systems must have a permanent label at each service equipment location to which the PV systems are connected, or the label must be located at an approved readily visible location. These labels must indicate the location of all rapid shutdown initiation devices. This requirement continues to mandate the same type of label, which includes a simple diagram of the building with a roof. This diagram is modified for clarity as a label for *roof-mounted PV systems*. This label is included in an informational note figure, which is not an enforceable part of the *NEC*. However, a label of this type or similar must be installed. A new last sentence in 690.56(C) requires a simple diagram of a building with a roof, including the words:

SOLAR PV SYSTEM IS EQUIPPED WITH RAPID SHUTDOWN.
TURN RAPID SHUTDOWN SWITCH TO THE "OFF" POSITION
TO SHUT DOWN PV SYSTEM
AND REDUCE SHOCK HAZARD IN ARRAY.

The remainder of this requirement is editorially modified.

FR: 8715
SR: 8102

Emergency Disconnect, 1 & 2 Family Dwellings

Code Language

694.22(C) Requirements for Disconnecting Means.
(C)(1) Location. ... (See *NEC* text)
For one-family and two-family dwellings, a disconnecting means or manual shutdown button or switch shall be located at a readily accessible location outside the building.

(See NEC for actual text)

Significance of the Change

Section 694.22 contains *Additional Provisions* for wind energy systems, including requirements for disconnecting means, equipment, requirements for disconnecting means, including location and marking and rules for equipment that is not readily accessible.

New 694.22(C)(1) is added to require an emergency shutdown device be located outside of one- and two-family dwelling units. This new first-level subdivision is added to provide the fire service, and other first responders, with the capability to remove power from a dwelling unit during an emergency. Together, with new requirements for readily accessible emergency disconnecting means in one- and two-family dwelling units for services in 230.85, generators in 445.18, storage batteries in 480.7(B), and energy storage systems in 706.15(A), these requirements will provide first responders with the ability to quickly and safely remove power from dwelling units during an emergency.

694.22(C)(1) now requires that wind energy systems installed for one-family and two-family dwellings include a disconnecting means or manual shutdown button or switch that is located at a readily accessible location outside the building. Note that a manual shutdown button is permitted to remotely (shunt trip) open the disconnecting means to the wind turbine.

Change Summary

- 694.22(C)(1) requires installations in one-family and two-family dwellings, include a means for first responders to disconnect.
- The disconnect must be readily accessible and outside of the building.
- A manual shutdown button is permitted to remotely (shunt trip) open the disconnecting means.

FR: 8493
SR: None

Multiple Sources, Multibuilding Campus Complexes

Code Language

695.3 Power Source(s) for Electric Motor-Driven Fire Pumps.

(B) Multiple Sources.

(B)(2) Individual Source and On-site Standby Generator. ... (See *NEC* text)

Exception to 695.3(B)(1) and (B)(2): An alternate source of power shall not be required where a back-up engine-driven fire pump, back-up steam turbine-driven fire pump, or back-up electric motor-driven fire pump with an independent power source in accordance with 695.3(A) or (C) is installed.

(C) Multibuilding Campus-Style Complexes.

(C)(3) Selective Coordination. ... (See *NEC* text)

(See NEC for actual text)

Change Summary

- The exception to 695.3(B)(1) is modified for clarity.
- This exception now permits a combination of power sources from 695.3(A), or a feeder source in 695.3(C)(1), and a source in 695.3(A).
- 695.3(C)(3) is modified to clarify that all supply-side overcurrent protective devices must be selectively coordinated.

FRs: 7722, 7729
SR: 7526

College Campus Multibuilding Campus Style Complex with Feeder sources as per 695.3(C)(1)

- - - **Service Conductors** - - -

Service PAPPL-1625

Service PAPPL-2807

Building PS-101

Building PS-100

Building PS-108

Fire Pump

Additional disconnecting means and associated OCPS's are permitted

Significance of the Change

Section 695.3 requires fire pumps to have a reliable source of power. 695.3(B) recognizes that a reliable source of power may not be available, and permits multiple sources. 695.3(B)(1) recognizes that reliable power may not be available and permits two or more of the power sources listed in 695.3(A). 695.3(B)(2) permits an approved combination of one or more of the sources in 695.3(A) and an on-site standby generator. The exception to 695.3(B)(2) relieves the requirement for an alternate source of power where a backup engine driven fire pump or a back-up steam turbine driven fire pump is installed. Additional text is added to this exception to relieve the requirement for an alternate source of power where a backup electric motor driven fire pump with an independent power source in accordance with 695.3(A) or (C) is installed. This new text does not permit a method that was not recognized in previous editions of the *NEC* with respect to the power sources in 695.3(A), it simply provides clarity. 695.3(B)(1) very clearly permits an approved combination of two or more power sources from 695.3(A). This revision will now permit a power source listed in 695.3(A) and a feeder source in 695.3(C)(1). It is extremely important to note that this revision [based on 695.3(C)] will only impact multi-building campus-style complexes.

695.3(C)(3) is modified to clarify that all supply-side overcurrent protective devices must be selectively coordinated. New text is added to address overcurrent devices in series to correlate with similar requirements in the *NEC*.

Services, Terminations

Significance of the Change

Section 695.6 contains requirements for power wiring of fire pumps. 695.6(A)(1) contains requirements for wiring of service supplied and on-site power production facility supplied conductors. This second-level subdivision requires conductors to be physically routed outside of buildings and to be installed as service entrance conductors, in accordance with 230.6. Section 230.6 provides five list items for the installation of service conductors that are considered to be outside of the building. For example, 230.6 list item (1) recognizes installation under not less than 2 inches of concrete beneath the building, and list item (2) recognizes installation within the building in a raceway that is encased in concrete or brick not less than 2 inches thick. A new exception is added to 695.6(A)(1) to clarify that within the fire pump room, the requirements of 230.6(1) and (2) are not required. This revision correlates with requirements in the exception to 695.6(A)(2)(4).

Requirements for terminations in fire pump controllers are located in 695.6(J) *Terminations*. This requirement is modified to delete references to "conduit hubs" and "conduit entry." The previous text of this requirement did not recognize raceway and cable fittings that are listed for the purpose of terminating in fire pump controllers. The revised text in all four list items of 695.6(J) now references raceway or cable fittings.

Code Language

695.6 Power Wiring.

(A) Supply Conductors.

(A)(1) Services and On-Site Power Production Facilities. ... (See *NEC* text)

Exception: The supply conductors within the fire pump room shall not be required to meet 230.6(1) or (2).

Informational Note: See 250.24(C) for routing the grounded conductor to the service equipment.

(J) Terminations. Where raceways or cable are terminated... (See *NEC* text)

(1) Raceway or cable fittings listed and identified for use in wet locations shall be used... (See *NEC* text)

(See NEC for actual text)

Change Summary

- Service conductors within the fire pump room are not required to meet 230.6(1) or (2).
- References to "conduit hubs" and "conduit entry" are deleted in 695.6(J).
- 695.6(J) now recognizes listed raceway and cable fittings.

FR: 7730, 7679

SR: 7534

Fire Pump Controllers and Transfer Switches

Code Language

695.10... (See *NEC* text) Fire pump controllers and transfer switches shall not be permitted to be reconditioned.

700.5(C)... (See *NEC* text) Automatic transfer switches shall not be permitted to be reconditioned.

701.5(C) Automatic Transfer Switches. ... (See *NEC* text) Automatic transfer switches shall not be permitted to be reconditioned.

702.5(A) General. ... (See *NEC* text) Transfer switches shall not be permitted to be reconditioned.

708.24(A) General. ... (See *NEC* text) Transfer equipment shall not be permitted to be reconditioned.

(See NEC for actual text)

Change Summary

- Fire pump controllers and transfer switches are not permitted to be reconditioned.

- Automatic transfer switches are not permitted to be reconditioned for emergency and legally required systems.

- Reconditioned transfer switches/equipment are also prohibited in Articles 702 and 708.

Courtesy of Eaton

Significance of the Change

This significant change includes requirements in five different articles. These revisions address reconditioning of equipment. The term *reconditioned* means that electromechanical systems, equipment, apparatus or components are restored to operating conditions. It is imperative to note that some equipment lends itself very well to the reconditioning process, and other equipment cannot be reconditioned. This process (reconditioning) is significantly different from the normal servicing of equipment that remains within a facility. Additionally, it is important to note the replacement of listed equipment on a one-to-one basis does not constitute "reconditioned equipment." Additional terms to describe this process include: *rebuilt*, *refurbished*, or *remanufactured*.

Text is added into 695.10, *Listed Equipment*, to clarify that fire pump controllers and transfer switches are not permitted to be reconditioned. 700.5(C) and 701.5(C) now contain new text to clarify that automatic transfer switches are not permitted to be reconditioned in *Emergency and Legally Required Standby Systems*. New text in 702.5(A) clarifies that transfer switches are not permitted to be reconditioned. 708.24(A) clarifies that transfer equipment is not permitted to be reconditioned in *Critical Operations Power Systems*.

See the "NEMA Policy on Reconditioned Electrical Equipment" for more information.

FR: None

SRs: 7522, 7584, 7586, 7517, 7588

Generator Control Wiring Methods

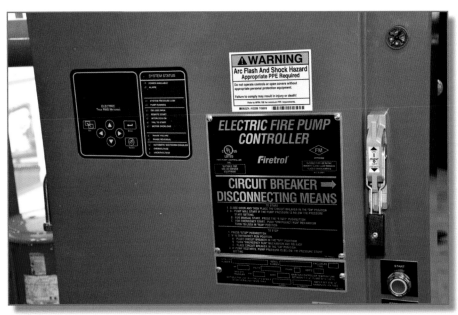

Code Language

695.14(F) Generator Control Wiring Methods. … (See *NEC* text) The integrity of the generator remote start circuit shall be monitored for broken, disconnected, or shorted wires. Loss of integrity shall start the generator(s).

The control conductors shall be protected to resist potential damage by fire or structural failure. Where routed through a building, the conductors shall be protected from fire for 2 hours using one of the following methods:

(1) The cable or raceway is encased in a minimum 50 mm (2 in.) of concrete.

(2) The cable or raceway is a listed fire-resistive cable system.

(3) The cable or raceway is protected by a listed electrical circuit protective system.

(See NEC for actual text)

Significance of the Change

Generator control conductors installed between the fire pump power transfer switch and a standby generator supplying the fire pump during the loss of normal power must be kept entirely independent of all other wiring as required in 695.14(F). The previous text of this requirement also mandated that any loss of integrity of the remote start circuit had to initiate visual and audible annunciation of generator malfunction at the generator and remote annunciator's and start the generator. New text now requires that the integrity of the generator remote start circuit must be monitored for broken, disconnected, or shorted wires, and any loss of integrity must start the generator. This revision is based upon a tentative interim amendment (TIA 17-17), that was issued for the 2017 *NEC*. This revision also correlates with similar text in 700.10(D)(3).

Generator control conductors are also required to be protected from potential damage by fire or structural failure. The parent text of 695.14(J) is also modified to clearly require that generator control conductors, where routed through a building, must be protected from fire for two hours using one of three methods provided in list items. List item (1) is modified to clarify that *cable or raceway* is encased in a minimum of 2 inches of concrete. List item (2) is modified to permit cable or raceways that are a *listed fire-resistive cable system*. List item 3 is modified to permit cable or raceways where protected by a *listed electrical circuit protective system*. The requirement for a two-hour fire rating is now in the parent text of 695.14(F).

Change Summary

- Generator remote start circuits must be monitored for broken, disconnected, or shorted wires and any loss of integrity must start the generator.
- Generator control conductors must be protected from fire for two hours using one of three permitted methods.
- Each permitted method is modified for clarity.

FR: 7732
SR: 7523

Chapter 7

Articles 700–770
Special Equipment

Significant Changes
TO THE *NEC®* 2020

Capacity and Rating

Code Language

700.4/701.4 Capacity and Rating.

(A) Rating. ... (See *NEC* text)

(B) Capacity. An emergency/legally required standby system shall have adequate capacity in accordance with Article 220 or by another approved method.

(C) Load Pickup, Load Shedding, and Peak Load Shaving.

(See NEC for actual text)

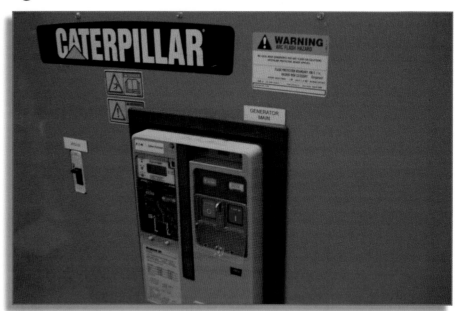

Courtesy of Eaton

Change Summary

- Requirements for capacity rating in 700.4 and 701.4 are correlated for clarity.
- 700.4(B) and 701.4(B) now permit capacity to be determined by Article 220 or another approved method.
- 701.4(C) *Load Pick Up, Load Shedding, and Peak Load Shaving* now correlates with requirements in 700.4.

Significance of the Change

Requirements for capacity and rating of alternate sources for emergency and legally required standby systems in 700.4 and 701.4 are revised for clarity, correlation, and to address how system capacity is permitted to be determined. 700.4(A) is retitled *Rating*, and the first sentence is deleted. 701.4 is separated into three first-level subdivisions to correlate with 700.4. These new subdivisions address (A) *Rating*, (B) *Capacity*, and (C) *Load Pick Up, Load Shedding, and Peak Load Shaving*. A new 700.4(B) *Capacity* is added to prescriptively address permitted methods to determine capacity. 700.4(B) and 701.4(B) now require emergency systems and legally required standby systems to have adequate capacity in accordance with Article 220 or by another approved method. Article 220 with purview over feeder load calculations can be applied, and other methods, such as historical data on demand can be used. The current *Code* language could be interpreted as requiring the emergency source to have a larger output rating than the ampacity rating of the normal power supply. By allowing *other approved methods*, the load calculation shall be permitted to be calculated under engineering supervision. It is extremely important to size a generator properly. Manufacturers suggest generators be operated at a minimum of 60–75% of their maximum rated load. The requirement in 701.4(C) is modified to correlate with 700.4(C). The term *maximum available fault current* is revised, and *maximum* is deleted. The newly defined term *available fault current* in Article 100 explains that it is the largest amount of current capable of being delivered at a point on the system during a short circuit.

FRs: 7505, 7576
SRs: 7665, 7629, 7669

Transfer Equipment

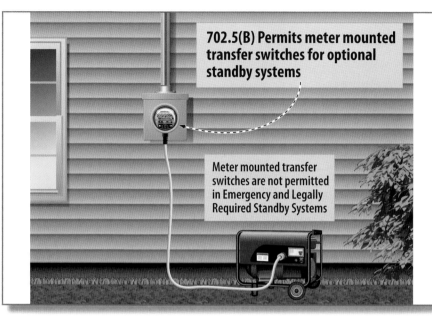

702.5(B) Permits meter mounted transfer switches for optional standby systems

Meter mounted transfer switches are not permitted in Emergency and Legally Required Standby Systems

Code Language

700.5/701(A) General. ... (See *NEC* text) Meter-mounted transfer switches shall not be permitted for emergency/legally required system use.

702.5 (A) General.

702.5 (B) Meter-Mounted Transfer Switches. Transfer switches installed between the utility meter and the meter enclosure shall be listed meter-mounted transfer switches and shall be approved. Meter-mounted transfer switches shall be of the manual type unless rated as determined by 702.4(B)(2).

702.5 (C) Documentation.

702.5 (D) Inadvertent Connection.

702.5 (E) Parallel Installation. Transfer equipment and electric power production systems installed to permit operation in parallel with the normal source shall also meet the requirements of Article 705.

(See NEC for actual text)

Significance of the Change

Requirements for transfer equipment in 700/701.5(A) *General*, are modified to prohibit meter-mounted transfer switches from being used for emergency or legally required system use. Additionally, requirements for transfer equipment to be listed are relocated from 700/701.5(C) into 700/701.5(A) *General* for clarity.

Section 702.5 provides requirements for transfer equipment for optional standby systems and is separated into five first-level subdivisions for clarity. The existing exception is relocated to follow 702.5(A) for clarity. New 702.5(B) permits the use of *Meter-Mounted Transfer Switches*, which must be listed meter-mounted transfer switches and must be approved. Meter-mounted transfer switches are required to be the manual type unless rated as determined by 702.4(B)(2). New 702.5(C) *Documentation* is modified to require the short-circuit current rating of the transfer equipment to be marked in *other than dwelling units*. The existing second paragraph in 702.5 is deleted because the standard for transfer switch equipment prohibits the use of supplemental overcurrent protection. 702.5(D) *Inadvertent Connection* continues to require installation to prevent inadvertent connection of all sources in any operation of the transfer equipment. Additionally, this requirement now mandates transfer equipment be listed. 702.5(E) *Parallel Installation* provides clarity with respect to two electric power production systems installed to permit operation in parallel with the normal source. These installations must also meet the requirements of Article 705.

Change Summary

- Meter-mounted transfer switches are prohibited in emergency and legally required systems.
- 702.5 is significantly revised and separated into five first-level subdivisions.
- 702.5(B) permits meter-mounted transfer switches.

FRs: 7507, 7580, 7830
SRs: 7588, 7600, 7586, 7584

Fire Protection

Code Language

700.10 Wiring, Emergency System.
(D) Fire Protection.
(D)(1) Occupancies.
(D)(2) Feeder-Circuit Wiring.
(D)(3) Feeder-Circuit Equipment.
(D)(4) Generator Control Wiring. Control conductors installed between the transfer equipment and the emergency generator shall be kept entirely independent of all other wiring and shall meet the conditions of 700.10(D)(2). The integrity of the generator remote start circuit shall be monitored for broken, disconnected, or shorted wires. Loss of integrity shall start the generator(s).

(See NEC for actual text)

Courtesy of Eaton

Change Summary

- 700.10(D) is editorially modified for clarity, adding new (D)(1) *Occupancies*.

- Existing list item (3) referencing healthcare facilities is deleted to correlate with *NFPA 99*.

- New text in 700.10(D)(4) provides clarity of requirements to ensure the integrity of the generator remote start circuit.

Significance of the Change

Requirements for fire protection of emergency system wiring in 700.10(D) are modified, adding a new second-level subdivision 700.10(D)(1) *Occupancies* for clarity. Existing list item (3) in the parent text, which identifies *health care occupancies where persons are not capable of self-preservation*, is deleted to resolve conflicts between this section and *NFPA 99*. Purview over health care facilities resides in *NFPA 99*. See tentative interim amendment 17-8. The remaining second-level subdivisions are editorially renumbered. 700.10(D)(2) *Feeder-Circuit Wiring* is modified to clarify that list item (3), which permits cables or raceways that are listed as a fire-resistive cable system, requires these systems to have a minimum 2-hour fire rating. 700.10(D)(2) and (D)(3) is modified to recognize a *fire protection system* to correlate with *NFPA 5000*. 700.10(D)(4) Generator Control Wiring, is modified to correlate with tentative interim amendment (TIA) 17-17. The previous text of this requirement mandated that any loss of integrity of the remote start circuit had to initiate visual and audible annunciation of generator malfunction at the generator and remote annunciators and start the generator. This requirement is revised to prescriptively identify the loss of integrity. New text now requires that the integrity of the generator remote start circuit, must be monitored for broken, disconnected, or shorted wires, and any loss of integrity must start the generator.

FRs: 7658, 8980
SR: None

Sources of Power, General Requirements

Significance of the Change

Part of the parent text in 700.12 is separated into two first-level subdivisions for clarity. 700.12(B) *Equipment Design and Location* is modified to require a 2-hour fire rating to correlate with requirements in 700.10(D). 700.12(B) list item (3), which references healthcare facilities, is deleted to resolve the conflict between this section and *NFPA 99*. 700.12(D)(1) is modified to delete the required time delay at a 15-minute setting to correlate with *NFPA 110*. 700.12(D)(2) is separated into four third-level subdivisions and editorially modified for clarity.

A new first-level subdivision 700.12(H) is added to recognize sources connected to a DC microgrid system. This requires the DC microgrid to be capable of being isolated from all nonemergency sources and must be of suitable rating and capacity to supply and maintain the total emergency load for not less than two hours at full demand. Where a dc microgrid system is the normal supply for the building, it shall not serve as the sole source of power for the emergency system.

700.12(I)(2) list item (3) is modified to delete the exception to recognize newer technology that results in fewer lighting branch circuits. This requirement addresses the branch circuit feeding unit equipment. The branch circuits supplying the normal lighting ahead of any switches are permitted to supply the unit equipment. Revised text now permits a separate branch circuit with a lock-on feature that originates from the same panelboard, where the normal lighting in any area is provided by one or more branch circuits. The separate branch circuit disconnect must be provided with a lock-on feature.

Code Language

700.12 General Requirements.
(A) Power Source Considerations.
(B) Equipment Design and Location.
… (See *NEC* text)
(D) Generator Set.
(D)(2)(a) On-Site Fuel Supply, (b) Fuel Transfer Pumps, (c) Public Gas System, Municipal Water Supply, (d) Automatic Fuel Transfer.
(H) DC Microgrid Systems.
(I)(2) Installation of Unit Equipment.
(I)(2)(3)(b) Where the normal lighting circuit is served by one or more branch circuits, a separate branch circuit, provided with a lock-on feature, that originates from the same panelboard as the normal lighting circuits. The branch circuit disconnecting means for this branch circuit shall be provided with a lock-on feature.

(See NEC for actual text)

Change Summary

- The parent text of 700.12 is separated into first-level subdivisions for clarity.
- A new 700.12(H) recognizes DC microgrid systems under listed conditions, as an emergency source.
- 700.12(I)(2) is modified to delete the exception in (I)(2)(3), and to clarify the existing requirement.

FR: 8095
SR: 7605

Emergency Illumination

Code Language

700.16 Emergency Illumination.

(A) General.

(B) System Reliability. Emergency lighting systems shall be designed and installed so that the failure of any illumination source cannot leave in total darkness any space that requires emergency illumination. Control devices in the emergency lighting system shall be listed for use in emergency systems. Listed unit equipment in accordance with 700.12(F) shall be considered as meeting the provisions of this section.

(C) Discharge Lighting.

(D) Disconnecting Means.

(See NEC for actual text)

Change Summary

- 700.16 *Emergency Illumination* is modified into four first-level subdivisions for clarity.
- 700.16(B) is modified to delete text referencing individual lighting elements, such as the burning out of a lamp, and now references an illumination source.
- Additional text in 700.16(B) requires control devices in emergency systems to be listed for use in emergency systems, to ensure system reliability.

FR: 7550
SR: None
SCR: 23
CC: 7607

Courtesy of Electronic Theatre Controls Incorporated

Significance of the Change

700.16 *Emergency Illumination* is modified into four first-level subdivisions for clarity. 700.16(B) is modified to clarify that emergency lighting systems must be designed and installed so that the failure of any *illumination source* cannot leave any area requiring emergency lighting in total darkness. The previous text was confusing and referenced the failure of any individual lighting elements, such as the *burning out of a lamp*. This reference to incandescent lighting was deleted, as it gave the impression we were only interested in the failure of a lamp or fluorescent tube.

Additional text is added to 700.16(B) to fully address comprehensive system reliability. This section now requires control devices in the emergency lighting system to be listed for use in emergency systems. Listed unit equipment in accordance with 700.12(F), is recognized as meeting the provisions of 700.16(B). This revision acknowledges the potential complexity of a modern emergency lighting system, and the many other elements that make up the lighting system. Failure of any element in that system could cause a failure of the emergency light source to illuminate. All control devices of the emergency lighting control system are now required to be listed for emergency system use, to ensure the reliability of emergency lighting.

Dimmer/Relay Systems, Directly Controlled Luminaires

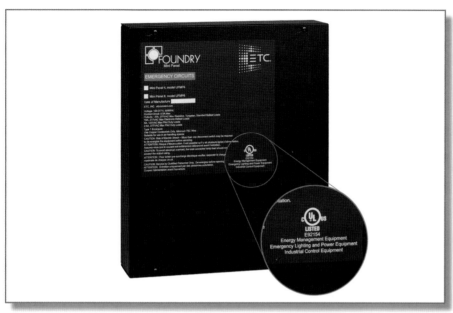

Courtesy of Electronic Theatre Controls Incorporated

Significance of the Change

Section 700.23 permits a dimmer or relay system with more than one dimmer and listed for use in emergency systems, to be used as a control device for emergency lighting. When normal power fails, these systems are permitted to selectively energize emergency illumination using a *control bypass function*. New text is added to permit a dimmer or relay system fed by a normal/emergency source from an upstream transfer switch, to obtain a normal power sensing function from a normal-only power source upstream of the transfer switch. Typically, these dimmer or relay systems are supplied from a normal/emergency source through an upstream transfer switch. In order to operate properly, the dimmer or relay system must monitor a normal only source other than its own normal/emergency feed in order to determine whether it is operating on normal or emergency power and whether a bypass of the control function is required.

The title of Section 700.24 is modified and permits emergency illumination through *Directly Controlled Emergency Luminaires* that respond to an external control input to bypass normal control upon loss of normal power. This text is modified to recognize that a directly controlled emergency luminaire may respond to an *external control input*, or *loss thereof*, to bypass normal control upon loss of normal power. Without this revision, users of this *Code* could interpret the loss of input as being noncompliant with this requirement. It is typical to see control circuits at less than 10 volts, and the loss of signal is quite often the trigger for full illumination when emergency power is present.

Code Language

700.23 Dimmer and Relay Systems... (See *NEC* text)

Where the dimmer or relay system is fed by a normal/emergency source from an upstream transfer switch, normal power sensing for this function shall be permitted to be from a normal-only power source upstream of the transfer switch... (See *NEC* text)

700.24 Directly Controlled Emergency Luminaires. Where emergency illumination is provided by one or more directly controlled emergency luminaires that respond to an external control input, or loss thereof, to bypass normal control... (See *NEC* text)

(See NEC for actual text)

Change Summary

- Emergency dimmer or relay systems may obtain a normal power sensing function from a normal-only power source upstream of the transfer switch.
- Directly controlled emergency luminaires may respond to an *external control input*, or *loss thereof*, to bypass normal control upon loss of normal power.

FR: 7561
SR: 7608

700.32, 701.32, & 708.54

Article 700 Emergency, 701 Legally Required, and 708 COPs

Part VI Overcurrent Protection

Selective Coordination

Code Language

700/701.32, 708.54 Selective Coordination. ... (See *NEC* text)

Informational Note: See Informational Note Figure 700.32 for an example of how emergency system overcurrent protective devices (OCPDs) selectively coordinate with all supply-side OCPDs.

OCPD D selectively coordinates with OCPDs C, F, E, B, and A.

OCPD C selectively coordinates with OCPDs F, E, B, and A.

OCPD F selectively coordinates with OCPD E.

OCPD B is not required to selectively coordinate with OCPD A because OCPD B is not an emergency system OCPD.

(See NEC for actual text)

Change Summary

- New informational notes and figures are added in 700.32, 701.32, and 708.54 for selective coordination.

- Significant clarity is provided for the *Code* user in the determination of which OCPDs must selectively coordinate.

- The Informational Note Figure provides guidance in the application of these requirements.

FR: None
SRs: 7616, 7619, 7622

Significance of the Change

Selective Coordination is the localization of an overcurrent condition, to restrict outages to the circuit or equipment affected, accomplished by the selection and installation of overcurrent protective devices and their ratings or settings for the full range of available overcurrents, from overload to the maximum available fault current, and for the full range of overcurrent protective device (OCPD) opening times associated with those overcurrents.

A new informational note (IN) and figure is added to requirements for selective coordination in 700.32 for *Emergency Systems*, 701.32 for *Legally Required Standby Systems*, and in 708.54 for *Critical Operations Power Systems (COPs)*.

There has been confusion in the determination of which overcurrent devices need to be selectively coordinated with respect to the normal supply of an *emergency, legally required*, and *COPs systems*. The requirements of 700.32, 701.32, and 708.54 are essentially the same and require overcurrent devices to be selectively coordinated with *all supply-side* overcurrent protective devices (OCPDs).

For example, in an emergency system, starting with the final branch-circuit OCPD and going upstream to the standby generator, all OCPDs must be selectively coordinated. Starting again with the final branch-circuit OCPD in an emergency system and going upstream to the normal source, all OCPDs downstream of the transfer switch must selectively coordinate with all normal side OCPDs. The OCPDs in the normal supply on the line side of the transfer switch are not required to selectively coordinate with each other.

Signs, Emergency Shutdown

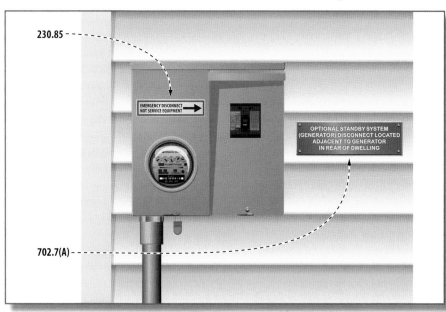

230.85

702.7(A)

EMERGENCY DISCONNECT
NOT SERVICE EQUIPMENT →

OPTIONAL STANDBY SYSTEM
(GENERATOR) DISCONNECT LOCATED
ADJACENT TO GENERATOR
IN REAR OF DWELLING

Code Language

702.7(A) Standby. A sign shall be placed at the service-entrance equipment for commercial and industrial installations that indicates the type and location of each on-site optional standby power source. For one- and two-family dwelling units, a sign shall be placed at the disconnecting means required in 230.85 that indicates the location of each permanently installed on-site optional standby power source disconnect or means to shut down the prime mover as required in 445.18(D).

(See NEC for actual text)

Significance of the Change

Section 702.7 *Signs* is modified to include signage for emergency shutdown of optional standby systems. The existing requirement is modified to apply for *commercial and industrial installations*. New Section 230.85 requires an emergency disconnect for all service conductors supplying one- and two-family dwelling units. This disconnecting means is required to be installed in a readily accessible outdoor location. The intent of this disconnect is to allow first responders to remove power from the dwelling unit in the event of a fire or other emergency.

702.7(A) is modified to require that a sign be placed at the disconnecting means required in 230.85, for all optional standby systems supplying one- and two-family dwelling units. This sign must indicate the location of each permanently installed on-site optional standby power source disconnect or means to shut down the prime mover, as required in 445.18(D). This new requirement specifically refers to new text in 445.18(D) that requires generators other than cord-and-plug-connected, to be provided with an emergency shutdown device located outside of the dwelling unit at a readily accessible location. This requirement applies to all permanently installed optional standby power sources and would include an energy storage system. Section 706.15(A) also requires a disconnecting means or remote control being installed outdoors one- and two-family dwellings at a readily accessible location.

This revision will provide first responders with the location of readily accessible outdoor disconnects for all optional standby power sources supplying the dwelling unit.

Change Summary

- New text in 702.7(A) requires a sign indicating the location of each permanently installed on-site optional standby power source disconnect or means to shut down the prime mover.

- This requirement applies only to one- and two-family dwelling units.

- The required sign must be placed at the disconnecting means required in 230.85.

FR: None
SR: 7632

Load-Side Source Connections

Code Language

705.12 Load-Side Source Connections.

(A) Dedicated Overcurrent and Disconnect.

(B) Bus or Conductor Ampere Rating.

(C) Marking.

(D) Suitable for Backfeed. Fused disconnects, unless otherwise marked, shall be suitable for backfeed... (See *NEC* text)

(E) Fastening.

(See NEC for actual text)

Change Summary

- 705.12 is retitled as *Load-Side Source Connections*, to correlate with revisions in 705.11 for *Supply Side Source Connections*.
- New text is added to clarify the ampacity of busbar under engineering supervision.
- New text is added to recognize fused disconnects, unless otherwise marked, as suitable for backfeed.

FR: 8902

SR: 8150

SCR: 2, 3

Courtesy of Eaton

Significance of the Change

Section 705.12 is significantly modified and retitled *Load-Side Source Connections*. This revision correlates with the changes in 705.11 for supply-side source connections. Previous text from 705.12(B) *Load-Side* is relocated as parent text in this section. Previous text in 705.12(A) is deleted, as it is now addressed in 705.11. New 705.12(A) requires each source interconnection of power sources be made at a dedicated circuit breaker or fusible disconnecting means. Requirements for bus or conductor amp ratings are relocated to 705.12(B). This requirement is separated into three second-level subdivisions. 705.12(B)(1) requires feeders to have an ampacity greater than or equal to 125% of the power source output circuit current. 705.12(B)(2) for feeder taps remains unchanged. 705.12(B)(3) addresses requirements for busbar connections. Clarity is provided for busbar connections designed under engineering supervision, by specifically referencing switchgear, switchboards, and panelboards. New text is added to permit connections on busbar that supply feed through lugs and conductors connected to the lugs opposite the main source of supply. Where this occurs, the ampacity of the busbar and connected feeders must not be less than the sum of the primary source overcurrent device and 125% of the power source output current. Marking requirements in 705.12(C) remain unchanged. 705.11(D) *Suitable for Backfeed*, is modified to permit fused disconnects, unless otherwise marked, as suitable for backfeed. The requirements for fastening listed plug-in type circuit breakers back fed from electric power sources in 705.12(E) remains unchanged.

Power Control Systems (PCS)

Courtesy of Eaton

Significance of the Change

Article 705 provides requirements for *Interconnected Electric Power Production Sources*. Installations with multiple energy sources (some with variable output), including energy storage systems, are becoming more common. Power control systems (PCS) are necessary to maximize the output of multiple energy sources and to prevent an overload situation when all energy sources are producing. New Section 705.13 *Power Control Systems* requires a PCS to be listed and evaluated to control the output of one or more power production sources, energy storage systems (ESS), and other equipment. The PCS limits the current to the ampacity of the conductors or the ratings of the busbars to which it is connected, in accordance with 705.13(A) through (E).

705.13(A) requires that the PCS monitor all currents. 705.13(B) requires that the sum of all controlled currents, plus all monitored currents from other sources, does not exceed the rating of the busbar or conductor supplied or the rating of an OCPD. 705.13(C) requires that the PCS provide overcurrent protection either by overcurrent devices or by a PCS, which is identified to function as an overcurrent device in the product listing. 705.13(D) requires that the rating of an OCPD for any single power source that is controlled, cannot exceed the rating of the busbar or conductors to which it is connected. 705.13(E) requires that access to the settings of the PCS be restricted to qualified persons. This restricted access must be in accordance with the requirements of 240.6.

Code Language

705.13 Power Control Systems.

(A) Monitoring.

(B) Settings.

(C) Overcurrent Protection. The PCS shall provide overcurrent protection either by overcurrent devices or by the PCS including the functionality as an overcurrent device in the product listing.

Informational Note: Some PCS are listed to provide overcurrent protection.

(D) Single Power Source Rating.

(E) Access to Settings. The access to settings of the PCS shall be restricted to qualified personnel in accordance with the requirements of 240.6(C).

(See NEC for actual text)

Change Summary

- New 705.13 provides requirements for Power control systems (PCS).
- These systems are necessary where multiple energy sources and/or energy storage systems exist.
- The PCS monitors all currents to ensure that an overload does not occur. The PCS may be listed as an overcurrent protective device.

FR: 8745
SR: 8151

Disconnecting Means, Source

Code Language

705.20 Disconnecting Means, Source. Means shall be provided to disconnect power source output circuit conductors... (See *NEC* text)

(1) Be one of the following types:

(a) A manual operable switch or CB

(b) A load-break-rated pull-out switch

(c) A power-operated... (See *NEC* text) remote-controlled switch... (See *NEC* text) CB... (See *NEC* text) manually operable locally and opens automatically when control power is interrupted

(d) A device listed or approved for the intended application

(5) Enclosures with doors or hinged covers with exposed live parts when open that require a tool to open or are lockable where readily accessible to unqualified persons

(See NEC for actual text)

Change Summary

• Requirements for disconnecting power source output circuit conductors from all other systems are significantly revised.

• Permitted types of disconnects are provided.

• Enclosures accessible to unqualified persons (general public), must require a tool to open or must be lockable to prevent unauthorized access.

FR: 8747
SR: 8153

Significance of the Change

Section 705.20 is significantly revised. In the 2017 *NEC*, this section simply required a disconnect for all ungrounded conductors of power production sources from all other conductors. Similar requirements previously existed in 705.21 *Disconnecting Means, Equipment* and 705.23 *Interactive System Disconnecting Means*, and those sections are deleted. Revisions to other articles regarding a particular power source have made these requirements unnecessary. Requirements for equipment disconnecting means for equipment that is part of an interconnected power production source system are best addressed in the specific articles applying to each source type. 705.20 requires a disconnecting means for power source output conductors. Requirements for this disconnecting means must comply with the eight list items provided. Permitted types of disconnect include a manual switch or circuit breaker, load break rated pullout, power-operated, or remote-controlled switch/circuit breaker that is both manually operable and automatic on loss of control power, or any device listed or approved for the application. The disconnect must be externally operable, open all ungrounded conductors of the circuit, must be readily accessible, must indicate open or closed position, and have sufficient rating for the available fault current. Where enclosures with doors or hinged covers that contain exposed energized parts, are accessible to unqualified persons (general public), those enclosures must require a tool to open or must be lockable to prevent unauthorized access. Disconnect marking per 690.13(B):

WARNING, ELECTRIC SHOCK HAZARD, TERMINALS ON THE LINE AND LOAD SIDE MAY BE ENERGIZED IN THE OPEN POSITION

Wiring Methods, Circuit Sizing and Current

Code Language

705.25 Wiring Methods.

(A) General. ... (See *NEC* text)

(B) Flexible Cords and Cables. ... (See *NEC* text) shall comply with Article 400 and shall be listed and identified as DG Cable, Distributed Generation Cable, hard service cord, or portable power cable, shall be suitable for extra-hard usage, shall be listed for outdoor use, and shall be water resistant... (See *NEC* text)

(C) Multiconductor Cable Assemblies.

705.28 Circuit Sizing and Current.

705.30 Overcurrent Protection.

(See NEC for actual text)

Significance of the Change

New Section 705.25 is added to address permitted *Wiring Methods*. The requirement in 705.25(A) permits all raceways and cable assemblies in Chapter 3 that are specifically listed, intended, and identified for use with power production systems and equipment. Wiring devices with integral enclosures must be provided with sufficient cable length to facilitate replacement where necessary. 705.25(B) requires that where flexible cords or cables are used to connect moving parts of a power production system or where flexible cord and cable is required for maintenance and repair, the installation must comply with Article 400, and the cable must be identified as one of the following: Type DG, *Distributed Generation Cable*, hard service cord, or portable power cable. These cable types must be suitable for extra-hard usage, be listed for outdoor use, and water-resistant. Cables exposed to sunlight must be sunlight resistant and flexible fine stranded cables must be terminated in accordance with 110.14.

The previous requirements of 705.60 and 705.65 are modified, revised for clarity, and relocated into 705.28 *Circuit Sizing and Current*. These requirements are modified to apply to all interconnected electric power production sources. Redundant requirements are removed, and correlation with requirements in Article 690 provides clarity and usability.

Previous requirements for overcurrent protection in 705.65 are revised for clarity, with redundant text removed and relocated into Section 705.30 *Overcurrent Protection*.

Change Summary

- New 705.25 provides a basic requirement for wiring methods used in interconnected electric power production sources.

- Type DG, *Distributed Generation Cable*, hard service cord, or portable power cable are permitted where flexibility is required.

- Previous requirements for overcurrent protection, circuit sizing, and current are revised and relocated.

FRs: 8660, 8663
SR: 8190

Qualified Personnel, Maintenance, Storage Batteries

Code Language

706.3 Qualified Personnel. The installation and maintenance of ESS equipment and all associated wiring and interconnections shall be performed only by qualified persons.

706.7 Maintenance. Energy storage systems shall be maintained in proper and safe operating condition... (See *NEC* text)

706.8 Storage Batteries. Storage batteries not associated with an ESS shall comply with Article 480.

(See NEC for actual text)

Courtesy of Tesla Energy

Change Summary

- New 706.3 requires that the installation and maintenance of all ESS equipment, wiring, and connections be performed by qualified persons only.
- New 706.7 requires all ESS systems be maintained in proper and safe operating condition.
- New 706.8 requires storage batteries that are not associated with an ESS be installed in accordance with Article 480.

Significance of the Change

Previous requirements in Section 706.3 to illustrate how Article 706 correlates with other parts of the *Code* was unnecessary and is deleted. This new section is now titled *Qualified Personnel* and mandates that the installation and maintenance of ESS equipment and all associated wiring is to be performed only by qualified persons. A new Section 706.7 *Maintenance* is added to correlate with the new requirements in 706.3. Energy storage systems are now required to be maintained in proper and safe operating condition. Where these systems are not properly installed or properly maintained, the result can be a catastrophic failure. Installation and maintenance must be performed by qualified persons only. Maintenance of the systems must be performed in accordance with manufacturer requirements and any applicable industry-standards. A written record of maintenance on the ESS that includes all records of repairs or replacements is required.

Significant revisions in both Articles 480 and 706 are made to remove redundant requirements and to locate requirements for storage batteries in Article 480. A new Section 706.8 *Storage Batteries*, now provides clarity and correlation between Article 480 and 706. This new section requires storage batteries that are not associated with an ESS to comply with Article 480.

FRs: 7857, 8924

SR: None

SCR: 25

Disconnecting Means

Courtesy of Tesla Energy

Significance of the Change

Requirements for *Energy Storage System Disconnects* (ESS), are relocated from 706.7 to 706.15 and revised. The revision in 706.15(A) is revised to permit the disconnecting means to be integral to a listed ESS. Requirements for lockable in the open position is logically relocated into 706.15(A). Existing text continues to require the disconnect be readily accessible. The general rule is that the disconnect be within sight of the ESS. Where that is impracticable, the disconnect must be installed as close as practicable, and that location must be marked immediately adjacent to the ESS. The marking must be durable and cannot be handwritten. New text is added to require a disconnecting means or remote control located outdoors at a readily accessible location for one- and two-family dwelling units. This revision correlates with requirements in 230.85 for an emergency service disconnect. Notification and marking requirements in 706.15(C) are modified to require the ESS disconnect to be marked *ENERGY STORAGE SYSTEM DISCONNECT*. List item (3) in 706.15(C) is modified to require an arc-flash label applied in accordance with acceptable industry practice. This requirement is very different from 110.16(B) because this requirement steers the *Code* user directly to Section 130.5 in *NFPA 70E*. An exception is added to exempt one- and two-family dwellings from the marking requirements in list items (1) through (4). 706.15(D) is retitled *Partitions Between Components* and is modified to clarify requirements for readily accessible disconnects where input or output circuits pass through a wall floor or ceiling. Additional clarity is provided permitting circuit breakers or fused disconnects for this purpose.

Code Language

706.15 Disconnecting Means.

(A) ESS Disconnecting Means. ... (See *NEC* text) integral to listed ESS equipment... (See *NEC* text)

(1) ... (See *NEC* text) shall be readily accessible.

(2) ... (See *NEC* text) located within sight of the ESS... (See *NEC* text)

(3) ... (See *NEC* text) lockable open... (See *NEC* text) with 110.25. For one-family and two-family dwellings, a disconnecting means or its remote ... (See *NEC* text) readily accessible location outside the building.

(B) Remote Actuation.

(C) Notification and Marking. ... (See *NEC* text) and be permanently marked "ENERGY STORAGE SYSTEM DISCONNECT... (See *NEC* text)

(3) An arc-flash label applied in accordance with acceptable industry practice

(D) Partitions Between Components.

(See NEC for actual text)

Change Summary

- The required disconnect is permitted to be integral to the ESS.
- A disconnect or remote control must be installed outdoors in a readily accessible location for one- and two-family dwelling units.
- Disconnects require an arc-flash label applied in accordance with acceptable industry practice.

FR: 8942
SRs: 7700, 7731

Bypass Isolation Automatic Transfer Switches

Code Language

708.24 Transfer Equipment.

(D) Bypass Isolation Automatic Transfer Switches. Where loads are supplied by only one automatic transfer switch, the automatic transfer switch shall include a bypass isolation switch to facilitate maintenance as required in 708.6(C) without jeopardizing continuity of power. When the bypass isolation transfer switch is in the bypass mode, either it shall automatically initiate transfer between power sources upon loss of the connected power source or it shall remain actively supervised by a qualified person who can manually initiate a transfer between power sources.

(See NEC for actual text)

Change Summary

- New 708.24 requires COPS loads supplied by only one transfer switch to include a bypass isolation switch.
- The bypass isolation switch allows the automatic transfer switch to be maintained under safe working conditions without loss of power.
- Requirements in 700.5(B) and 701.5(B) permit a means to bypass and isolate the transfer equipment, but it is not required.

FR: 8872
SR: None

Courtesy of Eaton

Significance of the Change

A new first-level subdivision (D) *Bypass Isolation Automatic Transfer Switches* is added in 708.24 *Transfer Equipment*. Where critical operations power system (COPS) loads are supplied by only one automatic transfer switch, the automatic transfer switch is now required to include a bypass isolation switch, which will facilitate maintenance as required inside in 708.6(C) without jeopardizing the continuity of power. This new requirement further clarifies that when the bypass isolation transfer switch is in the bypass mode, it must automatically initiate a transfer between power sources upon loss of the connected power source or it must remain actively supervised by a qualified person who can manually initiate a transfer between power sources. This new requirement is very different from those in Articles 700 for *Emergency Systems* and 701 for *Legally Required Standby Systems* with respect to bypass isolation switches. Requirements in 700.5(B) and 701.5(B) permit a means to bypass and isolate the transfer equipment but do not require it. 700.5(B) and 701.5(B) do require that where bypass isolation switches are used, inadvertent parallel operation must be avoided. This revision will allow the automatic transfer switch to be put into bypass mode so that maintenance can be performed safely and COPS loads are still supplied. Bypass isolation switches provide redundancy and continuous powering of the loads while the ATS is de-energized so that proper maintenance can be performed under safe work conditions. Reliability and continued operation without loss of power are critical in all COPS systems.

Scope and Equipment Approval

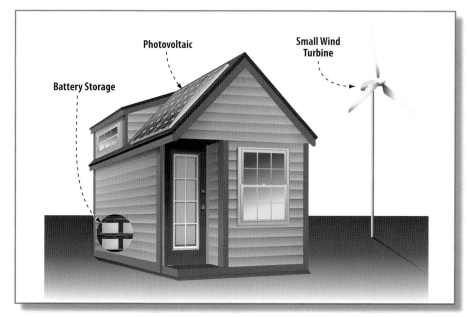

Code Language

710.1 Scope. This article covers electric power production systems that operate in island mode and installations not connected to an electric power production and distribution network... (See *NEC* text)

710.6 Equipment Approval. All equipment shall be approved for the intended use in accordance with one of the following:

(1) Be listed for the application

(2) Be evaluated for the application and have a field label applied... (See *NEC* text)

(See NEC for actual text)

Significance of the Change

The scope of Article 710 *Stand Alone Systems* is modified for clarity. This revision clarifies that Article 710 covers electric power production systems that operate in island mode and installations not connected to an electric power production and distribution network. This means there is no grid connection, no utility, no service. The new informational note to 710.6 provides necessary background information to help understand this scope revision. This article covers *stand-alone systems*. Inverters are identified as either *multimode* or *stand-alone* types. Stand-alone inverters operate *only* in island mode. Multimode inverters operate in either island mode or interactive mode when a utility grid connection is supplied. A multimode inverter will only operate in island mode if it is *never* connected to an electric utility supply, and in that case, falls under the scope of Article 710. An informational note is added to clarify the scope in 710.1.

Section 710.6 is modified in an attempt to further clarify the term *field labeled*. This section is titled *Equipment Approval* and is modified to require all equipment to be approved in accordance with two list items provided. List item (1) requires all equipment to be listed for the application. List item (2) requires all equipment be evaluated for the application and *have a field label applied*. The term *field labeled* is under the purview of the *NFPA 790* and *791* committee. The intent of this revision is to get a serialized label of some type, and not just a label identifying the organization that performed the field evaluation. The informational note added to 710.6 provides significant information on inverter types.

Change Summary

- Article 710 covers systems that operate in island mode and installations that are not connected to a power production network, such as a utility.

- 710.6 now requires all equipment be either listed for the application or field evaluated with a field label applied.

- A multimode inverter will only operate in island mode if it is *never* connected to an electric utility supply.

FR: 8718
SRs: 8202, 8209

710.10 & 710.12

Article 710 Stand-Alone Systems

Part N/A

Identification of Power Sources, Inverter Input

Code Language

710.10 Identification of Power Sources. A permanent plaque or directory shall be installed at a building supplied by a stand-alone system at each service equipment location, or at an approved readily visible location... (See *NEC* text) location of each power source disconnecting means for the building or be grouped with other plaques or directories for other on-site sources. Where multiple sources supply the building, ... (See *NEC* text) "CAUTION: MULTIPLE SOURCES OF POWER." The marking shall comply with 110.21(B).

Exception: ... (See *NEC* text)

710.12 Stand-Alone Inverter Input Circuit Current.

(See NEC for actual text)

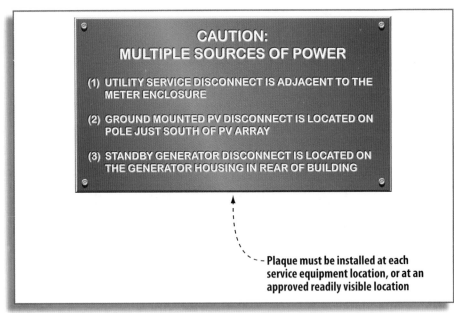

CAUTION:
MULTIPLE SOURCES OF POWER

(1) UTILITY SERVICE DISCONNECT IS ADJACENT TO THE METER ENCLOSURE

(2) GROUND MOUNTED PV DISCONNECT IS LOCATED ON POLE JUST SOUTH OF PV ARRAY

(3) STANDBY GENERATOR DISCONNECT IS LOCATED ON THE GENERATOR HOUSING IN REAR OF BUILDING

Plaque must be installed at each service equipment location, or at an approved readily visible location

Change Summary

- New 710.10 requires permanent plaques or directories at buildings supplied by stand-alone systems at each service equipment location or other approved location.
- Where multiple sources supply the building, the marking must include "CAUTION: MULTIPLE SOURCES OF POWER."
- Requirements in 690.8(A)(4) for inverter input current are relocated to 710.12.

Significance of the Change

New Section 710.10 *Identification of Power Sources* now correlates with other *NEC* requirements for a permanent plaque or directory of power sources at each service equipment location or other approved location. These plaques and directories provide necessary information for installer maintainers working on the systems. They also provide critical information when first responders must remove power from a building or structure before entering it in a fire or other emergency situation. First responders may encounter buildings and structures supplied by a utility service, dc micro grid system, energy storage system, or PV systems that are utility-interactive or stand-alone, with on-site battery sources, standby generators and more. Where multiple sources supply a building or structure, the plaque or directory must be marked: CAUTION: MULTIPLE SOURCES OF POWER. An exception is added to permit marking groups of power production sources where they are located in the same area.

A new Section 710.12 relocates requirements for *Stand-Alone Inverter Input Circuit Current* into Article 710. This requirement was previously located in 690.8(A)(4) for PV systems. This requires that the maximum current be the stand-alone continuous inverter input current rating when the inverter is producing rated power at the lowest input voltage.

FRs: 8721, 8724
SR: 8210

Functionally Grounded, Directory

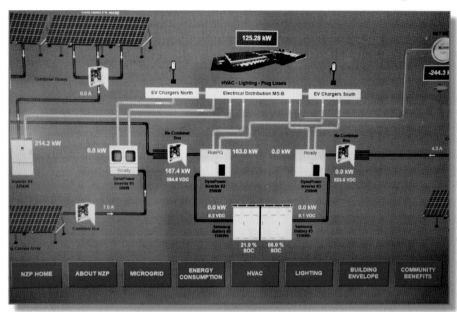

Code Language

712.2 Grounded, Functionally. A system that has an electrical ground reference for operational purposes that is not solidly grounded.

Informational Note: Examples of operational reasons for functionally grounded systems include ground-fault detection and performance-related issues for some power sources.

712.10 Directory.

(A) Source Directory.

(B) Building Directory. A building supplied by a dc microgrid system shall have a permanent plaque or directory installed outside the building at each service equipment location or at an approved readily visible location ... (See *NEC* text)

Exception... (See *NEC* text)

(See NEC for actual text)

Significance of the Change

The definition of *Resistively Grounded* in 712.2 is modified for clarity and to correlate with the definition in Article 690. The definition title is modified as *Grounded, Functionally* for clarity, and correlates with the definition in Article 690. These two definitions were different in 2017, but are the same in the 2020 *NEC*. This is a violation of the *NEC Style Manual*, and it is likely that these definitions will be moved to Article 100 in 2023. The reference to a *high resistance connection* is deleted. Functionally grounded, now means an electrical ground reference for operational purposes that is not solidly grounded. A new informational note provides examples of operational purposes, including but not limited to, ground fault protection.

Requirements for a directory of power sources in 712.10 are expanded. This section is separated into two first-level subdivisions. 712.10(A) *Source Directory* contains the previous text requiring a directory of all dc power sources supplying the micro grid to be installed at each source capable of acting as the primary dc source. A new 712.10(B) *Building Directory* is added to require all buildings supplied by a DC micro grid to have a plaque or directory installed outside the building at each service equipment location, or at an approved readily visible location. This new requirement correlates with other marking requirements for alternative energy sources. An exception is added permitting identification of groups of multiple power production sources.

Change Summary

- The definition of *Resistively Grounded* in 712.2 is retitled as *Grounded, Functionally*, and is modified.

- A *functional ground* is a reference for operational purposes, such as ground fault protection and is not solidly grounded.

- New requirements for a building directory of power sources is added in 712.10(B).

FRs: 8868, 7893
SRs: 7655, 7660

725.2 & 725.3

Article 725 Class 1, Class 2, and Class 3...

Part I General

Cable Bundle, Temperature Limitations, EGCs

Code Language

725.2 Cable Bundle. A group of cables that are tied together or in contact with one another in a closely packed configuration for at least 1.0 m (40 in.).

Informational Note: Random or loose installation of individual cables can result in less heating. Combing of the cables can result in less heat dissipation and more signal cross talk between cables.

725.3(O) Temperature Limitation of Class 2 and Class 3 Cables. The requirements of 310.14(A)(3) on the temperature limitation of conductors shall apply to Class 2 and Class 3 cables.

(P) Identification of Equipment Grounding Conductors. Equipment grounding conductors shall be identified in accordance with 250.119.

Exception: ... (See NEC text)

(See NEC for actual text)

Change Summary

- A new definition of *cable bundle* in 725.2 is added for clarity.
- A *cable bundle* is a group of cables tied together, in close contact or packed for at least 40 inches.
- Two new subdivisions in 725.3 require compliance with 310.14(A)(3) and 250.119.

FRs: 8779, 8807, 8804, 8805, 8806, 8926
SRs: 7933, 7947

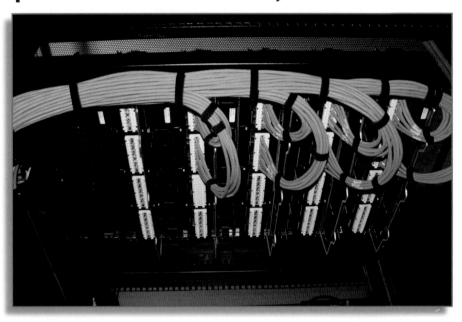

Significance of the Change

There are multiple references throughout Article 725 to *cable bundles* in requirements to address permitted ampacity. Without a definition, where cables are grouped for a short distance, for example, a short section of raceway for protection, the cables are bundled, and requirements for bundled cables would apply. A new definition of *Cable Bundle* is added in 725.2 to provide clarity. As defined, the cable bundle is a group of cables tied together, in close contact or packed for at least 40 inches. An associated informational note explains that where cables are installed without bundling, less heating will occur. Where cables are bundled there is less heat dissipation and more signal crosstalk between cables. Additional revisions in Article 100 relocates the definitions of *Circuit Integrity Cable*, *Class 1/2/3 Circuits*, and *Power Limited Tray Cable* to Article 100, as they are used in multiple Articles.

Section 725.3 *Other Articles* identifies requirements elsewhere in the *NEC* that apply to installations under the purview of Article 725. Two new first-level subdivisions are added. New 725.3(O) *Temperature Limitation of Class 2 and Class 3 Cables* requires compliance with 310.14(A)(3), which requires conductors not be applied in a manner that exceeds their operating temperature. Section 725.179(G) mandates that Class 2 and 3 cables have a temperature limitation of 60°C (140°F). New 725.3(P) requires that equipment grounding conductors be identified as required in 250.119. An exception is provided for identified types of cable for Class 2 and 3 circuits. Similar revisions occurred in 760.3.

Transmission of Power and Data

Significance of the Change

The parent text of Section 725.144 *Transmission of Power and Data* is modified for clarity. Informational Note (IN) No. 2 is modified to provide additional information on connectors for electronic equipment. New IN No. 3 explains that the requirements of Table 725.144 were derived for carrying power and data over four-pair copper balanced twisted-pair cabling. New IN No. 4 references guidelines for supporting power delivery over balanced twisted-pair cabling. New IN No. 5 references a standard for lighting systems, PoE. Based upon data provided in a fact-finding report, the values in Table 725.144 are modified and rounded to two decimal places. All of these values were slightly increased. IN No. 1 is modified to explain that elevated cable temperatures can reduce a cable's data transmission performance. New IN No. 2 explains that the current rating of connectors can limit the maximum amount of current below the ampacity that is shown in Table 725.144. In 725.144(A), the cable types listed are now limited to a Table ampacity determined at 86°F. For ambient temperatures higher than that the correction factors in 310.15(B) apply. A new exception is added for conductors 24 AWG or larger. Where these conductors do not exceed 0.3 amps, compliance with Table 725.144 is not required. 725.144(B) now permits cables with the suffix *LP*, at their rated ampacity. Where the number of LP cables bundled is 192 or less, and the selected ampacity of the cables in accordance with Table 725.144 exceeds the marked ampacity of the cable, the ampacity from the table is permitted to be used. Where the ambient temperature is above 86°F, the correction factors in 310.15(B) must be applied.

Code Language

725.144 Transmission of Power and Data. ... (See *NEC* text)

Informational Note No. 5: ... (See *NEC* text) American National Standard for Lighting Systems — Minimum Requirements for Installation of Energy Efficient Power over Ethernet (PoE) Lighting Systems, for information on installation of cables for PoE lighting systems

(A) Use of Class 2 or Class 3 Cables to Transmit Power and Data. ... (See *NEC* text) the ampacities in Table 725.144 shall ... (See *NEC* text) 30°C (86°F). For ambient temperatures above 30°C (86°F), the correction factors in Table 310.15(B)(1) or in the equation in 310.15(B) shall apply.

Exception: Compliance with Table 725.144 shall not be required for installations where conductors are 24 AWG or larger and the nominal current does not exceed 0.3 amperes in any conductor.

(B) Use of Class 2-LP or Class 3-LP Cables to Transmit Power and Data.

(See NEC for actual text)

Change Summary

- 725.144 is modified with multiple new explanatory informational notes.
- Significant revisions for cable ampacity are added.

FRs: 8941, 8932, 8934
SRs: 7980, 7973, 7975

Chapter 8

Articles 800–840
Communications Systems

Significant Changes

TO THE *NEC*® 2020

Article 800

General Requirements for Communications Systems

Code Language

Part I. General.

800.1 Scope.

800.2 Definitions.

800.3 Other Articles.

800.3(G) Reconditioned Equipment. The requirements of 110.21(A)(2) shall apply.

800.21 Access to Electrical Equipment Behind Panels Designed to Allow Access.

800.24 Mechanical Execution of Work.

800.25 Abandoned Cables.

800.26 Spread of Fire or Products of Combustion. ... (See *NEC* text)

Part II. Wires and Cables Outside and Entering Buildings. ... (See *NEC* text)

Part III. Grounding Methods. ... (See *NEC* text)

Part IV. Installation Methods Within Buildings. ... (See *NEC* text)

Part V. Listing Requirements. ... (See *NEC* text)

(See NEC for actual text)

Change Summary

- New Article 800 contains general requirements for all Chapter 8 articles.
- This revision removes significant redundancies in these articles.
- Reconditioned equipment under the purview of Chapter 8 must comply with the requirements of 110.21(A)(2).

FR: 7512

FCR: 211

SR: Multiple

Note: Too many to list!

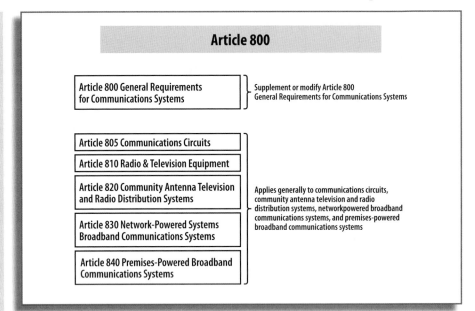

Significance of the Change

Chapter 8 of the *NEC* is titled *Communications Systems*, and consisted of five articles in 2017. They are Article 800 *Communications Circuits*, 810 *Radio and Television Equipment*, 820 *Community Antenna Television and Radio Distribution Systems*, 830 *Network-Powered Broadband Communications Systems*, and 840 *Premises-Powered Broadband Communications Systems*. These articles included a very significant amount of redundant requirements repeated again in each article. This revision results in a new Article 800 *General Requirements for Communications Systems*, to place common requirements in a single location applicable to all Chapter 8 Articles. The scope of new Article 800 in 800.1, explains that this article contains general requirements for communications systems that apply unless modified in Articles 805, 820, 830, or 840.

Existing Article 800 is moved to Article 805 *Communications Circuits*. The net result is clarity and usability because all of the redundant requirements are now rolled into Article 800.

Reconditioned equipment is now addressed in 800.3(G) and mandates that the requirements of 110.21(A)(2) apply. This requires reconditioned equipment to be marked with the name, trademark, or other descriptive marking of the organization responsible for reconditioning the equipment, along with the date of the reconditioning. The equipment must be marked as *reconditioned* and the original listing mark must be removed. There is an exception for industrial occupancies.

Communications Wire and Cables

Significance of the Change

Existing Article 800 is moved to Article 805 *Communications Circuits*.

A new first-level subdivision is added to identify additional communications limited power cables suitable for carrying power and data. New 805.179(D) *Types CMP-LP, CMR-LP, CMG-LP, and CM-LP Limited Power (LP) Cables* requires the communications limited power cables be identified as suitable for carrying power and data to a specified limit without exceeding the temperature rating of the cable where the cable is installed in cable bundles in free air or installed within a raceway, cable tray, or cable routing assembly. In order to designate the current limitation in each conductor, these cables must be marked with the suffix "-LP(XXA)," where XX designates the current limit in amperes per conductor. An informational note is added and provides examples of the cable markings. An example of the marking on a communications cable with an LP rating is *CMP-LP (0.6A)(75°C) 23AWG 4-pair*, which indicates that it is a 4-pair plenum cable with 23 AWG conductors, a temperature rating of 75°C, and a current limit of 0.6 amp.

A new first-level subdivision 805.179(G) *Optional Markings* is added to permit manufacturers to mark cables to indicate special characteristics of the cable material. An informational note is provided with examples, that include limited-smoke, halogen-free, low-smoke halogen-free, and sunlight resistance.

Code Language

805.179(D) Types CMP-LP, CMR-LP, CMG-LP, and CM-LP Limited Power (LP) Cables. ... (See *NEC* text) shall be listed as suitable for carrying power and data up to a specified current limit for each conductor without exceeding the temperature rating of the cable where the cable is installed in cable bundles in free air or installed within a raceway, cable tray, or cable routing assembly. ... (See *NEC* text) marked with the suffix "-LP(XXA)," where XX designates the current... (See *NEC* text)

800.179(G) Optional Markings. Cables shall be permitted to be surface marked to indicate special characteristics of the cable materials.

Informational Note: ... (See *NEC* text), halogen-free, low-smoke halogen-free, and sunlight resistance.

(See NEC for actual text)

Change Summary

- New 805.179(D) requires cable types with the suffix LP to be listed as suitable for carrying power and data.
- These cables must not exceed the temperature rating of the cable where the cable is installed in cable bundles in free air or installed within a raceway, cable tray, or cable routing assembly.
- New 805.179(G) permits optional cable markings.

FR: 7786
SR: 7741

840.94 & 840.102

Article 840 Premises-Powered Broadband Communications Systems

Part III Protection and IV Grounding Methods

Premises Circuits Leaving the Building

Code Language

840.94 and 840.102 Premises Circuits Leaving the Building. Where circuits leave the building to power equipment remote to the building or outside the exterior zone of protection defined by a 46 m (150 ft) radius rolling sphere... (See *NEC* text)

840.94... (See *NEC* text) 800.90 and 800.93 shall apply.

840.102... (See *NEC* text) the installation of communications wires and cables shall comply with 800.100 and 800.106, and the installation of coaxial cables shall comply with 820.100 and 800.106.

Informational Note: See NFPA 780-2017, *Standard for the Installation of Lightning Protection Systems*, for the application of the term *rolling sphere*.

(See NEC for actual text)

Change Summary

- Premises powered broadband communications systems may require power circuits to leave the premises.

- Two new sections are added to require these circuits be protected and properly grounded.

- These requirements apply where the circuits leaving the premises to power equipment are outside of the exterior zone of protection, which is a 150-foot radius.

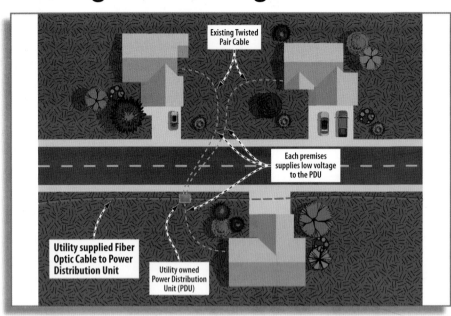

Existing Twisted Pair Cable

Each premises supplies low voltage to the PDU

Utility supplied Fiber Optic Cable to Power Distribution Unit

Utility owned Power Distribution Unit (PDU)

Significance of the Change

Article 840 covers premises powered broadband communications systems. These systems typically consist of optical fiber, twisted pair, or coaxial cables, which supply a broadband signal to the premises. This signal is typically separated into telephone, hi-speed Internet, and other services. The power for the network terminal is supplied by the premises. It is typical for a battery to be installed or a UPS in the event of the loss of power to the premises.

In some cases, the utility company or service provider will install circuits from the premises to the utility equipment outside of the premises. Utilities and service providers install these circuits to avoid having the utility company run copper cable to the premises, which would require establishing a meter point and providing batteries. These circuits, which are derived from the premises, are exposed in the same manner any outdoor conductors would be to nearby lightning strikes and other damage. Two new sections are added to require protection for these conductors.

Where circuits leave the building to power remote equipment that is outside of the exterior zone of protection, they must be provided with protective devices in accordance with 805.90. The exterior zone of protection is a 150-foot radius. These circuits must have non-current carrying metallic sheaths grounded in accordance with 805.93, and they must be additionally grounded in accordance with 800.100, 800.106 and 820.100.

FRs: 7889, 7891
SR: 7750